PARAMEDIC CARE: Principles & Practice

SPECIAL CONSIDERATIONS
OPERATIONS

Workbook

SECOND EDITION

BRADY

PARAMEDIC CARE: Principles & Practice

SPECIAL CONSIDERATIONS OPERATIONS

Workbook

SECOND EDITION

Robert S. Porter

BRYAN E. BLEDSOE, D.O., F.A.C.E.P., EMT-P
Emergency Physician
Midlothian, Texas
and
Adjunct Associate Professor of Emergency Medicine
The George Washington University Medical Center
Washington, DC

ROBERT S. PORTER, M.A., NREMT-P
Senior Advanced Life Support Educator
Madison County Emergency Medical Services
Canastota, New York
and
Flight Paramedic
AirOne, Onondaga County Sheriff's Department
Syracuse, New York

RICHARD A. CHERRY, M.S., NREMT-P
Clinical Assistant Professor of Emergency Medicine
Assistant Residency Director
Upstate Medical University
Syracuse, New York

PEARSON
Prentice
Hall

Upper Saddle River, NJ 07458

Publisher: *Julie Levin Alexander*
Publisher's Assistant: *Regina Bruno*
Executive Editor: *Marlene McHugh Pratt*
Senior Managing Editor for Development:
 Lois Berlowitz
Project Manager: *Triple SSS Press Media Development*
Editorial Assistant: *Matthew Sirinides*
Director of Marketing: *Karen Allman*
Senior Marketing Manager: *Katrin Beacom*
Channel Marketing Manager: *Rachele Strober*
Marketing Coordinator: *Michael Sirinides*
Director of Production and Manufacturing:
 Bruce Johnson
Managing Editor for Production: *Patrick Walsh*
Production Liaison: *Faye Gemmellaro*
Production Editor: *Heather Willison/Carlisle Publisher*
 Services
Manufacturing Manager: *Ilene Sanford*
Manufacturing Buyer: *Pat Brown*
Creative Director: *Cheryl Asherman*
Senior Design Coordinator: *Christopher Weigand*
Cover Design: *Christopher Weigand*
Cover Photography: *Eddie Sperling*
Cover Image Manipulation: *Studio Montage*
Composition: *Carlisle Publishers Services*
Printer/Binder: *Banta-Harrisonburg*
Cover Printer: *Phoenix Color*

Studentaid.ed.gov the U.S. Department of Education's Website on college planning assistance, is a valuable tool for anyone intending to pursue higher education. Designed to help students at all stages of schooling, including international students, returning students, and parents, it is a guide to the financial aid process. This Website presents information on applying to and attending college, as well as on funding your education and repaying loans. It also provides links to useful resources, such as state education agency contact information, assistance in filling out financial aid forms, and an introduction to various forms of student aid.

NOTICE ON CARE PROCEDURES

It is the intent of the authors and publisher that this Workbook be used as part of a formal EMT-Paramedic program taught by qualified instructors and supervised by a licensed physician. The procedures described in this Workbook are based upon consultation with EMT and medical authorities. The authors and publisher have taken care to make certain that these procedures reflect currently accepted clinical practice; however, they cannot be considered absolute recommendations.

The material in this Workbook contains the most current information available at the time of publication. However, federal, state, and local guidelines concerning clinical practices, including, without limitation, those governing infection control and universal precautions, change rapidly. The reader should note, therefore, that the new regulations may require changes in some procedures.

It is the responsibility of the reader to familiarize himself or herself with the policies and procedures set by federal, state, and local agencies as well as the institution or agency where the reader is employed. The authors and the publisher of this Workbook disclaim any liability, loss, or risk resulting directly or indirectly from the suggested procedures and theory, from any undetected errors, or from the reader's misunderstanding of the text. It is the reader's responsibility to stay informed of any new changes or recommendations made by any federal, state, and local agency as well as by his or her employing institution or agency.

NOTICE ON CPR AND ECC

The national standards for Cardiopulmonary Resuscitation (CPR) and Emergency Cardiovascular Care (ECC) are reviewed and revised on a regular basis and may change slightly after this manual is printed. It is important that you know the most current procedures for CPR and ECC, both for the classroom and your patients. The most current information may always be downloaded from www.bradybooks.com or obtained from the appropriate credentialing agency.

Pearson Education Ltd.
Pearson Education Singapore, Pte. Ltd.
Pearson Education Canada, Ltd.
Pearson Education—Japan

Pearson Education Australia PTY, Limited
Pearson Education North Asia Ltd.
Pearson Educación de Mexico, S.A. de C.V.
Pearson Education Malaysia, Pte. Ltd.
Pearson Education, Upper Saddle River, NJ

10 9 8 7 6 5 4 3 2 1
ISBN 0-13-117842-3

Dedication

*To Kris and sailing: Pleasant distractions from writing about
and practicing prehospital emergency medicine.*

CONTENTS
Self-Instructional Workbook
Paramedic Care: Principles & Practice, 2nd Edition

SPECIAL CONSIDERATIONS/OPERATIONS

INTRODUCTION

To the Self-Instructional Workbook

Paramedic Care: Principles & Practice, 2nd Edition

Welcome to the self-instructional Workbook for *Paramedic Care: Principles & Practice*. This Workbook is designed to help guide you through an educational program for initial or refresher training that follows the guidelines of the 1998 U.S. Department of Transportation EMT-Paramedic National Standard Curriculum. The Workbook is designed to be used either in conjunction with your instructor or as a self-study guide you use on your own.

This Workbook features many different ways to help you learn the material necessary to become a paramedic, including those listed below.

Features

Review of Chapter Objectives

Each chapter of *Paramedic Care: Principles & Practice* begins with objectives that identify the important information and principles addressed in the chapter reading. To help you identify and learn this material, each Workbook chapter reviews the important content elements addressed by these objectives as presented in the text.

Case Study Review

Each chapter of *Paramedic Care: Principles & Practice* includes a case study, introducing and highlighting important principles presented in the chapter. The Workbook reviews these case studies and points out much of the essential information and many of the applied principles they describe.

Content Self-Evaluation

Each chapter of *Paramedic Care: Principles & Practice* presents an extensive narrative explanation of the principles of paramedic practice. The Workbook chapter (or chapter section) contains between 10 and 50 multiple-choice questions to test your reading comprehension of the textbook material and to give you experience taking typical emergency medical service examinations.

Special Projects

The Workbook contains several projects that are special learning experiences designed to help you remember the information and principles necessary to perform as a paramedic. Special projects include crossword puzzles, fill-in-the-blank, and a variety of other exercises.

Content Review

The Workbook provides a comprehensive review of the material presented in this volume of *Paramedic Care: Principles & Practice*. After the last text chapter has been covered, the Workbook presents an extensive content self-evaluation component that helps you recall and build upon the knowledge you have gained by reading the text, attending class, and completing the earlier Workbook chapters.

National Registry Practical Evaluation Forms

Supplemental materials found at the back of the Workbook include the National Registry Practical Evaluation Forms. These or similar forms will be used to test your practical skills throughout your training and, usually, for state certification exams. By reviewing them, you have a clearer picture of what is expected of you during your practical exam and a better understanding of the type of evaluation tool that is used to measure your performance.

Patient Scenario Flash Cards

At the end of this Workbook are scenario flash cards, which are designed to help you practice the processes of investigating both the chief complaint and the past medical history. Each card contains the dispatch information and results of the scene size-up and then prompts you to inquire into either the patient's major symptoms or his past medical history.

Acknowledgments

Contributor

We wish to acknowledge the extraordinary talent and efforts of Bob Elling, who prepared the material in this Workbook. In developing study guides, questions, and activities, he has upheld the highest standards of EMS instruction.

Bob Elling, MPS, REMT-P, has been an active field medic and EMS Administrator/Educator since 1978. He continues to work part time as a paramedic with the Colonie EMS Department. He is currently a full-time faculty member at the Institute of Prehospital Emergency Medicine at Hudson Valley Community College in Troy, New York. He is also a Professor of Management with the American College of Prehospital Medicine.

Reviewers

The following reviewers provided many excellent suggestions for improving this Workbook. Their assistance is greatly appreciated.

Lance Corey, NREMT-P, I/C
Oceana County EMS,
Hart, Michigan

Edward B. Kuvlesky, NREMT-P
Battalion Chief
Indian River County EMS
Indian River County, Florida

K. Lee Watson, NREMT-P
Martinsville—Henry County Rescue Squad
Martinsville, Virginia

HOW TO USE
The Self-Instructional Workbook
Paramedic Care: Principles & Practice, 2nd Edition

The self-instructional Workbook accompanying *Paramedic Care: Principles & Practice* may be used as directed by your instructor or independently by you during your course of instruction. The recommendations listed below are intended to guide you in using the Workbook independently.

- Examine your course schedule and identify the appropriate text chapter or other assigned reading.

- Read the assigned chapter in *Paramedic Care: Principles & Practice* carefully. Do this in a relaxed environment, free of distractions, and give yourself adequate time to read and digest the material. The information presented in *Paramedic Care: Principles & Practice* is often technically complex and demanding, but it is very important that you comprehend it. Be sure that you read the chapter carefully enough to understand and remember what you have read.

- Carefully read the Review of Chapter Objectives at the beginning of each Workbook chapter (or section). This material includes both the objectives listed in *Paramedic Care: Principles & Practice* and narrative descriptions of their content. If you do not understand or remember what is discussed from your reading, refer to the referenced pages and reread them carefully. If you still do not feel comfortable with your understanding of any objective, consider asking your instructor about it.

- Reread the case study in *Paramedic Care: Principles & Practice*, and then read the Case Study Review in the Workbook. Note the important points regarding assessment and care that the Case Study Review highlights and be sure that you understand and agree with the analysis of the call. If you have any questions or concerns, ask your instructor to clarify the information.

- Take the Content Self-Evaluation at the end of each Workbook chapter (or section), answering each question carefully. Do this in a quiet environment, free from distractions, and allow yourself adequate time to complete the exercise. Correct your self-evaluation by consulting the answers at the back of the Workbook, and determine the percentage you have answered correctly (the number you got right divided by the total number of questions). If you have answered most of the questions correctly (85 to 90 percent), review those that you missed by rereading the material on the pages listed in the Answer Key and be sure you understand which answer is correct and why. If you have more than a few questions wrong (less than 85 percent correct), look for incorrect answers that are grouped together. This suggests that you did not understand a particular topic in the reading. Reread the text dealing with that topic carefully, and then retest yourself on the questions you got wrong. If incorrect answers are spread throughout the chapter content, reread the chapter and retake the Content Self-Evaluation to ensure that you understand the material. If you don't understand why your answer to a question is incorrect after reviewing the text, consult with your instructor.

- In a similar fashion, complete the exercises in the Special Projects section of the Workbook chapters (or sections). These exercises are specifically designed to help you learn and remember the essential principles and information presented in *Paramedic Care: Principles & Practice*.

- When you have completed this volume of *Paramedic Care: Principles & Practice* and its accompanying Workbook, prepare for a course test by reviewing both the text in its entirety and your class notes. Then take the Content Review examination in the Workbook. Again, review your score and any questions you have answered incorrectly by referring to the text and rereading the page or pages where the material is presented. If you note groupings of wrong answers, review the entire range of pages or the full chapter they represent.

If, during your completion of the Workbook exercises, you have any questions that either the textbook or Workbook doesn't answer, write them down and ask your instructor about them. Prehospital emergency medicine is a complex and complicated subject, and answers are not always black-and-white. It is also common for different EMS systems to use differing methods of care. The questions you bring up in class, and your instructor's answers to them, will help you expand and complete your knowledge of prehospital emergency medical care.

The authors and Brady Publishing continuously seek to ensure the creation of the best materials to support your educational experience. We are interested in your comments. If, during your reading and study of material in *Paramedic Care: Principles & Practice*, you notice any error or have any suggestions to improve either the textbook or Workbook, please direct your comments via the Internet to the following address:

hiawatha@localnet.com

You can also visit the Brady Website at:
www.bradybooks.com/paramedic

GUIDELINES TO BETTER TEST-TAKING

The knowledge you will gain from reading the textbook, completing the exercises in the Workbook, listening in your paramedic class, and participating in your clinical and field experience will prepare you to care for patients who are seriously ill or injured. However, before you can practice these skills, you will have to pass several classroom written exams and your state's certification exam. Your performance on these exams will depend not only on your knowledge but also on your ability to answer test questions correctly. The following guidelines are designed to help your performance on tests and to better demonstrate your knowledge of prehospital emergency care.

1. Relax and be calm during the test.

A test is designed to measure what you have learned and to tell you and your instructor how well you are doing. An exam is not designed to intimidate or punish you. Consider it a challenge, and just try to do your best. Get plenty of sleep prior to the examination. Avoid coffee or other stimulants for a few hours before the exam, and be prepared.

Reread the text chapters, review the objectives in the Workbook, and review your class notes. It might be helpful to work with one or two other students and ask each other questions. This type of practice helps everyone better understand the knowledge presented in your course of study.

2. Read the questions carefully.

Read each word of the question and all the answers slowly. Words such as "except" or "not" may change the entire meaning of the question. If you miss such words, you may answer the question incorrectly even though you know the right answer.

EXAMPLE:
The art and science of Emergency Medical Services involves all of the following EXCEPT:

    A. sincerity and compassion.
    B. respect for human dignity.
    C. placing patient care before personal safety.
    D. delivery of sophisticated emergency medical care.
    E. none of the above.

The correct answer is C, unless you miss the "EXCEPT."

3. Read each answer carefully.

Read each and every answer carefully. While the first answer may be absolutely correct, so may the rest, and thus the best answer might be "all of the above."

EXAMPLE:
Indirect medical control is considered to be:

    A. treatment protocols.
    B. training and education.
    C. quality assurance.
    D. chart review.
    E. all of the above.

While answers A, B, C, and D are correct, the best and only acceptable answer is "all of the above," E.

4. Delay answering questions you don't understand and look for clues.

When a question seems confusing or you don't know the answer, note it on your answer sheet and come back to it later. This will ensure that you have time to complete the test. You will also find that other questions in the test may give you hints to answer the one you've skipped over. It will also prevent you from being frustrated with an early question and letting it affect your performance.

EXAMPLE:

Upon successful completion of a course of training as an EMT-P, most states will

    A. certify you. (correct)
    B. license you.
    C. register you.
    D. recognize you as a paramedic.
    E. issue you a permit.

Another question, later in the exam, may suggest the right answer:

The action of one state in recognizing the certification of another is called:

    A. reciprocity. (correct)
    B. national registration.
    C. licensure.
    D. registration.
    E. extended practice.

5. Answer all questions.

Even if you do not know the right answer, do not leave a question blank. A blank question is always wrong, while a guess might be correct. If you can eliminate some of the answers as wrong, do so. It will increase the chances of a correct guess.

A multiple-choice question with five answers gives a 20 percent chance of a correct guess. If you can eliminate one or more incorrect answers, you increase your odds of a correct guess to 25 percent, 33 percent, and so on. An unanswered question has a 0 percent chance of being correct.

Just before turning in your answer sheet, check to be sure that you have not left any items blank.

EXAMPLE:

When a paramedic is called by the patient (through the dispatcher) to the scene of a medical emergency, the medical control physician has established a physician/patient relationship.

    A. True
    B. False

A true/false question gives you a 50 percent chance of a correct guess.

The hospital health professional responsible for sorting patients as they arrive at the emergency department is usually the:

    A. emergency physician.
    B. ward clerk.
    C. emergency nurse.
    D. trauma surgeon.
    E. both A and C. (correct)

Neonatology

Review of Chapter Objectives

With each chapter of the Workbook, we identify the objectives and the important elements of the text content. You should review these items and refer to the pages listed if any points are not clear.

After reading this chapter, you should be able to:

1. Define *newborn* and *neonate*. **p. 4**

A newborn is a baby in the first few hours of its life, also called a **newly born infant**. A neonate is a baby less than 1 month old.

2. Identify important antepartum factors that can affect childbirth. **p. 5**

Antepartum factors are those that occur before the onset of labor. Examples of important antepartum factors that can adversely affect childbirth include multiple gestation, inadequate prenatal care, a mother who is younger than 16 years of age or older than 35, a history of perinatal morbidity or mortality, post-term gestation, drugs or medications, and a mother with a history of toxemia, hypertension, or diabetes.

3. Identify important intrapartum factors that can determine high-risk newborn patients. **p. 5**

Intrapartum factors are those that occur during childbirth. Examples of intrapartum factors that can help determine high-risk newborn patients include a mother with premature labor, meconium-stained amniotic fluid, rupture of membranes more than 24 hours prior to delivery, use of narcotics within 4 hours of delivery, an abnormal presentation, prolonged labor or precipitous delivery, and a prolapsed cord or bleeding.

4. Identify the factors that lead to premature birth and low-birth-weight newborns. **pp. 23, 28–29**

A premature or low-birth-weight newborn is an infant born prior to 37 weeks of gestation or with a birth weight ranging from 0.6 to 2.2 kg (1 pound, 5 ounces, to 4 pounds, 13 ounces). Factors that lead to premature birth or low-birth-weight newborns include, among others, maternal narcotic use or trauma. For a full list of factors, see Chapter 14, "Obstetrics," in *Paramedic Care: Medical Emergencies*, Volume 3 of the series.

5. Distinguish between primary and secondary apnea. **p. 6**

When an infant is born, it may experience hypoxia. This is usually relieved by the initial gasps for air. If this asphyxia continues, respiratory movement may cease altogether. The infant may then enter a period of apnea known as **primary apnea**. In most cases, simple stimulation and exposure to oxygen will reverse bradycardia and assist in the development of pulmonary perfusion. With ongoing asphyxia, the infant will enter a period known as **secondary apnea**. Always assume that apnea in the newborn is secondary apnea and rapidly treat it with ventilatory assistance.

6. Discuss pulmonary perfusion and asphyxia.   p. 6

With the first breaths, the lungs rapidly fill with air, which displaces the remaining fetal fluid. The pulmonary arterioles and capillaries open, decreasing pulmonary vascular resistance. The blood is now diverted from the ductus arteriosus to the pulmonary circulation. However, if hypoxia or severe acidosis occurs, the pulmonary vascular bed may constrict and the ductus may reopen. This will retrigger fetal circulation with its attendant shunting, ongoing hypoxia, and ultimately asphyxia (if the situation is not managed quickly and correctly).

7. Identify the primary signs utilized for evaluating a newborn during resuscitation.   p. 9

The newborn should be assessed immediately after birth. The primary signs used for evaluating a newborn during resuscitation include respiratory rate, heart rate, and skin color. The newborn's respiratory rate should average 40–60 breaths per minute. The normal heart rate is between 150 and 180 beats per minute at birth, slowing to 130–140 beats per minute thereafter. A pulse less than 100 beats per minute indicates distress and requires emergency intervention. Some cyanosis of the extremities is common immediately after birth. However, if the newborn is cyanotic in the central part of the body or if peripheral cyanosis persists, the newborn must be treated with 100 percent oxygen.

8. Identify the appropriate use of the APGAR scale.   pp. 9–10

The APGAR scale—designed for use at 1 and 5 minutes after birth—helps distinguish between newborns who need only routine care and those who need greater assistance. The system also predicts long-term survival. A severely distressed newborn (one with an APGAR score of less than 4) requires immediate resuscitation.

9. Calculate the APGAR score given various newborn situations.   p. 9

To calculate the APGAR score, a value of 0, 1, or 2 is given for each of the following categories: pulse rate (heart rate), grimace (irritability), activity (muscle tone), and respiratory rate.

10. Formulate an appropriate treatment plan for providing initial care to a newborn.   pp. 10–13

Treatment of the newborn begins by preparing the environment and assembling the equipment needed for delivery and immediate care of the newborn. The initial care of the newborn follows the same priorities as for all patients. Complete the initial assessment first. Correct any problems detected in the initial assessment before proceeding to the next step. The majority of term newborns require no resuscitation beyond suctioning of the airway, mild stimulation, and maintenance of body temperature by drying and warming with blankets.

11. Describe the indications, equipment needed, application, and evaluation of the following management techniques for the newborn in distress:

    a. Blow-by oxygen   pp. 18, 20
    Blow-by oxygen—the process of blowing oxygen across a newborn's face—is applied if central cyanosis is present or if the adequacy of ventilations is uncertain. If possible, the oxygen should be warmed and humidified.

    b. Ventilatory assistance   pp. 18, 20–21
    Positive-pressure ventilation should be applied to a newborn if any of the following conditions exist: heart rate less than 100 beats per minute, apnea, or persistence of central cyanosis after administration of supplemental oxygen. A bag-valve-mask unit is the device of choice. A self-inflating bag of appropriate size should be used (450 mL is optimal). If prolonged ventilation is required, it may be necessary to disable the pop-off valve.

    c. Endotracheal intubation   pp. 17–21
    This technique involves placement of an endotracheal (ET) tube into the trachea of a newborn, usually for suctioning meconium. Endotracheal intubation requires appropriately sized tubes

©2006 Pearson Education, Inc.
Paramedic Care: Principles & Practice, Vol. 5

without cuffs and a laryngoscope. After suctioning, a fresh tube should be inserted for mechanical ventilation. (See Procedure 1–2 for more details.) Endotracheal intubation should be carried out in the following situations: The bag-valve mask does not work, tracheal suctioning is needed, prolonged ventilation will be required, a diaphragmatic hernia is suspected, or an inadequate respiratory effort is found.

d. Orogastric tube   p. 21

A nasogastric, or orogastric, tube is used to relieve significant gastric distention, most often caused by a leak around an uncuffed endotracheal tube. The tube should be inserted through the nose or mouth, then through the esophagus into the stomach. An endotracheal tube should be in place to avoid misplacing the gastric tube into the trachea. Make sure the newborn is well oxygenated and that the tube is correctly measured (from the tip of the newborn's nose, around the ear, to the xiphoid process). Lubricate the end of the tube before inserting and then check placement by injecting 10 cc of air into the tube and auscultating a bubbling sound (or sound of rushing air) over the epigastrium.

e. Chest compressions   p. 21

Chest compressions should be applied to newborns with heart rates of less than 60 beats per minute or with heart rates between 60 and 80 beats per minute *that do not increase* with 30 seconds of positive-pressure ventilation and supplemental oxygen. Begin chest compressions by encircling the newborn's chest, placing both thumbs on the lower one third of the sternum. Compress the sternum 1.5 to 2.0 cm (1/2 to 3/4 inch) at a rate of 120 times per minute. Maintain a ratio of three compressions to one ventilation. Reassess the newborn after 20 cycles of compressions (1-minute intervals). Discontinue compressions if the spontaneous heart rate exceeds 80 beats per minute.

f. Vascular access   pp. 21–22

Vascular access—a method for administering fluids and drugs—should be considered if ventilation and oxygenation fail to correct cardiopulmonary arrests or in cases of persistent bradycardia, hypovolemia, respiratory depression secondary to narcotics, and metabolic acidosis. Vascular access can most readily be managed by using the umbilical vein. The umbilical cord contains three vessels—two arteries and one vein, with the vein being the largest of the three. Equipment for venous access includes a scalpel blade, a 5-Fr. umbilical catheter, a three-way stopcock, umbilical tape, and saline. Be sure to save enough of the umbilical stump (cut to 1 cm above the abdomen) in case neonatal personnel have to place additional lines. Also, if the catheter is inserted too far, it may become wedged against the liver, and it will not function.

---

12. Discuss the routes of medication administration for the newborn.   pp. 21–23, 24

Medications for the newborn may be administered by peripheral vein cannulation, intraosseous cannulation, umbilical vein cannulation, and endotracheal tube.

---

13. Discuss the signs of hypovolemia in a newborn.   p. 30

Signs of hypovolemia in the newborn include pale color and cool skin, weak peripheral pulses, prolonged capillary refill (in normal ambient temperatures), changes in mental status, and diminished urination.

---

14. Discuss the initial steps in resuscitation of a newborn.   pp. 17–23

Resuscitation of the newborn follows an inverted pyramid. In chronological order, initial steps include drying, warming, positioning, suctioning, and tactical stimulation; administration of supplemental oxygen; bag-valve ventilation; and chest compressions. If these steps fail, advanced measures include intubation and administration of medications.

---

15. Discuss the effects of maternal narcotic usage on the newborn.   p. 23

Maternal narcotic use has been shown to produce low-birth-weight infants. Such infants may demonstrate withdrawal symptoms—tremors, startles, and decreased alertness. They also face a serious risk of respiratory depression at birth.

16. Determine the appropriate treatment for the newborn with narcotic depression. p. 23

Naloxone, which is extremely safe even at high doses, is the treatment of choice for respiratory depression secondary to maternal narcotic use *within 4 hours of delivery*. Ventilatory support must be provided prior to administration of naloxone. Due to the long duration of the narcotic, which may exceed the duration of the naloxone, repeat administration will be needed. Keep in mind, however, that the naloxone may induce a withdrawal reaction in an infant born to a *narcotic-addicted* mother. Medical direction may advise that naloxone NOT be administered if the mother is drug addicted, recommending prolonged ventilatory support instead.

17. Discuss appropriate transport guidelines for a newborn. pp. 23, 25

Paramedics are frequently called upon to transport a high-risk newborn from a facility where stabilization has occurred to a neonatal intensive care unit. During transport you will help maintain the newborn's body temperature, control oxygen administration, and maintain ventilatory support. Often, a transport isolette with its own heat, light, and oxygen source is available. If a self-contained isolette is not available for transport, you might wrap the newborn in several blankets, keep the infant's head covered, and place hot-water bottles containing water heated to no more than 40°C (104°F) near, but not touching, the newborn. DO NOT use chemical packs to keep the newborn warm.

18. Determine appropriate receiving facilities for low- and high-risk newborns. pp. 5, 23, 25

Low-risk newborns need to be taken to a hospital with an obstetrical unit, whereas high-risk newborns are often taken directly or transferred to a facility with a neonatal intensive care unit (NICU).

19. Describe the epidemiology, including the incidence, morbidity/mortality, risk factors and prevention strategies, pathophysiology, assessment findings, and management for the following neonatal problems:

a. Meconium aspiration pp. 26–27

Meconium-stained amniotic fluid occurs in approximately 10–15 percent of deliveries, mostly in post-term or small-for-gestational-age newborns. Meconium aspiration accounts for a significant proportion of neonatal deaths. Fetal distress and hypoxia can cause meconium to be passed into the amniotic fluid. Either *in utero* or more often with the first breath, thick meconium is aspirated into the lungs, resulting in small-airway obstruction and aspiration pneumonia. The infant may have respiratory distress within the first hours, or even the first minutes, of life as evidenced by tachypnea, retraction, grunting, and cyanosis in severely affected newborns. The partial obstruction of some airways may lead to a pneumothorax.

An infant born through thin meconium may not require treatment, but depressed infants born through thick, particulate (pea-soup) meconium-stained fluid should be intubated immediately, prior to the first ventilation. Before stimulating such infants to breathe, apply suction with a meconium aspirator attached to an endotracheal tube. Connect to suction at 100 cm/H$_2$O or less to remove meconium from the airway. Withdraw the ET tube as suction is applied. It may be necessary to repeat this procedure to clear the airway. The patient should then be taken to a facility that can manage a high-risk neonate.

b. Apnea p. 27

This condition is a common finding in the preterm infant or infants weighing less than 1,500 grams (3 pounds, 5 ounces), infants exposed to drugs, or infants born after prolonged or difficult labor and delivery. Typically, the infant fails to breathe spontaneously after stimulation, or the infant experiences respiratory pauses of greater than 20 seconds. Apnea can be due to hypoxia, hypothermia, narcotic or central nervous system depressants, weakness of the respiratory muscles, septicemia, metabolic disorders, or central nervous system disorders.

Management begins with tactile stimulation, followed by bag-valve-mask ventilation, with the pop-off valve disabled. If the infant does not breathe on his own, or if the heart rate is below 60 with adequate ventilation and chest compressions, perform tracheal intubation with direct visualization. Gain circulatory access, and monitor the heart rate continuously. If the apnea is due to a narcotic administered within the past 4 hours, consider naloxone. Remember, however, that the use of a narcotic antagonist is generally contraindicated if the mother is a drug abuser. Throughout the treatment, keep the infant warm to prevent hypothermia.

c. Diaphragmatic hernia pp. 27–28

This is a rare condition seen in approximately 1 out of every 2,200 live births. The defect is caused by the failure of the pleurperitoneal canal to close completely. The survival rate for newborns who require mechanical ventilation in the first 18 to 24 hours is approximately 50 percent, and it approaches 100 percent if there is no distress in the first 24 hours of life.

Protrusion of abdominal viscera through the hernia into the thoracic cavity occurs in varying degrees. Assessment findings may include little to severe distress present from birth; dyspnea and cyanosis unresponsive to ventilations; small, flat (scaphoid) abdomen; bowel sounds in the chest; and heart sounds displaced to the right. If you suspect a diaphragmatic hernia, position the infant with his head and thorax higher than the abdomen and feet. This will help to displace the abdominal organs downward. Place a nasogastric or orogastric tube and apply low, intermittent suctioning. DO NOT use bag-valve-mask ventilation, which can worsen the condition by causing gastric distension. If necessary, cautiously administer positive-pressure ventilation through an endotracheal tube. A diaphragmatic hernia usually requires surgical repair, which should be explained to the parents along with the need for quick transport.

d. Bradycardia p. 28

Bradycardia is most commonly caused by hypoxia in newborns. However, the bradycardia may also be due to several other factors, including increased intracranial pressure, hypothyroidism, or acidosis. In cases of hypoxia, the infant experiences minimal risk if the hypoxia is corrected quickly. In providing treatment, follow the procedures in the inverted pyramid. Resist the inclination to treat the bradycardia with pharmacological measures alone. Keep the newborn warm and transport to the nearest facility.

e. Prematurity pp. 28–29

A premature newborn is an infant born prior to 37 weeks of gestation or with weight ranging from 0.6 to 2.2 kg (1 pound, 5 ounces, to 4 pounds, 13 ounces.) Mortality decreases weekly with gestation beyond the onset of fetal viability. Premature newborns are at greater risk of respiratory suppression, head or brain injury caused by hypoxemia, changes in blood pressure, intraventricular hemorrhage, and fluctuations in serum osmolarity. They are also more susceptible to hypothermia than full-term newborns. The degree of immaturity determines the physical characteristics of a premature newborn. Premature newborns often appear to have a larger head relative to body size. They may have large trunks and short extremities, transparent skin, and few wrinkles.

Prematurity should not be a factor in short-term treatment. Resuscitation should be attempted if there is any sign of life, and the measures of resuscitation should be the same as those for newborns of normal weight and maturity. Maintain a patent airway and avoid potential aspiration of gastric contents.

f. Respiratory distress/cyanosis pp. 29–30

Prematurity is the single most common factor causing respiratory distress and cyanosis in the newborn. The problem occurs most frequently in infants weighing less than 1,200 grams (2 pounds, 10 ounces) and less than 30 weeks of gestation. Premature infants have an immature central respiratory control center and are easily affected by environmental or metabolic changes. Contributing factors to respiratory distress include lung or heart disease, central nervous system disorders, meconium aspiration, metabolic problems, obstruction of the nasal passages, shock and sepsis, and diaphragmatic hernia. Expect the following assessment findings: tachypnea, paradoxical breathing, intercostal retractions, nasal flaring, and expiratory grunt.

In providing treatment, follow the inverted pyramid, paying particular attention to airway and ventilation. Suction as needed and provide high-flow high-concentration oxygen. If prolonged ventilation will be required, consider placing an endotracheal tube. Perform chest compressions, if indicated. Consider dextrose ($D_{10}W$ or $D_{25}W$) solution if the newborn is hypoglycemic. Maintain body temperature and transport to the most appropriate facility.

g. Seizures
pp. 30–31

Neonatal seizures differ from seizures in a child or an adult, because generalized tonic-clonic convulsions rarely occur in the first month of life. Types of seizures in the neonate include:

- **Subtle seizures**—consist of chewing motions and excessive salivation, blinking, sucking, swimming movements of the arms, pedaling movements of the legs, apnea, and color changes.
- **Tonic seizures**—characterized by rigid posturing of the extremities and trunk; sometimes associated with fixed deviation of the eyes.
- **Focal clonic seizures**—consist of rhythmic twitching of muscle groups in the extremities and face.
- **Multifocal seizures**—exhibit signs similar to focal clonic seizures, except multiple muscle groups are involved, and clonic activity randomly migrates.
- **Myoclonic seizures**—characterized by brief focal or generalized jerks of the extremities or parts of the body that tend to involve distal muscle groups.

The causes of neonatal seizures include sepsis, fever, hypoglycemia, hypoxic-ischemic encephalopathy, metabolic disturbances, meningitis, development abnormalities, or drug withdrawal. Assessment findings of seizures include decreased level of consciousness and seizure activity as already described. Treatment focuses on airway management, oxygen saturation, and administration of an anticonvulsant. You might administer a benzodiazepine (usually lorazepam) for status epilepticus or dextrose ($D_{10}W$ or $D_{25}W$) for hypoglycemia.

h. Fever
p. 31

Neonates do not develop fever as easily as older children. Therefore, any fever in a neonate requires extensive evaluation because it is more likely to be caused by a life-threatening condition such as pneumonia, sepsis, or meningitis. In fact, fever may be the only sign of meningitis in a neonate. Because of their immature development, they do not exhibit the classic symptoms such as a stiff neck. Assessment findings of a fever include changes in mental status (irritability or somnolence), decreased feeding, skin warm to the touch, and rashes or petechiae. Term infants may form beads of sweat on their brows, but not on the rest of their bodies. Premature infants, on the other hand, will have no visible sweat at all.

Treatment of the neonate with a fever will, for the most part, be limited to ensuring a patent airway and adequate ventilation. Do not use cold packs, which may drop the temperature too quickly and may also cause seizures. If the newborn becomes bradycardic, provide chest compressions.

i. Hypothermia
pp. 31–32

Hypothermia presents a common and life-threatening condition for newborns. The high surface-to-volume relationship in newborns makes them extremely sensitive to environmental temperatures, especially right after delivery when they are wet. In treating hypothermia—a body temperature below 35°C (95°F)—try to control the loss of heat through evaporation, conduction, convection, and radiation. Also remember that hypothermia can be an indicator of sepsis in the newborn. Regardless of the cause, the increase in the metabolic demands can produce a variety of related conditions including metabolic acidosis, pulmonary hypertension, and hypoxemia.

In assessing hypothermic newborns, remember that they do not shiver. Instead, expect the following findings: pale color, skin cool to the touch (especially in the extremities), acrocyanosis, respiratory distress, possible apnea, bradycardia, central cyanosis, initial irritability, and lethargy in later stages. Management focuses on ensuring adequate ventilations and oxygenation. Chest compressions may be necessary with bradycardia.

j. Hypoglycemia
pp. 32–33

Newborns are the only age group that can develop severe hypoglycemia and not have diabetes mellitus. Hypoglycemia is more common in premature or small-for-gestational-age infants, the smaller twin, and newborns of diabetic mothers, as these infants have decreased glucose utilization. Hypoglycemia may be due to a number of factors, including inadequate glucose intake or increased glucose utilization, stress (which can cause blood sugar to fall to a critical level), respiratory illnesses, hypothermia, toxemia, CNS hemorrhage, asphyxia, meningitis, and sepsis. Infants receiving glucose infusions can develop hypoglycemia if the infusion is suddenly stopped.

Infants with hypoglycemia may be asymptomatic, or they may exhibit symptoms such as apnea, color changes, respiratory distress, lethargy, seizures, acidosis, and poor myocardial contractility. Assessment findings may include twitching or seizures, limpness, lethargy, eye-rolling, high-pitched cry, apnea, irregular respirations, and possible cyanosis. Treatment begins with management of airway and ventilations. Administer chest compressions, if needed. With medical direction, administer dextrose ($D_{10}W$ or $D_{25}W$). Remember—persistent hypoglycemia is a serious condition and can have catastrophic effects on the brain.

k. Vomiting   **p. 33**

Vomiting in a neonate may result from a variety of causes and rarely presents as an isolated symptom. Vomiting—the forceful ejection of stomach contents—rarely occurs during the first weeks of life and may be confused with regurgitation or "spitting up." Causes of vomiting include a tracheoesophageal fistula, an upper gastrointestinal obstruction, increased intracranial pressure, or an infection. Vomit containing dark blood signals a life-threatening illness. Keep in mind, however, that vomiting of mucus, which may occasionally be streaked with blood, in the first few hours after birth is not uncommon.

Assessment findings may include distended stomach, signs of infection, increased intracranial pressure, or drug withdrawal. Because vomitus can be aspirated, management considerations focus on ensuring a patent airway to prevent aspiration. If you detect respiratory difficulty, suction or clear the vomitus from the airway and oxygenate as needed. Fluid administration may be necessary to prevent dehydration. Remember that, as with older patients, vagal stimulation may cause bradycardia in the neonate.

l. Diarrhea   **pp. 33–34**

Diarrhea can cause severe dehydration and electrolyte imbalances in the neonate. Normally five to six stools per day can be expected, especially in breast-fed infants. Causes of diarrhea in a neonate include bacterial or viral infection, gastroenteritis, lactose intolerance, phototherapy, neonatal abstinence syndrome (NAS), thyrotoxicosis, and cystic fibrosis. In managing an infant with diarrhea, remember body substance isolation (BSI) precautions. Management consists of maintenance of airway and ventilations, adequate oxygenation, and chest compressions, if indicated. With medical direction, administer fluid therapy to prevent or treat dehydration.

m. Common birth injuries   **p. 34**

A birth injury occurs in an estimated 2 to 7 of every 1,000 live births in the United States. About 5 to 8 of every 100,000 infants die of birth trauma and 25 of every 100,000 die of anoxic injuries. These injuries account for 2 to 3 percent of infant deaths. Risk factors for birth injury include prematurity, postmaturity, cephalopelvic disproportion, prolonged labor, breech presentation, explosive delivery, and a diabetic mother.

Birth injuries can take various forms. Cranial injuries may include molding of the head and overriding of the parietal bones, erythema, abrasions, ecchymosis, subcutaneous fat necrosis, subconjunctival and retinal hemorrhage, subperiosteal hemorrhage, and fracture of the skull. Often the infant will develop a large scalp hematoma, called a *caput succedaneum*, during the birth process, but this condition will usually resolve over a week's time. Other birth injuries include peripheral nerve injury, injury to the liver, rupture of the spleen, adrenal hemorrhage, fractures of the clavicle or extremities, and hypoxia-ischemia.

Assessment findings may include diffuse (sometimes ecchymotic) edematous swelling of soft tissues around the scalp, paralysis below the level of the spinal cord injury, paralysis of the upper arm with or without paralysis of the forearm, diaphragmatic paralysis, movement on only one side of the face when crying, inability to move the arm freely on the side of the fractured clavicle, lack of spontaneous movement of the affected extremity, hypoxia, and shock. Management of a newborn who has suffered a birth injury is specific to injury but always centers on protection of the airway, provision of adequate ventilation, and chest compressions, if necessary.

n. Cardiac arrest   **p. 35**

The incidence of neonatal cardiac arrest is related primarily to hypoxia. The condition can be caused by primary or secondary apnea, bradycardia, persistent fetal circulation, or pulmonary hypertension. Unless appropriate interventions are initiated immediately, the outcome is poor.

Risk factors for cardiac arrest in newborns include bradycardia, intrauterine asphyxia, prematurity, drugs administered to or taken by the mother, congenital neuromuscular diseases, congenital malformations, and intrapartum hypoxemia. Assessment findings may include peripheral cyanosis, inadequate respiratory effort, and ineffective or absent heart rate. In managing the neonatal cardiac arrest, follow the inverted pyramid for resuscitation and administer drugs or fluids according to medical direction.

o. Post arrest management   **p. 35**

Postarrest management involves maintenance of the infant's body temperature, prompt transport to the appropriate facility, and delicate handling of the parents or caregivers.

20. Given several neonatal emergencies, provide the appropriate procedures for assessment, management, and transport.   **pp. 4–36**

During your classroom, clinical, and field training, you will assess and develop a management plan for the real and simulated patients you attend. Use the information presented in this chapter, the information on neonatal emergencies in the field provided by your instructors, and the guidance given by your clinical and field preceptors to develop the skills needed to assess, manage, and transport the newborn and neonate patient. Continue to refine these skills once your training ends and you begin your career as a paramedic.

Case Study Review

It is important to review each emergency response you participate in as a paramedic. Similarly, we will review the case study that precedes each chapter. We will address the important points of the response as addressed by the chapter. Often, this will include the scene size-up, patient assessment, patient management, patient packaging, and transport.

Reread the case study on page 4 in Paramedic Care: Special Considerations/Operations *and then read the following discussion. This case study draws attention to one of the complications that may occur at a prehospital delivery of a newborn.*

In this case, you arrive on scene to attend one patient, a woman who has just gone into labor, and quickly find yourself managing a second patient—a newly born infant who remains blue and limp, even after suctioning. The situation can be highly stressful, especially with the two parents nearby. You recall the steps in the inverted pyramid for resuscitating a distressed newborn. You quickly dry the infant and wrap her in a dry blanket, reducing the life-threatening risk of hypothermia. As you prepare to suction, you remember that you will also need to apply tactile stimulation, either by flicking the soles of the newborn's feet or by gently rubbing her back.

When the baby does not "pink up," many thoughts probably run through your mind. You know, for example, that a prolonged lack of oxygen can cause permanent brain damage—and death. Use of the APGAR score is out of the question. You must immediately provide the patient with oxygen. Again following the inverted pyramid, you administer supplemental oxygen (preferably warmed and humidified) using the "blow-by" method. When the patient's heart rate remains below 100 beats per minute, you begin positive-pressure ventilation with a bag-valve-mask unit, the device of choice. Perhaps you also depress the pop-off valve to deactivate it and ensure adequate ventilation.

Because the baby starts breathing spontaneously, you do not have to initiate endotracheal intubation or chest compressions. You still use the pulse oximeter to ensure adequate oxygen saturation. In preparing the newborn for transport, keep in mind the risk of hypothermia and cover the baby's head to prevent unnecessary heat loss. En route to the hospital, with the baby receiving blow-by oxygen, you finally compute the APGAR score. You come up with a 9, 1 point below the maximum!

Remember, too, that the mother is a patient as well and needs a physical assessment and frequent monitoring. Your calm, professional conduct throughout the call helped reassure the parents—the two other people in your care—of their daughter's safety. In recognition of a job well done, they name her after you.

Content Self-Evaluation

Each chapter in this Workbook includes a short content review. The questions are designed to test your ability to remember what you read. At the end of this Workbook, you can find the answers to the questions, as well as the pages where the topic of each question was discussed in the text. If you answer the question incorrectly or are unsure of the answer, review the pages listed.

MULTIPLE CHOICE

_____ 1. Examples of antepartum factors indicating possible complications in newborns would include multiple gestation and:
   A. premature labor.
   B. inadequate prenatal care.
   C. abnormal presentation.
   D. prolapsed cord.
   E. prolonged labor.

_____ 2. Examples of intrapartum factors indicating possible complications in newborns would include the use of narcotics within 4 hours of delivery and:
   A. meconium-stained amniotic fluid.
   B. post-term gestation.
   C. a mother under 16 years old.
   D. toxemia or diabetes.
   E. a mother over 35 years old.

_____ 3. When the fetus is in the uterus, the respiratory system is:
   A. working at a very rapid speed.
   B. working at a very slow speed.
   C. essentially nonfunctional.
   D. essentially functional.
   E. flushed with meconium.

_____ 4. Factors that stimulate the baby's first breath include:
   A. mild acidosis.
   B. hypoxia.
   C. hypothermia.
   D. initiation of stretch reflexes in the lungs.
   E. all of the above.

_____ 5. Persistent fetal circulation is a condition in which the:
   A. ductus arteriosus remains closed.
   B. ductus arteriosus reopens.
   C. pulmonary vascular bed dilates.
   D. both A and C.
   E. both B and C.

_____ 6. Always assume that apnea in the newborn is secondary apnea and rapidly treat it with ventilatory assistance.
   A. True   B. False

_____ 7. Most of the fetal development that could lead to congenital problems occurs during the:
   A. first trimester.
   B. second trimester.
   C. third trimester.
   D. onset of labor.
   E. intrapartum period.

_____ 8. Some infants are born with a defect in their spinal cord. In some cases, the spinal cord and associated structures may be exposed. This abnormality is called diaphragmatic hernia.
A. True   B. False

_____ 9. A congenital hernia of the umbilicus found in the neonate is called a(n):
A. choanal atresia.
B. Pierre Robin syndrome.
C. spina bifida.
D. meningomyelocele.
E. omphalocele.

_____ 10. A congenital condition characterized by a small jaw combined with a cleft palate, downward displacement of the tongue, and an absent gag reflex is called a(n):
A. cleft lip.
B. omphalocele.
C. cleft palate.
D. Pierre Robin syndrome.
E. choanal atresia.

_____ 11. The APGAR score should be assigned at 1 and 10 minutes after the infant's birth.
A. True   B. False

_____ 12. The G in APGAR stands for:
A. gravida.
B. gestation.
C. grimace.
D. gray tone.
E. none of the above.

_____ 13. A dark green material found in the intestine of the full-term newborn is called:
A. bile.
B. meconium.
C. mucus.
D. vomitus.
E. hyperbilirubinemia.

_____ 14. Loss of heat by the newborn can occur through:
A. evaporation.
B. convection.
C. conduction.
D. radiation.
E. all of the above.

_____ 15. Immediately after birth, the newborn's core temperature can drop 4° or more from its birth temperature.
A. True   B. False

_____ 16. Prior to cutting the umbilical cord, it should not be "milked" as this can cause:
A. polycythemia.
B. anemia.
C. hyperbilirubinemia.
D. hemophilia.
E. both A and C.

_____ 17. An increase in the level of bilirubin in the blood can cause:
   A. jaundice.
   B. pallor.
   C. cyanosis.
   D. flushing.
   E. anemia.

_____ 18. The most important indicator of neonatal distress is the fetal respiratory rate.
   A. True   B. False

_____ 19. EMS units should contain all of the following equipment in their neonatal resuscitation kit EXCEPT a(n):
   A. meconium aspirator.
   B. laryngoscope with size 3 and 4 blades.
   C. device to secure the endotracheal tube.
   D. umbilical catheter and 10 mL syringe.
   E. DeLee suction trap.

_____ 20. Following the inverted pyramid of neonatal resuscitation, which would be done first?
   A. intubation
   B. bag-valve-mask ventilations
   C. chest compressions
   D. drying and warming
   E. administration of medications

_____ 21. In distressed newborns, monitor the heart rate with external electronic monitors.
   A. True   B. False

_____ 22. The danger of deep suctioning a newborn is that it can cause a(n):
   A. vagal response.
   B. increased heart rate.
   C. decreased respiratory rate.
   D. allergic reaction.
   E. tachypnea.

_____ 23. Suctioning of a newborn should last no longer than 10 seconds.
   A. True   B. False

_____ 24. Normal newborn respirations are approximately _____ times a minute.
   A. 10–30
   B. 20–50
   C. 30–60
   D. 40–70
   E. 60–90

_____ 25. Insertion of an endotracheal tube is recommended when prolonged ventilation of a newborn will be required.
   A. True   B. False

_____ 26. Initiate chest compressions in the newborn with which of the following?
   A. heart rate greater than 100
   B. heart rate less than 60
   C. no respirations
   D. heart rate between 60 and 80 that does not improve
   E. both A and D

_____ 27. The proper sized catheter to cannulate the umbilical vein is:
    A. 14 ga.
    B. 22 ga.
    C. 10 fr.
    D. 5 fr.
    E. 2 fr.

_____ 28. Naloxone may induce withdrawal in the newborn of a mother who is drug addicted.
    A. True
    B. False

_____ 29. Remove the endotracheal tube as you suction the neonate with possible meconium aspiration.
    A. True
    B. False

_____ 30. Which of the following is NOT a causative factor for apnea?
    A. CNS depressants
    B. Caffeine
    C. Septicemia
    D. Metabolic disorders
    E. Weak respiratory muscles

_____ 31. The most common cause of bradycardia in the newborn is:
    A. increasing intracranial pressure.
    B. narcotic overdoze.
    C. cerebral palsy.
    D. hypoxia.
    E. congenital cardiac problems.

_____ 32. Which of the following is a reason premature infants lose heat more readily?
    A. decreased subcutaneous fat
    B. increased surface area to weight ratio
    C. immature temperature control mechanisms
    D. cannot shiver and generate heat
    E. all of the above

_____ 33. The initial bolus of fluid for the dehydrated neonate is:
    A. 10 mL/kg.
    B. 20 mL/kg.
    C. 40 mL/kg.
    D. 60 mL/kg.
    E. none of the above.

_____ 34. Hypothermia is a common and life-threatening condition in neonates.
    A. True
    B. False

_____ 35. Hypoglycemia is only associated with severe diabetes mellitus in the newborn.
    A. True
    B. False

Special Project

The APGAR Scale

The APGAR scoring system will help you distinguish between newborns who need only routine care and those who needed greater assistance. To gain practice in using this system, complete the following exercises.

Part I

You have just assisted in the delivery of a newborn. Your quick assessment reveals a blue baby with very slow movement of the extremities. Your initial vital signs indicate a slow respiratory rate and a heart rate around 80 to 90 beats per minute. The infant seems distressed but does not cry when touched. Complete the first 1-minute APGAR score for this infant using the following chart.

The APGAR Score					
Sign	0	1	2	Score 1 min.	5 min.
Appearance (Skin color)	Blue, pale	Body pink, extremities blue	Completely pink		
Pulse Rate (Heart rate)	Absent	Below 100	Above 100		
Grimace (Irritability)	No response	Grimace	Cries		
Activity (Muscle tone)	Limp	Some flexion of extremities	Active motion		
Respiratory Effort	Absent	Slow and irregular	Strong cry		
			TOTAL SCORE =		

Part II

You have begun to follow the inverted pyramid by drying, warming, positioning, suctioning, and providing tactile stimulation to the newborn. Based upon the inverted pyramid, what would be the next steps if the infant does not "perk up"? Indicate these steps, in the correct order, on the following incomplete diagram.

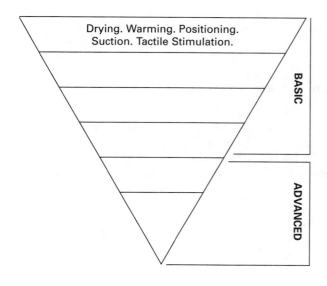

Part III

Fortunately, the stimulation that you provided has been helpful. At this time, both the family and your crew feel immense relief as the infant begins to cry and thrash about. A quick assessment of the vitals reveals a pulse rate well over 100 beats per minute. The infant's body is now pink, but the extremities are still a bit blue. Recalculate the APGAR score, using the chart in Part I, now that 5 minutes have quickly gone by.

2 Pediatrics

Review of Chapter Objectives

After reading this chapter, you should be able to:

1. **Discuss the paramedic's role in the reduction of infant and childhood morbidity and mortality from acute illness and injury.**   **pp. 41–43**

When considering the reduction of pediatric morbidity and mortality, your role as a paramedic centers around two key concepts. First, you must realize that pediatric injuries have become a major health concern. Second, you should remember that children are at a higher risk of injury than adults and that they are more likely to be adversely affected by the injuries that they suffer.

In addition to pediatric injuries, paramedics are often responsible for treating the ill child. There are many aspects of disease and disease processes that are unique to children. It is important that the paramedic be familiar with these, as early intervention is often the key to reduced morbidity and mortality.

2. **Identify methods/mechanisms that prevent injuries to infants and children.**   **pp. 42–43**

As a paramedic, you can help reduce the rate of injury by taking advantage of opportunities to share "teaching points" in your daily life, both personally and professionally. Take part in, or offer to organize, school or community programs in injury prevention or health care. Engage student interest in the EMS profession by volunteering to speak at "career days," emphasizing those aspects of your job that relate to young people. Use nonurgent ambulance calls as a chance to educate family members or caregivers on the importance of "child-proofing" a home or neighborhood. Work with appropriate agencies in initiating or conducting safety inspections, block watches, and more.

3. **Describe Emergency Medical Services for Children (EMSC) and how it can affect patient outcome.**   **p. 42**

Emergency Medical Services for Children (EMSC) is a federally funded program aimed at improving the health of pediatric patients who suffer life-threatening illnesses and injuries. EMSC falls under the management of the Maternal and Child Health Bureau, which is an agency of the U.S. Department of Health and Human Services. As part of a nationally coordinated effort, the EMSC program has identified a number of pediatric health care concerns, including community education, data collection, quality improvement, injury prevention, access, prehospital care, emergency care, definitive care, finance, rehabilitation, a systems approach to pediatric care, and ongoing health care from birth to young adulthood.

4. **Identify the common family responses to acute illness and injury of an infant or child.** pp. 44–45

As you might expect, the reaction of parents or caregivers to a pediatric emergency will vary. Initial responses by parents or caregivers might include shock, grief, denial, anger, guilt, fear, or complete loss of control. Their behavior may change during the course of the emergency.

5. **Describe techniques for successful interaction with families of acutely ill or injured infants and children.** pp. 44–45

Communication is the key to successful interaction with families of acutely ill or injured pediatric patients. Preferably only one paramedic will speak with adults at the scene. This will reduce any chance of providing conflicting information and allow a second paramedic to focus on the child. If parents or caregivers sense your confidence and professionalism, they will regain control and trust your suggestions for care. As with the child, most parents and caregivers feel overwhelmed by fear.

If conditions permit, you should allow one of the parents or caregivers to remain with the child at all times. Some family members may be extremely emotional in emergency situations. The child will react more positively to a family member who appears calm and reassuring. If a parent or caregiver is "out of control," have another person take him or her away from the immediate area to settle down. Maintain a reasonable level of suspicion if a child shows a pattern of injuries, some old and some new. In such cases, the parent or caregiver may try to cover up what may be an abusive situation. They may also try to block examination and treatment.

6. **Identify key anatomical, physiological, growth, and developmental characteristics of infants and children and their implications.** pp. 45–49

Children are broken into age groups because they differ in terms of anatomical, physiological, growth, and developmental characteristics. The following are some of the differences:

Newborns (first hours after birth). The term *newborn* refers to a baby in the first hours of extrauterine life. These patients are assessed using the APGAR scoring system, which was described in Chapter 1. Resuscitation of the newborn generally follows the inverted pyramid described in Chapter 1 and the guidelines established in the Neonatal Advanced Life Support (NALS) curriculum.

Neonates (ages birth to 1 month). The neonate typically loses up to 10 percent of its birth weight as it adjusts to extrauterine life. This lost weight, however, is ordinarily recovered within 10 days. Gestational age affects early growth. Children born at term (40 weeks) should follow accepted developmental guidelines. Infants born prematurely will not be as developed, either neurologically or physically, as their term counterparts.

The neonatal stage of development centers on reflexes. The neonate's personality also begins to form. Common illnesses in this age group include jaundice, vomiting, and respiratory distress. The approach to this age group should include several factors. First, the child should always be kept warm. Observe skin color, muscle tone, and respiratory activity. The absence of tears when crying may indicate dehydration. The lungs should be auscultated early during this exam, while the infant is quiet. Obviously, the history must be obtained from the parents or caregivers. However, it is also important to observe the child.

Infants (ages 1 to 5 months). Infants should have doubled their birth weight by 5 to 6 months of age and can follow the movement of others with their eyes. Muscle control develops in a cephalo-caudal ("head-to-tail") progression, with control spreading from the trunk toward the extremities. Although the infant's personality continues to form, it still centers strongly on the parents or caregivers. Concentrate on keeping these patients warm and comfortable, allowing them to remain in the parent's or caregiver's lap, if possible. A pacifier or bottle can be used to help keep the baby quiet during the examination.

Infants (ages 6 to 12 months). Patients in this age group are active and enjoy exploring the world with their mouths. In this stage of development, the risk of foreign body airway obstruction

(FBAO) becomes a serious concern. Infants 6 months and older have more fully formed personalities and express themselves more readily than younger babies. They have considerable anxiety toward strangers. They don't like lying on their backs, and they tend to cling to their mothers, though the fathers "will do." Common illnesses and accidents include febrile seizures, vomiting, diarrhea, dehydration, bronchiolitis, car crashes, croup, child abuse, poisonings, falls, airway obstructions, and meningitis. These children should be examined while sitting in the lap of the parent or caregiver. The exam should progress in a toe-to-head order, since starting at the face may upset the child. If time and conditions permit, allow the child to become familiar with you before beginning the examination.

Toddlers (ages 1 to 3 years). Great strides in gross motor development occur during this stage. Children tend to run underneath or stand on almost anything. As they grow older, toddlers become braver and more curious or stubborn. They begin to stray away from the parents or caregivers more frequently. Yet these remain the only people who can comfort them quickly, and most children will cling to a parent or caregiver if frightened. At ages 1 to 3, language development begins. Although the majority of the medical history comes from interaction with the parent or caregiver, it is possible to ask the toddler simple questions.

Accidents of all types are the leading cause of injury deaths in pediatric patients ages 1 to 15 years. Common accidents in this age group include motor vehicle collisions, homicides, burn injuries, drownings, and pedestrian collisions. Common illnesses and injuries in the toddler age group include vomiting, diarrhea, febrile seizures, poisonings, falls, child abuse, croup, and meningitis. Keep in mind that FBAO is still a high risk for toddlers.

Be cautious when treating toddlers. Approach toddlers slowly and try to gain their confidence. Conduct the exam in a toe-to-head order. The child may be difficult to examine and may resist being touched. Be sure to tell the child if something will hurt. If at all possible, avoid procedures on the dominant arm/hand, which the child will try to pull away.

Preschoolers (ages 3 to 5 years). Children in this age group show a tremendous increase in fine and gross motor development. Language skills increase greatly. However, if frightened, these children often refuse to speak. They usually have vivid imaginations and may see monsters as part of their world. Preschoolers may have tempers and will express them. During this stage of development, children fear mutilation and may feel threatened by treatment. Avoid frightening or misleading comments. When evaluating a child in this age group, question the child first, keeping in mind that imagination may interfere with the facts. The child often has a distorted sense of time, thus you must rely on the parents or caregivers to fill in the gaps. Common illnesses and injuries in this age group include croup, asthma, poisonings, auto collisions, burns, child abuse, ingestion of foreign bodies, drownings, epiglottitis, febrile seizures, and meningitis.

Start the examination with the chest and evaluate the head last. Do not lie or try to trick the child. Avoid baby talk. If time and situation permit, give the preschooler health care choices.

School-age children (ages 6 to 12 years). School-age children are active and carefree. Growth spurts sometimes lead to clumsiness. The personality continues to develop, and these children are proud and protective of their parents and caregivers. Common illnesses and injuries for this age group include drownings, auto collisions, bicycle accidents, falls, fractures, sports injuries, child abuse, and burns.

When examining school-age children, give them responsibility for providing the history. However, remember that children may be reluctant to provide information if they sustained an injury while doing something forbidden. The parents or caregivers can fill in the pertinent details. During assessment, respect the modesty of school-age children. Also, remember to be honest and tell the child what is wrong.

Adolescents (ages 13 to 18 years). Adolescence covers the period from the end of childhood to the start of adulthood (age 18). It begins with puberty, roughly at age 13 for males and age 11 for females. Puberty is highly child specific and can begin at various ages. Adolescents vary significantly in their development. Those over age 15 are physically nearer to adults in terms of their vital signs but emotionally may still be children. Regardless of physical maturity, remember that teenagers as

©2006 Pearson Education, Inc.
Paramedic Care: Principles & Practice, Vol. 5

a group are "body conscious." The slightest possibility of a lasting scar may be a tremendous issue to the adolescent patient. Common illnesses and injuries in this age group include mononucleosis, asthma, auto collisions, sports injuries, drug and alcohol problems, suicide gestures, and sexual abuse. Remember that pregnancy is also possible in female adolescents.

In examining an adolescent patient, it may be wise to conduct the interview away from the parents or caregivers. If you must perform a detailed physical exam, respect the teenager's sense of privacy. If the patient exhibits modesty or bodily shame, have a paramedic of the same sex as the teenager conduct the exam. Although patients in this age group are not legally adults, keep in mind that most of them see themselves as grown up and will take offense at the use of the word "child."

7. Outline differences in adult and childhood anatomy, physiology, and "normal" age-group-related vital signs. pp. 49–54

Anatomical or physiological differences in infants and children as compared with adults include:

- A proportionally larger tongue
- Smaller airway structures
- Abundant secretions
- Deciduous (baby) teeth
- Flat nose and face
- Head heavier relative to body and less-developed neck structures and muscles
- Fontanelle and open sutures (soft spots) palpable on top of a young infant's head
- Thinner, softer brain tissue
- Head larger in proportion to the body
- Shorter, narrower, more elastic (flexible) trachea
- Short neck
- Abdominal breathers with a faster respiratory rate
- In the case of newborns, breathe primarily through the nose (obligate nose breathers)
- Larger body surface relative to their body mass
- Softer bones
- More exposed spleen and liver
- More easily dehydrated
- Less blood and in greater danger of developing severe shock or bleeding to death from a relatively minor wound
- Immature temperature control mechanism (unstable in babies)

Age-related differences in vital signs include:

- Pulse rates (average) by age group:
  —Newborn: 100–180
  —Infant 0–5 months: 100–160
  —Infant 6–12 months: 100–160
  —Toddler 1–3 years: 80–110
  —Preschooler 3–5 years: 70–110
  —School-age child 6–10 years: 65–110
  —Early adolescent 11–14 years: 60–90
- Respiratory rates (average) by age group:
  —Newborn: 30–60
  —Infant 0–5 months: 30–60
  —Infant 6–12 months: 30–60
  —Toddler 1–3 years: 24–40
  —Preschooler 3–5 years: 22–34
  —School-age child 6–10 years: 18–30
  —Early adolescent 11–14 years: 12–26

- Blood pressure (average/mmHg at rest) by age group:

	Systolic Approx. 90 plus 2 × age	Diastolic Approx. 2/3 systolic
—Preschooler 3–5 years:	Average 98 (78–116)	Average 65
—School-age child 6–10 years:	Average 105 (80–122)	Average 69
—Early adolescent 11–14 years:	Average 114 (88–140)	Average 76

8. Describe techniques for successful assessment and treatment of infants and children. pp. 54–67

Many of the components of the initial patient assessment can be done during a visual examination of the scene ("assessment from the doorway"). Whenever possible, involve the parent or caregiver in efforts to calm or comfort the child. Depending on the situation, you may decide to allow the parent or caregiver to remain with the child during treatment and transport. The developmental stage of the patient and the coping skills of the parents or guardians will be key factors in making this decision.

When interacting with parents or other responsible adults, pay attention to the way in which parents or caregivers interact with the child. Are the interactions appropriate to the emergency? Are family members concerned? Are they angry? Are they overly emotional or entirely indifferent?

From the time of dispatch, you will continually acquire information relative to the patient's condition. As with all patients, personal safety must be your first priority. In treating pediatric patients, follow the same guidelines in approaching the scene as you would with any other patient. Observe for potentially hazardous situations and make sure you take appropriate BSI precautions. Remember that infants and young children are at especially high risk for infection.

9. Discuss the appropriate equipment used to obtain pediatric vital signs. pp. 65–67

Remember that poorly taken vital signs are of less value than no vital signs at all. Therefore, you must have the correct equipment to obtain pediatric vital signs. Items include appropriate-sized blood pressure cuffs, a pediatric stethoscope, and so on. Modern noninvasive monitoring devices all have their application to emergency care. These devices may include pulse oximeter, automated blood pressure devices, self-registering thermometers, and ECGs. However, these devices may frighten a child. Before applying any monitoring device, explain what you are going to do and then demonstrate the device.

10. Determine appropriate airway adjuncts, ventilation devices, and endotracheal intubation equipment; their proper use; and complications of use with infants and children. pp. 67–80

As a general rule, use airway adjuncts in pediatric patients only if prolonged artificial ventilations are required. There are two reasons for this. First, infants and children often improve quickly through the administration of 100 percent oxygen. Second, airway adjuncts may create greater complications in children than in adults.

Keeping this in mind, be sure to have available the appropriate-sized airway adjuncts for each pediatric age group. Basic equipment includes oral and nasal airway's, a pediatric BVM, smaller sized suction catheters, smaller sized masks for the BVM, age-appropriate nasogastric tubes, and a pediatric laryngoscope, blades, and ET tubes. It is also a good idea to carry a Broselow tape, which, after measuring the child's height, displays the appropriate sizes of tubes.

The biggest complication of airway management for the pediatric patient is the possibility of overinflation, which allows air to gather in the stomach. Gastric distention can cause pressure on the diaphragm, making full expansion of the lungs difficult. For specific techniques in airway management in the pediatric patient, review the steps and scan sheets in the textbook, especially those dealing with advanced airway and ventilatory management.

When an endotracheal tube is placed in the pediatric patient appropriately, visualize the tube passing the vocal cords, check for bilateral breath sounds and absent sounds over the epigastrium. Esophageal detector devices may give false-positive responses (due to uncuffed tubes) and, hence, colormetric detector or waveform capnography are preferred. Continuous or periodic evaluation of tube placement is recommended as ET tubes may displace during transport.

11. **List the indications and methods of gastric decompression for infants
and children.**   pp. 80–81, 82

If gastric distention is present in a pediatric patient, you may consider placing a nasogastric (NG) tube. In infants and children, gastric distention may result from overly aggressive artificial ventilations or from air swallowing. Placement of an NG tube will allow you to decompress the stomach and the proximal bowel of air. An NG tube can also be used to empty the stomach of blood or other substances. Indications for use of nasogastric intubation include an inability to achieve adequate tidal volumes during ventilation due to gastric distention and the presence of gastric distention in an unresponsive patient.

As with nasopharyngeal airways, an NG tube is contraindicated in pediatric patients who have sustained head or facial trauma. Because the NG tube might migrate into the cranial sinuses, consider the use of an orogastric tube instead. Other contraindications include possible soft-tissue damage in the nose and inducement of vomiting.

In determining the correct length of NG tube, measure the tube from the top of the nose, over the ear, to the tip of the xiphoid process. To insert an NG tube, you should:

- Oxygenate and continue to ventilate, if possible.
- Measure the NG tube from the tip of the nose, over the ear, to the tip of the xiphoid process.
- Lubricate the end of the tube. Then pass it gently downward along the nasal floor to the stomach.
- Auscultate over the epigastrium to confirm correct placement. Listen for bubbling while injecting 10 to 20 cc of air into the tube.
- Use suction to aspirate stomach contents.
- Secure the tube in place.

12. **Define pediatric respiratory distress, failure, and arrest.**   pp. 90–91

The severity of respiratory compromise can be quickly classified into the following categories:

Respiratory distress. The mildest form of respiratory impairment is classified as respiratory distress. The most noticeable finding is the increased work of breathing. The signs and symptoms of respiratory distress include a normal mental status deteriorating to irritability or anxiety, tachypnea, retractions, nasal flaring (in infants), good muscle tone, head bobbing, grunting, and cyanosis that improves with supplemental oxygen. If not corrected immediately, respiratory distress will lead to respiratory failure.

Respiratory failure. Respiratory failure occurs when the respiratory system is not able to meet the demands of the body for oxygen intake and for carbon dioxide removal. It is characterized by inadequate ventilation and oxygenation. During respiratory failure, the carbon dioxide level begins to rise because the body is not able to remove carbon dioxide. This ultimately leads to respiratory acidosis. The signs and symptoms of respiratory failure include irritability or anxiety deteriorating to lethargy, marked tachypnea later deteriorating to bradypnea, marked retractions later deteriorating to agonal respirations, poor muscle tone, marked tachycardia later deteriorating to bradycardia, and central cyanosis. Respiratory failure is a very ominous sign. If immediate intervention is not provided, the child will deteriorate to full respiratory arrest.

Respiratory arrest. The end result of respiratory impairment, if untreated, is respiratory arrest. The cessation of breathing typically follows a period of bradypnea and agonal respirations. The signs and symptoms of respiratory arrest include unresponsiveness deteriorating to coma, bradypnea deteriorating to apnea, absent chest wall movement, bradycardia deteriorating to asystole, and profound cyanosis. Respiratory arrest will quickly deteriorate to full cardiopulmonary arrest if appropriate interventions are not made. The child's chances of survival markedly decrease when cardiopulmonary arrest occurs.

13. **Differentiate between upper airway obstruction and lower airway disease.**   pp. 92–99

Obstruction of the upper airway can be caused by many factors and may be partial or complete. Obstruction can result from inflamed or swollen tissues, which may be caused by infection or by aspirating a foreign body. Two medical conditions that can lead to upper airway obstruction in pediatric patients include croup and epiglottitis. Appropriate care depends on prompt and immediate identification of the disorder and its severity.

Suspect lower airway distress when the following conditions exist: an absence of stridor, presence of wheezing during exhalation, and increased work of breathing. Common causes of lower airway disease include respiratory diseases such as asthma, bronchiolitis, and pneumonia. Although infrequent, you may also encounter cases of foreign body lower airway aspiration, especially in toddlers and preschoolers.

14. Describe the general approach to the treatment of children with respiratory distress, failure, or arrest from upper airway obstruction or lower airway disease. pp. 93–99

The general approach to the child with respiratory distress or failure from an upper or lower airway problem is to assess the child in the least stressful way possible and to administer oxygen. If the child has a complete upper airway obstruction, the appropriate FBAO maneuvers will need to be quickly done. If the child is in respiratory arrest, begin BVM resuscitation and consider the need for ET tube insertion. An NG tube may be useful to minimize gastric distention. If the child is in respiratory failure, assisted ventilations should also be considered.

In cases of upper airway obstruction, keep this precaution in mind: Because it is difficult to distinguish croup from epiglottitis in the prehospital setting, never examine the oropharynx. If epiglottitis is present, examination of the oropharynx may result in laryngospasm and complete airway obstruction. In fact, if the patient is maintaining his or her airway, *do not put anything into the child's mouth*, including a thermometer. In the case of foreign body aspiration, do not attempt to look into the child's mouth if the obstruction is partial. Instead make the child comfortable and administer humidified oxygen. If the obstruction is complete, clear the airway with accepted basic life support techniques. However, DO NOT perform blind finger sweeps, because this can push a foreign body deeper into the airway.

When treating lower airway diseases, the primary goal is to support ventilations through the use of supplemental, humidified oxygen and appropriate pharmacological therapy such as bronchodilator medications (asthma and bronchiolitis). If prolonged ventilation will be required, perform endotracheal intubation.

15. Discuss the common causes and relative severity of hypoperfusion in infants and children. pp. 99–103

The second major cause of pediatric cardiopulmonary arrest—after respiratory impairment—is shock. Shock can most simply be defined as inadequate perfusion of the tissues with oxygen and other essential nutrients and inadequate removal of metabolic waste products.

When compared with the incidence of shock in adults, shock is an unusual occurrence in children because their blood vessels constrict so efficiently. However, when the blood pressure does drop, it drops so far and so fast that the child may quickly develop cardiopulmonary arrest. A number of factors place infants and young children at risk for shock. Newborns and neonates can develop shock as a result of loss of body heat. Other causes include dehydration (from vomiting and/or diarrhea), infection (particularly septicemia), trauma, and blood loss. Less common causes of shock in infants and children include allergic reactions, poisoning, and cardiac events.

As in adults, the severity of shock in a pediatric patient is classified as compensated shock, decompensated shock, and irreversible shock. It can also be categorized as *cardiogenic* or *noncardiogenic*. Cardiogenic shock results from an inability of the heart to maintain an adequate cardiac output to the circulatory system and tissues. Cardiogenic shock in a pediatric patient is ominous and often fatal. Noncardiogenic shock—types of shock that result from causes other than inadequate cardiac output—is more frequently encountered in pediatric patients, because they have a much lower incidence of cardiac problems than adults. Causes of noncardiogenic shock may include hemorrhage, abdominal trauma, systemic bacterial infection, spinal cord injury, and others.

16. Identify the major classifications of pediatric cardiac rhythms. pp. 104–108

Dysrhythmias in children are uncommon. When dysrhythmias occur, bradydysrhythmias are the most common. Supraventricular tachydysrhythmias are very uncommon. Dysrhythmias can cause pump failure, ultimately leading to cardiogenic shock. Children have a very limited capacity to in-

©2006 Pearson Education, Inc.
Paramedic Care: Principles & Practice, Vol. 5

crease stroke volume. The primary mechanism through which they increase cardiac output is through changes in the heart rate. The treatment of dysrhythmias is specific for the dysrhythmia in question.

17. Discuss the primary etiologies of cardiopulmonary arrest in infants and children. pp. 90–91, 99

The primary causes of cardiopulmonary arrest in infants and children include untreated respiratory failure, immaturity of the cardiac conductive system, bradycardia, hypoxia, vagal stimulation (rare), drug overdose, drowning, multiple system trauma, electrocution, pericardial tamponade, tension pneumothorax, acidosis, hypothermia, hypoglycemia, and FBAO.

18. Discuss age-appropriate sites, equipment, techniques, and complications of vascular access for infants and children. pp. 83–85

Intravenous techniques for children are basically the same as for adults. (See Volume 1, Chapter 10, "Medication Administration.") However, additional veins may be accessed in an infant. These include veins of the neck and scalp, as well as of the arms, hands, and feet. The external jugular vein, however, should only be used in life-threatening situations.

The use of intraosseous (IO) infusion has become popular in the pediatric patient. This is especially true when large volumes of fluid must be administered, as occurs in hypovolemic shock, and when other means of venous access are unavailable. The indications for IO include the existence of shock or cardiac arrest, an unresponsive patient, or an unsuccessful attempt at a peripheral IV insertion. The contraindications for IO infusion include the presence of a fracture in the bone chosen for infusion and a fracture of the pelvis or extremity fracture proximal to the chosen site.

In performing IO perfusion, you can use a standard 16- or 18-gauge needle (either hypodermic or spinal). However, an intraosseous needle is preferred and significantly better. Basic steps are as follows: Prep the anterior surface of the leg below the knee with antiseptic solution (povidone iodine), and insert the needle in a twisting fashion 1 to 3 cm below the tuberosity. Insertion should be slightly inferior in direction (to avoid the growth plate) and perpendicular to the skin. Signs of correct placement of the needle into the marrow cavity include a lack of resistance as the needle passes through the bony cortex, the ability of the needle to stand upright without support, the ability to aspirate bone marrow into a syringe, or free flow of the infusion without infiltration into the subcutaneous tissues.

19. Describe the primary etiologies of altered levels of consciousness in infants and children. pp. 89–116, 121–122, 132

The primary causes of an altered level of consciousness in infants and children include infection (fever), traumatic brain injury, respiratory failure (hypoxia), hypoperfusion, and dysrhythmias. Although metabolic causes such as seizures and hypoglycemia are fairly uncommon, they can and do produce altered levels of consciousness in children. Shunt failures may also present as altered mental status.

20. Identify common lethal mechanisms of injury in infants and children. pp. 116–119

The most common pediatric mechanisms of injury (MOI) include falls, motor vehicle crashes, car vs. pedestrian collisions, drownings and near drownings, penetrating injuries, burns, and physical abuse.

21. Discuss anatomical features of children that predispose or protect them from certain injuries. pp. 122–125

Head. Small children have larger heads in proportion to the rest of their bodies. For this reason, when they fall or are thrown through the air, they often land head first, predisposing them to serious head injury. The larger relative mass of the head and lack of neck muscle strength also provide increased momentum in acceleration-deceleration injuries and a greater stress on the cervical spine. Because the skull is softer and more compliant in infants and young children than in adults, brain injuries occur more readily.

Chest and abdomen. Infants and young children lack the rigid rib cages of adults. Therefore, they suffer fewer rib fractures and more intrathoracic injuries. Remember that chest injuries are the second most common cause of pediatric trauma death. Because of the compliance of the chest wall, severe intrathoracic injury can be present without signs of external injury. Likewise, their relatively underdeveloped abdominal musculature affords minimal protection to the viscera, particularly the spleen.

Extremities. Because children have more flexible bones than adults, they tend to have incomplete fractures such as bend fractures, buckle fractures, and greenstick fractures. Therefore, you should treat "sprains" and "strains" as fractures and immobilize accordingly. In younger children, the bone growth plates have not yet closed. Some growth plate fractures can lead to permanent disability if not managed correctly.

Body surface. There are three distinguishing features of the pediatric patient's skin and body surface area (BSA). First, the skin of an infant or child is thinner than that of an adult. Second, infants and children generally have less subcutaneous fat. Finally, they have a larger BSA-to-weight ratio. As a result of these features, children risk greater injury from extremes in temperature or thermal exposure. They lose fluids and heat more quickly than adults and have a greater likelihood of dehydration and hypothermia. They also burn more easily and deeper than adults, which explains why burns are one of the leading causes of death among pediatric trauma patients.

22. Describe aspects of infant and child airway management that are affected by a potential cervical spine injury. pp. 119–120

An infant's open airway is in the neutral or extended position but not in the hyperextended position. This needs to be kept in mind when positioning the infant who may have sustained a neck injury where there can be little to no movement of the neck for fear of worsening the potential neck injury. Children under the age of 6 usually have large heads in proportion to the rest of their bodies. Therefore, it is often necessary to pad behind the shoulders when a cervical collar is applied as a part of the spinal immobilization. Keep infants, toddlers, and preschoolers with the cervical spine injury in a neutral in-line position by placing padding from the shoulders to the hips.

Always make sure that you use the appropriate-sized pediatric immobilization equipment. These supplies may include rigid cervical collars, towel or blanket rolls, foam head blocks, commercial pediatric immobilization devices, vest-type or short wooden backboards, and long boards with the appropriate padding.

23. Identify infant and child trauma patients who require spinal immobilization. p. 86

Children are not small adults. Although spinal injuries are not as common as in adults, they do occur, especially because of a child's disproportionately larger and heavier head. Any time an infant or child sustains a significant head injury, assume that a neck injury may be present. Children can suffer a spinal cord injury with no noticeable damage to the vertebral column as seen on cervical spine X-rays. Thus, negative cervical spine X-rays do not necessary assure that a spinal cord injury does not exist. As a result, children should remain immobilized until a spinal cord injury has been ruled out by hospital personnel.

Remember that many children, especially those under age 5, will protest or fight restraints. Try to minimize the emotional stress by having a parent or caregiver stand near or touch the child.

24. Discuss fluid management and shock treatment for infant and child trauma patients. pp. 100–103, 120–121

Fluid management and shock treatment for pediatric trauma patients should include administration of supplemental oxygen and establishment of intravenous access. However, DO NOT delay transport to gain venous access. Management of the airway and breathing takes priority over management of circulation, because circulatory compromise is less common in children than in adults.

When obtaining vascular access, remember the following:

- If possible, insert a large-bore catheter into a peripheral vein.
- Intraosseous access in children less than 6 years of age is an alternative when a peripheral IV cannot be obtained.

- Once venous access is obtained, administer an initial fluid bolus of 20 mL/kg of lactated Ringer's solution or normal saline.
- Reassess the patient's vital signs and give additional boluses of 20 mL/kg up to 100 mL/kg if there is no improvement.
- If improvement does not occur after the second bolus, there is likely to be a significant blood loss that may require surgical intervention. Rapid transport is essential.

25. Determine when pain management and sedation are appropriate for infants and children. p. 121

Many pediatric injuries are painful and analgesics are indicated. These include burns, long bone fractures, dislocations, and others. Unless there is a contraindication, pediatric patients should receive analgesics. Commonly used analgesics include meperidine, morphine, and fentanyl. It is best to avoid using synthetic analgesics (e.g., butorphanol [Stado], nalbuphine [Nubain]) because their effects on children are unpredictable. Also, certain pediatric emergencies may benefit from sedation. These include such problems as penetrating eye injuries, prolonged rescue from entrapment in machinery, cardioversion, and other painful procedures. Always consult medical direction if you feel pediatric analgesia or sedation may be required.

26. Define child abuse, child neglect, and sudden infant death syndrome (SIDS). pp. 125–129

Child abuse is the intentional effort by a parent or caregiver to harm a child physically, psychologically, or sexually. Abuse can also take the form of **child neglect** (either physical or emotional), in which the physical, mental, and/or emotional well-being of the child is ignored.

Sudden infant death syndrome (SIDS) is defined as the sudden death of an infant during the first year of life from an illness of unknown etiology, with peak incidence occurring at 2 to 4 months.

27. Discuss the parent/caregiver responses to the death of an infant or child. p. 126

The responses of the parent or caregiver to the death of a child include the normal grief reactions. Initially, there may be shock, disbelief, and denial. Other times, the parents or caregivers may express anger, rage, hostility, blame, or guilt. Often, there is a feeling of inadequacy as well as helplessness, confusion, and fear. The grief process is likely to last for years, as in the case of a SIDS death.

28. Define children with special health care needs and technology-assisted children. pp. 130–133

In recent years medical technology has lowered infant mortality rates and allowed a greater number of children with special needs to live at home. Some of these infants and children include:

- Premature babies
- Infants and children with lung disease, heart disease, or neurologic disorders
- Infants and children with chronic diseases, such as cystic fibrosis, asthma, childhood cancers, cerebral palsy, and others
- Infants and children with altered functions from birth (e.g., spina bifida, congenital birth defects, and cerebral palsy)

On some calls, you may be asked to treat technology-assisted children who depend, in varying degrees, upon special equipment. Commonly found devices include tracheostomy tubes, apnea monitors, home artificial ventilators, central intravenous lines, gastric feeding tubes, gastrostomy tubes, and shunts. (For more on these devices, see Chapter 6, "Acute Interventions for the Chronic-Care Patient.")

29. Discuss basic cardiac life support (CPR) guidelines for infants and children. pp. 67–74

The CPR guidelines for infants and children are periodically revised. The Brady website at www.bradybooks.com provides the most up-to-date information on these standards.

30. **Integrate advanced life support skills with basic cardiac life support for infants and children.** pp. 74–85, 104–108

This is a skills objective that should be practiced in the classroom lab setting. You should work through simulated "mega-codes" that involve both BLS and ALS responders administering all the appropriate treatments as specified in their regional protocols and the American Heart Association's PALS algorithms.

31. **Discuss the indications, dosage, route of administration, and special considerations for medication administration in infants and children.** pp. 84–86

When administering medications to any patient of any age, the paramedic needs to know the indications, contraindications, correct dose, correct route of administration, and any expected side effects of the medication. Specifically, when administering the medications to infants and children, be very careful and accurate with the dose. Most medication doses are weight specific, so it will be necessary to have a rough idea of the weight of the patient or to use some other tool such as the Broselow tape.

The objectives of medication therapy in pediatric patients include:

- Correction of hypoxemia
- Increased perfusion pressure during chest compressions
- Stimulation of spontaneous or more forceful cardiac contractions
- Acceleration of the heart rate
- Correction of metabolic acidosis
- Management of pain (see objective 25)
- Treatment of seizures (see objective 33)

In administering medications to pediatric patients, consult with medical direction.

32. **Discuss appropriate transport guidelines for low- and high-risk infants and children.** pp. 86, 89

In managing a pediatric patient, never delay transport to perform a procedure that can be done en route to the hospital. After deciding on necessary interventions—first BLS, then ALS—determine the appropriate receiving facility. In reaching your decision, consider three factors: time of transport, specialized facilities, and specialized personnel. If you live in an area with specialized prehospital crews such as critical care crews and neonatal nurses, their availability should weigh in your decision. Consider whether the patient would benefit from transfer by one of these crews. (For more on transport guides for low- and high-risk infants, see Chapter 1, "Neonatology.")

33. **Describe the epidemiology, including the incidence, morbidity/mortality risk factors, prevention strategies, pathophysiology, assessment, and treatment of infants and children with:**

   a. Respiratory distress/failure pp. 90–99
   Respiratory emergencies constitute the most common reason EMS is summoned to care for a pediatric patient. Respiratory illnesses can cause respiratory compromise due to their effect on the alveolar/capillary interface. Some illnesses are quite minor, causing only minor symptoms, while others can be rapidly fatal. Your approach to the child with a respiratory emergency will depend on the severity of respiratory compromise (see objectives 12 and 13). If the child is alert and talking, then you can take a more relaxed approach. However, if the child appears ill and exhibits marked respiratory difficulty, then you must immediately intervene to prevent respiratory arrest and possible cardiopulmonary arrest.

   Pediatric patients with late respiratory failure or respiratory arrest require aggressive treatment. This includes:

- Establishment of an airway
- Administration of high-flow, high-concentration, supplemental oxygen
- Mechanical ventilation with a BVM device attached to a reservoir delivering 100 percent oxygen

- Endotracheal intubation if mechanical ventilation does not rapidly improve the patient's condition
- Consideration of gastric decompression with an orogastric or nasogastric tube if abdominal distention is impeding ventilation
- Consideration of needle decompression of the chest if a tension pneumothorax is suspected
- Consideration of cricothyrotomy if complete obstruction is present and the airway cannot be obtained by any other method
- Obtaining venous access, and transporting to a facility equipped to handle critically ill children

b. Hypoperfusion   pp. 99–103

As noted, shock is the second major cause of pediatric cardiopulmonary arrest. For an overview of the causes and degrees of severity of hypoperfusion in infants and children, see objective 15.

   The definitive care of shock takes place in the emergency department of a hospital. Because shock is a life-threatening condition in pediatric patients, it is important to recognize early signs and symptoms—or even the possibility of shock in a situation where the signs and symptoms have not yet developed. In a situation in which you suspect a possibility of shock, provide oxygen to boost tissue perfusion and transport as quickly as possible. Also, keep the patient in a supine position and take steps to protect the child from hypothermia and agitation that might worsen the condition. In some cases (compensated shock), fluid therapy as ordered by medical direction can buy time until the patient arrives an appropriate treatment center. (See objective 24 for more on fluid therapy and shock management.)

c. Cardiac dysrhythmias   pp. 104–108

Dysrhythmias in children are uncommon. When dysrhythmias occur, bradydysrhythmias are the most common. Supraventricular tachydysrhythmias are very uncommon. Dysrhythmias can cause pump failure, ultimately leading to cardiogenic shock. Children have a very limited capacity to increase stroke volume. The primary mechanism through which they increase cardiac output is through changes in the heart rate. The treatment of dysrhythmias is specific for the dysrhythmia in question.

d. Neurologic emergencies   pp. 108–110

Neurologic emergencies in childhood are fairly uncommon. However, seizures can and do occur. In fact, they are a frequent reason for summoning EMS. In addition to seizures, meningitis tends to show up more often in children than in adults. Although your chances of encountering either of these two conditions are small, both are life threatening and should be promptly identified and treated.

   Seizures. The etiology for seizures is often unknown. However, several risk factors have been identified. They include fever, hypoxia, infections, idiopathic epilepsy (epilepsy of unknown origin), electrolyte disturbances, head trauma, hypoglycemia, toxic ingestions or exposure, tumor, or CNS malformations. Management of pediatric seizures is essentially the same as for the seizing adult. Place patients on the floor or on the bed. Be sure to lay them on their side, away from furniture. Do not restrain patients, but take steps to protect them from injury. Maintain the airway, but do not force anything, such as a bite stick, between the teeth. Administer supplemental oxygen. Then take and record all vital signs. If the patient is febrile, remove excess layers of clothing, while avoiding extreme cooling. If status epilepticus is present, institute the following steps:

- Start an IV of normal saline or lactated Ringer's and perform a glucometer evaluation.
- Administer diazepam as follows:
  —**Children 1 month to 5 years:** 0.2 to 0.5 mg slowly IV push every 2 to 5 minutes to a maximum of 2.5 milligrams.
  —**Children 5 years and older:** 1 mg slowly IV push every 2 to 5 minutes to a maximum of 5 milligrams.
- Contact medical direction for additional dosing. Diazepam can be administered rectally if an IV cannot be established.
- If the seizure appears to be due to a fever and a long transport time is anticipated, medical direction may request the administration of acetaminophen to lower the fever. Acetaminophen is supplied as an elixir or as suppositories. The dose should be 15 mg/kg body weight.

Meningitis. Meningitis is an infection of the meninges, the lining of the brain and spinal cord. Meningitis can result from either a virus and a bacteria. These infections can be rapidly fatal if they are not promptly recognized and treated appropriately. Prehospital care of the pediatric patient with meningitis is supportive. Rapidly complete the initial assessment and transport the child to the emergency department. If shock is present, treat the child with IV fluids (20 mL/kg) and oxygen.

e. Trauma pp. 116–125

Trauma is the number one cause of death in infants and children. Most pediatric injuries result from blunt trauma. As noted in objective 21, children have thinner and more pliable body walls that allow forces to be more readily transmitted to body contents, increasing the possibility of injury to internal tissues and organs. If you serve in an urban area, you can expect to see a higher incidence of penetrating trauma, mostly intentional and mostly from gunfire or knife wounds. Significant incidences of penetrating trauma are also seen outside the cities, mostly unintentional from hunting and agricultural accidents.

Although pediatric patients can be injured in the same way as adults, children tend to be more susceptible to certain types of injuries than grown-ups. Falls, for example, are the single most common cause of injury in children. Other mechanisms of injury include motor vehicle collisions, car vs. pedestrian injuries, drownings and near-drownings, penetrating injuries, burns, and physical abuse.

The treatment of trauma is injury specific. It involves management of the ABCs, management of the injury (e.g., spinal immobilization, splinting of fractures, control of bleeding), and treatment for possible shock.

f. Abuse and neglect pp. 127–129

Child abuse is the second leading cause of death in infants less than 6 months of age. An estimated 2,000 to 5,000 children die each year as a result of abuse or neglect. Abused children share several common characteristics. Often the child is seen as "special" and different from others. Premature infants and twins stand a higher risk of abuse than other children. Many abused children are less than 5 years of age. Children with physical and mental handicaps as well as those with other special needs are at greater risk. So are uncommunicative (autistic) children. Boys are more often abused than girls. A child who is not what the parents wanted (e.g., the "wrong" gender) is at increased risk of abuse, too.

Signs of abuse or neglect can be startling. As a guide, the following findings should trigger a high index of suspicion:

- Any obvious or suspected fractures in a child under 2 years of age
- Multiple injuries in various stages of healing, especially burns and bruises
- More injuries than usually seen in children of the same age or size
- Injuries scattered on many areas of the body
- Bruises or burns in patterns that suggest intentional infliction
- Increased intracranial pressure in an infant
- Suspected intra-abdominal trauma in a young child
- Any injury that does not fit with the description of the cause given

Information in the medical history may also raise the index of suspicion. Examples include:

- A history that does not match the nature or severity of the injury
- Vague parental accounts or accounts that change during the interview
- Accusations that the child injured himself intentionally
- Delay in seeking help
- Child dressed inappropriately for the situation
- Revealing comment by bystanders, especially siblings

Suspect child neglect if you spot any of the following conditions:

- Extreme malnutrition
- Multiple insect bites
- Long-standing skin infections
- Extreme lack of cleanliness

- Verbal or social skills far below those you would expect for a child of similar age and background
- Lack of appropriate medical care

In cases of child abuse or neglect, the goals of management include appropriate treatment of injuries, protection of the child from further abuse, and notification of proper authorities.

g. Special health-care needs, including technology-assisted children pp. 130–133

For most of human history, infants and children with devastating congenital conditions or diseases either died or remained confined to a hospital. In recent decades, however, medical technology has lowered infant mortality rates and allowed a greater number of children with special needs to live at home. For examples of children with special needs and some of the technological devices used to assist them, see objective 28.

In treating pediatric patients with special needs, remember that they require the same assessment as other patients. (Recall that in the initial assessment, "disability" refers to a patient's neurological status—not to the child's special need.) Keep in mind that the child's special need is often an ongoing process, which may make the parent or caregiver an excellent source of information. In most cases, you should concentrate on the acute problem—the reason for the call. In managing patients with special needs, try to keep several thoughts in mind.

- Avoid using the term *disability* in reference to the child's special need. Instead, think of the patient's many abilities.
- Never assume that the patient cannot understand what you are saying.
- Involve the parents, caregivers, or the patient, if appropriate, in treatment. They manage the illness or congenital condition on a daily basis.
- Treat the patient with a special need with the same respect as any other patient.

h. SIDS pp. 125–126

The incidence of SIDS in the United States is approximately 2 deaths per 1,000 births. It is the leading cause of death between 2 weeks and 1 year of age, with peak incidence occurring at 2 to 4 months. SIDS occurs most frequently in the fall and winter months. It tends to be more common in males than in females. It is more prevalent in premature and low-birth-weight infants, in infants of young mothers, and in infants whose mothers did not receive prenatal care. Infants of mothers who used cocaine, methadone, or heroin during pregnancy are at greater risk. Occasionally, a mild upper respiratory infection will be reported prior to the death. SIDS is not caused by external suffocation from blankets or pillows. Neither is it related to allergies to cow's milk or regurgitation and aspiration of stomach contents. It is not thought to be hereditary.

Current theories vary about the etiology of SIDS. Some authorities feel it may result from an immature respiratory center in the brain that leads the child to simply stop breathing. Others think there may be an airway obstruction in the posterior pharynx as a result of pharyngeal relaxation during sleep, a hypermobile mandible, or an enlarged tongue. Studies strongly link SIDS to a prone sleeping position. Soft bedding, waterbed mattresses, smoking in the home, and/or an overheated environment are other potential associations. A small percentage of SIDS may be abuse related.

Unless the infant is obviously dead, undertake active and aggressive care of the infant to assure the family or caregivers that everything possible is being done. A first responder or other personnel should be assigned to assist the parents or caregivers and to explain the procedure. At all points, use the baby's name.

34. Given several preprogrammed simulated pediatric patients, provide the appropriate assessment, treatment, and transport. pp. 41–133

During your classroom, clinical, and field training, you will be presented with real and simulated pediatric patients. Assess and treat them. Use the information provided in this chapter and the information and skills you gain from your instructors and clinical and field preceptors to develop your skill in caring for these patients. Continue to refine newly learned skills once your training ends and you begin your paramedic career.

Case Study Review

Reread the case study on pages 40 and 41 in Paramedic Care: Special Considerations/Operations *and then read the following discussion.*

This case study examines the treatment of a severely dehydrated pediatric patient—a common condition encountered on calls involving infants and young children.

This case involves an infant who has been unable to hold down any food for 3 days. In just a short time, she has developed signs and symptoms that point to possible shock, which the paramedics immediately notice. Their initial assessment starts as soon they observe the quality of the baby's skin (pale, cool, clammy) and the noticeably sunken anterior fontanelle. As the paramedics take vital signs and assess the level of consciousness, they note that the baby cries but does not produce tears. After taking appropriate BSI precautions, they wisely check the infant's diaper to see if it is dry or wet. (If it had been wet, they would have checked the quality of the urine. Dehydrated patients, when they do urinate, have very dark yellow urine because it is a concentrated solute with less solvent [water] than usual.) The dry diaper and the mother's comment confirms a suspicion of dehydration, giving the crew enough information to develop a treatment plan.

The paramedics take this patient very seriously and begin transport before starting fluid therapy. En route to the hospital, they start an IV, which is not always an easy task in a patient this small. They probably keep in mind the use of an intraosseous needle in case an IV cannot be placed. For a patient this dehydrated, it would not be surprising that she might have needed a second bolus of 20 mL/kg of the normal saline. Of course, as is always the case, a parent should be nearby to assist in comforting the patient.

During your paramedic career, you can expect to take part in a call similar to this one. Dehydration in infants and small children is a common condition, and you should be prepared to respond, assess, and manage the patient accordingly. Remember that dehydration is one of the causes of hypoperfusion (shock) in pediatric patients.

Content Self-Evaluation

MULTIPLE CHOICE

_____ 1. The leading cause of death in pediatric patients in the United States is:
   A. AIDS.
   B. asthma.
   C. trauma.
   D. neglect.
   E. cardiac arrest.

_____ 2. Factors that account for high rates of pediatric injury include all of the following EXCEPT:
   A. weather.
   B. geography.
   C. dangers in the home.
   D. HMOs.
   E. motor vehicle accidents.

_____ 3. The federally funded program aimed at improving the health of pediatric patients who suffer from life-threatening illnesses and injuries is called:
   A. EMSC.
   B. PBTLS.
   C. PALS.
   D. APLS.
   E. TRIPP.

©2006 Pearson Education, Inc.
Paramedic Care: Principles & Practice, Vol. 5

_____ 4. The most common response of children to illness or injury is:
   A. denial.
   B. fear.
   C. excitement.
   D. indifference.
   E. grief.

_____ 5. Treatment of a pediatric patient begins with:
   A. obtaining vital signs.
   B. placement of an ET tube.
   C. administration of oxygen.
   D. focused head-to-toe exam.
   E. communications and psychological support.

_____ 6. While caring for the pediatric patient, whenever possible, the paramedic should:
   A. avoid discussing painful procedures.
   B. administer high-flow high-concentration oxygen.
   C. allow a parent or caregiver to stay with the child.
   D. use correct medical and anatomical terms.
   E. stand in an authoritative posture.

_____ 7. The term _neonate_ describes a baby who is:
   A. newly born.
   B. 10 days or less in age.
   C. up to 1 month in age.
   D. 1 to 5 months in age.
   E. 6 months or more in age.

_____ 8. The age group for which foreign body airway obstruction (FBAO) becomes a concern is:
   A. infants, ages 1–5 months.
   B. infants, ages 6–12 months.
   C. toddlers.
   D. preschoolers.
   E. school-age children.

_____ 9. An infant's airway differs from that of an adult in all of the following ways EXCEPT that it:
   A. is narrower at all levels.
   B. has a softer and more flexible trachea.
   C. is less likely to be blocked by secretions.
   D. has a greater likelihood of soft-tissue injury.
   E. is more prone to obstruction by the tongue.

_____ 10. In comparing pediatric heart and respiratory rates with those of an adult, infants and young children have:
   A. about the same heart and respiratory rates as an adult.
   B. slower heart rates and slower respiratory rates.
   C. slower heart rates and faster respiratory rates.
   D. faster heart rates and slower respiratory rates.
   E. faster heart rates and faster respiratory rates.

_____ 11. Unlike an adult, the trachea of a child can collapse if the neck and head are hyperextended because:
   A. the trachea is softer and more flexible.
   B. a child's tongue takes up more space proportionately.
   C. the cricoid rings are firmer.
   D. a child's larynx is higher.
   E. the airway is wider at all levels.

_____ 12. The two abdominal organs that are most likely to suffer traumatic injury in a pediatric patient are the:
A. kidney and gallbladder.
B. liver and spleen.
C. stomach and small intestine.
D. colon and appendix.
E. bladder and pancreas.

_____ 13. A child's larger BSA-to-weight ratio causes a pediatric patient to be:
A. resilient to temperature changes.
B. prone to hypothermia.
C. difficult to assess.
D. prone to excess subcutaneous fat.
E. less likely to lose fluids quickly.

_____ 14. Although infants and children have a circulating blood volume proportionately larger than adults, their absolute blood volume is:
A. about the same.
B. smaller.
C. even larger.
D. rate dependent.
E. variable.

_____ 15. The pediatric assessment triangle focuses on airway, breathing, and circulation.
A. True   B. False

_____ 16. In an infant or small child, tachypnea, an abnormally rapid rate of breathing, may indicate:
A. fear.
B. pain.
C. inadequate oxygenation.
D. exposure to cold.
E. all of the above.

_____ 17. A respiratory rate of 18 to 30 breaths per minute would be considered normal for a(n):
A. newborn.
B. 6-month-old infant.
C. toddler.
D. preschooler.
E. school-age child.

_____ 18. Which of the following approaches is the correct method for conducting the physical examination of an infant or a very young child?
A. toe-to-head
B. head-to-chest
C. head-to-toe
D. chest-to-head
E. both A and B

_____ 19. To obtain the blood pressure of a pediatric patient, the cuff should be _____ the width of the patient's arm.
A. one fourth
B. one third
C. one half
D. two thirds
E. three fourths

_____ 20. Poorly taken vital signs are of less value than no vital signs at all.
A. True   B. False

_____ 21. Medication administration in the pediatric patient is modified to the patient's:
A. age.
B. height.
C. weight.
D. level of distress.
E. level of consciousness.

_____ 22. The hallmark of pediatric management is:
A. frequent pulse checks.
B. prompt transport.
C. administration of fluids.
D. adequate oxygenation.
E. diagnosis of medical conditions.

_____ 23. As a rule, an oropharyngeal airway should only be used on pediatric patients who:
A. have sustained head or facial trauma.
B. are known to suffer from seizures.
C. show signs of cardiac arrest.
D. exhibit a vagal response.
E. lack a gag reflex.

_____ 24. The only indication for cricothyrotomy in the pediatric patient is:
A. a foreign body airway obstruction.
B. desire to suction the airway.
C. failure to obtain an airway by any other method.
D. desire to ventilate by a BVM.
E. both A and C.

_____ 25. An indication for performing an endotracheal intubation in a pediatric patient includes:
A. need to gain access for suctioning.
B. necessity of providing a route for drug administration.
C. need for prolonged artificial ventilations.
D. failure to provide adequate ventilations with a BVM.
E. all of the above.

_____ 26. The optimal positioning of the head for pediatric intubation in the absence of a spinal injury is:
A. neutral.
B. hyperextended.
C. sniffing.
D. head-tilt.
E. spine.

_____ 27. If gastric distention is present in a pediatric patient, a paramedic might consider placing a(n):
A. oropharyngeal airway.
B. nasopharyngeal airway.
C. needle cricothyrotomy.
D. nasogastric tube.
E. endotracheal tube.

_____ 28. In obtaining vascular access in a pediatric patient, the external jugular vein should only be used in life-threatening situations.
A. True
B. False

_____ 29. The indications for use of intraosseous infusion include all of the following EXCEPT:
A. in a patient less than 6 years old.
B. for existence of shock or cardiac arrest.
C. for presence of a facture in the pelvis.
D. for an unresponsive patient.
E. for failure to place a peripheral IV.

_____ 30. You are more likely to use electrical therapy on pediatric patients than adult patients.
A. True   B. False

_____ 31. All of the following are symptoms of epiglottitis EXCEPT:
A. a rapid onset.
B. occasional stridor.
C. a barking cough.
D. drooling.
E. a fever of approximately 102 to 104° F.

_____ 32. In treating a patient with epiglottitis, a paramedic should:
A. take blood pressure regularly.
B. attempt to visualize the oropharynx.
C. take the child's temperature orally.
D. place the child in a supine position.
E. none of the above.

_____ 33. Common causes of lower airway distress include all of the following EXCEPT:
A. pneumonia.   D. bronchiolitis.
B. asthma.   E. status asthmaticus.
C. croup.

_____ 34. When a child experiences a severe asthma attack without wheezing, this is:
A. an ominous sign.
B. because of a lack of expectorant.
C. a sign of improvement.
D. because of an inability to cough.
E. common, and should not alarm the paramedic.

_____ 35. All of the following are signs and symptoms of shock in a child EXCEPT:
A. pale, cool, clammy skin.
B. impaired mental status.
C. absence of tears when crying.
D. increased urination.
E. a rapid respiratory rate.

_____ 36. Cardiogenic shock is more frequently encountered in prehospital pediatric care than noncardiogenic shock.
A. True   B. False

_____ 37. When dysrhythmias do occur in children, the most common form is a(n):
A. bradydysrhythmia.
B. supraventricular tachydysrhythmia.
C. ventricular tachydysrhythmia.
D. asystole.
E. ventricular fibrillation.

_____ 38. A pediatric patient is seen by a paramedic for a seizure. Assessment and history reveal that the child has a fever of 101°F, was very sleepy and irritable before the seizure, and has had no similar episodes. The child complained of a stiff neck and headache earlier in the day. You suspect that the episode may have been caused by:
A. febrile convulsions.
B. meningitis.
C. hypoglycemia.
D. hypoxia.
E. hyperglycemia.

_____ 39. Whenever a glucometer reading reveals a blood sugar of less than 70 mg/dL, a paramedic might suspect:
- A. hypoxia.
- B. hyperglycemia.
- C. hypoglycemia.
- D. ketoacidosis.
- E. dehydration.

_____ 40. The single most common cause of trauma-related injuries in children is:
- A. motor vehicle collisions.
- B. burns.
- C. falls.
- D. physical abuse.
- E. drownings.

_____ 41. Appropriate-sized pediatric immobilization equipment includes all of the following, EXCEPT:
- A. towel or blanket roll.
- B. vest-type device (KED).
- C. sandbag.
- D. straps and cravats.
- E. padding.

_____ 42. All of the following are true statements about SIDS, EXCEPT that it:
- A. occurs most frequently in the fall and winter.
- B. is not caused by external suffocation by blankets.
- C. tends to be more common in females than in males.
- D. is not thought to be hereditary.
- E. is possibly linked to a prone sleeping position.

_____ 43. Child abuse can take the form of:
- A. psychological abuse.
- B. physical abuse.
- C. sexual abuse.
- D. neglect.
- E. all of the above.

_____ 44. In cases of suspected child abuse, management goals include all of the following, EXCEPT:
- A. protection of the child from further injury.
- B. notification of proper authorities.
- C. appropriate treatment of injuries.
- D. cross-examination of the parents or caregivers.
- E. documentation of all findings and statements.

_____ 45. A surgical connection that runs from the brain to the abdomen in a pediatric patient is called a(n):
- A. central IV.
- B. tracheostomy.
- C. shunt.
- D. inner cannula.
- E. epigastric tube.

MATCHING

Write the letter of the term in the space provided next to the appropriate description.

- A. greenstick fracture
- B. hypoglycemia
- C. bronchiolitis
- D. hyperglycemia
- E. epiglottitis
- F. febrile seizures
- G. tracheostomy
- H. cardiogenic shock
- I. bacterial tracheitis
- J. croup
- K. buckle fracture
- L. neonate
- M. stoma
- N. distributive shock
- O. status epilepticus
- P. bent fractures
- Q. GCS
- R. EMSC
- S. congenital
- T. growth plate

_____ 46. surgical incision in the neck held open by a metal or plastic tube

_____ 47. permanent surgical opening in the neck through which the patient breathes

_____ 48. scoring system for monitoring the neurological status of a patient with a possible head injury

_____ 49. fracture characterized by angulation and deformity in the bone without an obvious break

_____ 50. fracture characterized by a raised or bulging projection at the fracture site

_____ 51. fractures characterized by an incomplete break in the bone

_____ 52. abnormally high concentration of glucose in the blood

_____ 53. laryngotracheobronchitis; common viral infection of young children

_____ 54. abnormally low concentration of glucose in the blood

_____ 55. seizures that occur as a result of a sudden increase in temperature

_____ 56. prolonged seizure or multiple seizures with no regaining of consciousness between them

_____ 57. marked decrease in peripheral vascular resistance and consequent hypertension

_____ 58. inability of the heart to meet the metabolic needs of the body, resulting in inadequate tissue perfusion

_____ 59 viral infection of the medium-sized airways, occurring most frequently during the first year of life

_____ 60. bacterial infection of the airway, subglottic region

_____ 61. bacterial infection of the epiglottis, usually occurring in children older than age four

_____ 62. area in a long bone in which growth in bone length occurs

_____ 63. federally funded program aimed at improving the health of pediatric patients who suffer from life-threatening illnesses and injuries

_____ 64. child less than 1 month old

_____ 65. present at birth

Special Project

Burn Injuries

Burn injuries are the leading cause of accidental death in the home for children under 14 years of age. As with other assessment tools, you must modify the "rule of nines" to estimate the extent of a burn in a pediatric patient. Read the following short patient description and complete the diagram on the following page. Then answer the questions that follow.

You have been called to the scene of a fire at a single-family residence. The dispatcher tells you that a 2-year-old female patient has been critically burned. Upon arrival at the scene, first responders with the fire department lead you to the little girl. They report that the patient has full-thickness burns on the entire right arm, entire right leg, and the anterior trunk.

THE RULE OF NINES

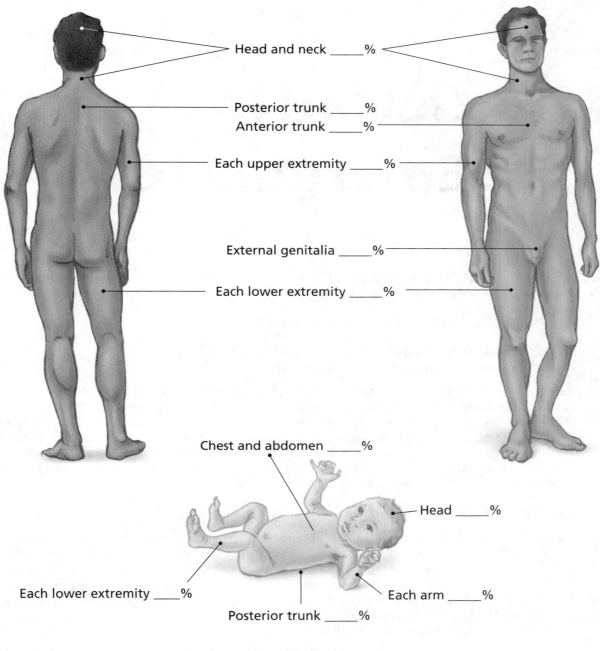

Head and neck _____%

Posterior trunk _____%
Anterior trunk _____%

Each upper extremity _____%

External genitalia _____%

Each lower extremity _____%

Chest and abdomen _____%

Head _____%

Each arm _____%

Each lower extremity _____%

Posterior trunk _____%

1. If the patient had been an adult, what would the rule of nines add up to?_____

2. What does the rule of nines add up to for this toddler?_____

3. Why do the percentages differ?_____

4. Suppose the burns had been less extensive. What alternative method for calculating the burn area might be used?_____

x

3

Geriatric Emergencies

Review of Chapter Objectives

After reading this chapter, you should be able to:

1. **Discuss the demographics demonstrating the increasing size of the elderly population in the United States.** pp. 142–143

Between 1960 and 1990, the number of elderly people in the United States nearly doubled. By late 2000, the total reached more than 35 million, with nearly 337,000 people age 95 and older. As the twenty-first century opened, demographers talked about the "graying of America," a process in which the number of elderly is pushing up the average age of the U.S. population as a whole. In 2030, when the post–World War II baby boomers enter their 80s, more than 70 million people will be age 65 or older. By 2040, the elderly will represent roughly 20 percent of the population. In other words, one in five Americans will be age 65 or older.

2. **Assess the various living environments of elderly patients.** pp. 143–145

The elderly live in both independent and dependent living environments. Many continue to live alone or with their partner until well into their 80s or 90s. The "oldest" old are the most likely to live alone, and, in fact, nearly half of those age 85 and older live by themselves. The great majority of these people—an estimated 78 percent—are women. This is because married men tend to die before their wives, and widowed men tend to remarry more often than widowed women. Elderly persons living alone represent one of the most impoverished and vulnerable parts of society.

Usually the elderly own their own homes or apartments. In addition to these traditional residences, they may choose among a variety of options for assisted living. Among the elderly who receive help, more than 43 percent rely on paid assistance. Another 54 percent use unpaid assistance, and 3 percent use both types of help. Those elderly who turn to dependent care arrangements select live-in nursing, life-care communities, congregate care, or personal-care homes. Approximately 5 percent of the elderly live in nursing homes.

3. **Discuss society's view of aging and the social, financial, and ethical issues facing the elderly.** pp. 142–143

After years of working and/or raising a family, an elderly person must not only find new roles to fulfill but, in many cases, must overcome the societal label of "old person." A lot of elderly people disprove ageism—and all the stereotypes it engenders—by living happy, productive, and active lives. Others, however, feel a sense of social isolation or uselessness. Physical and financial difficulties reinforce these feelings and help create an emotional context in which illnesses can occur. Successful medical treatment of elderly patients involves an understanding of the broader social content in which they live.

As a group, most elderly people worry about income, aggravated by fixed retirement payments or loss of benefits when a partner dies. Tight finances and limited mobility may prevent an independent elderly person from maintaining adequate nutrition and safety. As a result, elderly patients may be at increased risk of accidental hypothermia, carbon monoxide poisoning, or fires. They may also reduce their medications, or "half dose," to save money.

In the course of caring for elderly patients, ethical concerns frequently arise. You may be confronted with multiple decision makers, particularly in dependent living environments. You may also have a question about the patient's competency to give informed consent or refusal of treatment. Finally, you may be faced with advanced directives, such as "living wills" and Do Not Resuscitate (DNR) orders.

4. Describe the resources available to assist the elderly, and create strategies to refer at-risk patients to appropriate community services. pp. 147–150

In treating the elderly, remember that the best intervention is prevention. The goal of any health care service, including EMS, should be to help keep people from becoming sick or injured in the first place. As a paramedic, you can reduce morbidity among the elderly by taking part in community education programs and by cooperating with agencies or organizations that support the elderly. The specific resources may differ from community to community, but some possibilities include senior centers, Meals on Wheels, religious organizations with programs for the elderly, governmental agencies, or national and state associations such as the AARP, Alzheimer's Association, or the Association for Senior Citizens.

Many EMS agencies have developed a means for referring elderly patients to appropriate follow-up services. Consider preparing a checklist with descriptions of services in your area as well as the names of contact people and their phone numbers. The checklists can be given to elderly patients as needed.

5. Discuss common emotional and psychological reactions to aging, including causes and manifestations. pp. 143–145, 150, 190–191, 194–196

When behavioral or psychological problems develop later in life, they are often dismissed as normal age-related changes. This attitude denies an elderly person the opportunity to correct a treatable condition and/or overlooks an underlying physical disorder. Studies have shown that the elderly retain their basic personalities and their adaptive cognitive abilities. Intellectual decline and regressive behavior are not normal age-related changes and could in fact have a physiological cause, such as head trauma.

It is important to keep in mind the emotionally stressful situations facing many elderly people such as isolation, loneliness, loss of independence, loss of strength, fear of the future, and more. The elderly are at risk for alcoholism as well as facing a higher incidence of secondary depression as a result of neuroleptic medications such as Haldol or Thorazine.

The emotional well-being of the elderly impacts upon their overall physical health. Therefore, it is important that you note evidence of altered behavior in any elderly patient that you assess and examine. Also, keep in mind that many emotional conditions, such as depression, are normal reactions to stressful situations and can be resolved with appropriate counseling and treatment. Finally, remember that medical disorders in the elderly often present as functional impairment and should be treated as an early warning of a possibly undetected medical problem.

6. Apply the pathophysiology of multisystem failure to the assessment and management of medical conditions of the elderly patient. p. 151

The body becomes less efficient with age, increasing the likelihood of malfunction. The body of an elderly patient is susceptible to all the disorders of young people, but its maintenance, defense, and repair processes are weaker. As a result, the elderly often suffer from more than one illness or disease at a time. On average, six medical disorders may coexist in an elderly person and perhaps even more in the old-old. Furthermore, disease in one organ system may result in the deterioration of other systems, compounding existing acute and/or chronic conditions.

Because of concomitant diseases (comorbidity) in the elderly, complaints may not be specific to any one disorder. Common complaints of the elderly include fatigue and weakness, dizziness/vertigo/syncope, falls, headaches, insomnia, dysphagia, loss of appetite, inability to void, and/or constipation/diarrhea.

Elderly patients often accept medical problems as a part of aging and fail to monitor changes in their condition. In some cases, such as a silent myocardial infarction, pain may be diminished or absent. In others, a complaint may seem trivial, such as constipation.

Although many medical problems in the young and middle-aged populations present with a standard set of signs and symptoms, the changes involved in aging lead to different presentations. In pneumonia, for example, some classic symptoms such as fever, chest pain, and a cough may be diminished or absent.

7. Compare the pharmacokinetics of an elderly patient to that of a young patient, including drug distribution, metabolism, and excretion. pp. 151–152

In general, a person's sensitivity to drugs increases with age. When compared with younger patients, the elderly experience more adverse drug reactions, more drug-drug interactions, and more drug-disease interactions. Because of age-related pharmacokinetic changes such as a loss of body fluids and atrophy of organs, drugs concentrate more readily in the plasma and tissues of elderly patients. As a result, drug dosages often must be adjusted to prevent toxicity. Additionally, due to differences in the GI tract, medications are metabolized and excreted at a slower rate in the elderly patient.

8. Discuss the impact of polypharmacy, dosing errors, increased drug sensitivity, and medication noncompliance on assessment and management of the elderly patient. pp. 151–152

If medications are not correctly monitored, polypharmacy can cause a number of problems among the elderly. In taking a medical history of an elderly patient, remember to ask questions to determine if the patient is taking a prescribed medication as directed. Noncompliance with drug therapy, usually underadherence, is common among the elderly. Up to 40 percent do not take medications as prescribed. Of these individuals, 35 percent experience some type of medical problem.

Factors that can decrease compliance in the elderly include limited income, memory loss (due to decreased or diseased neural activity), limited mobility, sensory impairment (cannot hear/read/understand directions), multiple or complicated drug therapies, fear of toxicity, child-proof containers (especially difficult for arthritic patients), and lengthy drug therapy plans.

9. Discuss the use and effects of commonly prescribed drugs for the elderly patient. pp. 151–152, 188, 192

Functional changes in the kidneys, liver, and gastrointestinal system slow the absorption and elimination of many medications in the elderly. In addition, the various compensatory mechanisms that help buffer against medication side effects are less effective in the elderly than in younger patients.

Approximately 30 percent of all hospital admissions are related to drug-induced illness. About 50 percent of all drug-related deaths occur in people over the age of 60. Accidental overdoses may occur more frequently in the aged due to confusion, vision impairment, self-selection of medications, forgetfulness, and concurrent drug use. Intentional drug overdose also occurs in attempts at self-destruction. Another complicating factor is the abuse of alcohol among the elderly.

10. Discuss the problem of mobility in the elderly, and develop strategies to prevent falls. pp. 152–153

Regular exercise and a good diet are two of the most effective prevention measures for ensuring mobility among the elderly. Some elderly may suffer from a severe medical problem, such as crippling arthritis. They may fear for their personal safety, either from accidental injury or intentional injury, such as robbery. Certain medications also may increase their lethargy. Whatever the cause, a lack of mobility can have detrimental physical and emotional effects. Some of these include poor

©2006 Pearson Education, Inc.
Paramedic Care: Principles & Practice, Vol. 5

nutrition, difficulty with elimination, poor skin integrity, a greater predisposition for falls, loss of independence and/or confidence, depression from "feeling old," and isolation.

Falls present an especially serious problem for the elderly. Fall-related injuries represent the leading cause of accidental death among the elderly and the seventh highest cause of death overall. As a result, the paramedic should consider strategies for making a home safe for the elderly and point these out to the elderly patient or family of the elderly patient, whichever may be appropriate. Examples of hazards that can easily be corrected include torn or slippery rugs, chairs without armrests, chairs with low backs, chairs with wheels, obstructing furniture, slippery bathtubs, dim lighting, high cabinet shelves, missing handrails on stairways, and high steps on stairways.

11. Discuss age-related changes in sensations in the elderly, and describe the implications of these changes for communication and patient assessment. pp. 153, 154, 157, 160

Most elderly patients suffer from some form of age-related sensory changes. Normal physiological changes may include impaired vision or blindness, impaired or loss of hearing, an altered sense of taste or smell, and/or a lower sensitivity to pain or touch. Any of these conditions can affect your ability to communicate with the patient. In general, be prepared to spend more time obtaining histories from elderly patients.

12. Discuss the problems with continence and elimination in the elderly patient, and develop communication strategies to provide psychological support. pp. 153–155

The elderly often find it embarrassing to talk about problems with continence and elimination. They may feel stigmatized, isolated, and/or helpless. When confronted with these problems, DO NOT make a big deal out of them. Respect the patient's dignity, and assure the person that, in many cases, the problem is treatable.

Remember, too, that problems with continence and elimination are not necessarily caused by aging. They may be the result of drug therapy or medical conditions such as diabetes. As a result, in assessing a patient with incontinence or constipation, inquire about their medications and any chronic medical disorders. Also keep in mind the variety of other conditions that can result from problems with continence or elimination. In the case of incontinence, for example, a patient may experience rashes, skin infections, skin breakdown (ulcers), urinary tract infections, sepsis, and falls or fractures (caused by a frequent need to eliminate). In elderly people with cerebrovascular disease or impaired baroreceptor reflexes, efforts to force a bowel movement can lead to a transient ischemic attack (TIA) or syncope.

13. Discuss factors that may complicate the assessment of the elderly patient. pp. 150, 155–160

In assessing an elderly patient, keep in mind the variety of causes of functional impairment. If identified early, an environmental or disease-related condition can often be reversed. Your success depends upon a thorough understanding of age-related changes and the implications of these changes for patient assessment and management. You will need to recall at all times the complications that can arise from comorbidity (having more than one disease at a time) and polypharmacy (concurrent use of a number of drugs).

Communications challenges may also complicate the assessment. Patients may be blind, have speech difficulties, or have some kind of hearing loss that can make assessment more difficult. They also often have a lower sensitivity to pain or touch.

In general, assessment of the elderly patient follows the same basic approach used with any other patient. However, you should keep in mind these points:

- Set a context for illness, taking into account the patient's living situation, level of activity, network of social support, level of dependence, medication history (both prescriptive and nonprescriptive), and sleep patterns.
- Pay close attention to an elderly person's nutrition, noting conditions that may complicate or discourage eating.
- Keep in mind that elderly patients may minimize or fail to report important symptoms. Therefore, try to distinguish the patient's chief complaint from the patient's primary problem.

- Because of the presence of multiple chronic diseases, treat the patient on a "threat-to-life" basis.
- Recall at all times that alterations in the temperature-regulating mechanism can result in a lack of fever, or a minimal fever, even in the presence of a severe infection.
- When confronted with a confused patient, try to determine whether the patient's mental status represents a significant change from normal for him. DO NOT assume that a confused, disoriented patient is "just senile," thus failing to assess for a serious underlying problem.
- Remember that some patients are often easily fatigued and cannot tolerate a long physical examination. Also, because of problems with temperature regulation, the patient may be wearing several layers of clothing.
- Be aware that the elderly patient may minimize or deny symptoms because of a fear of institutionalization or a loss of self-sufficiency.
- Try to distinguish signs of chronic disease from acute problems. For example:
  —Peripheral pulses may be difficult to evaluate because of peripheral vascular disease and arthritis.
  —The elderly may have nonpathological crackles (rales) upon lung auscultation.
  —The elderly often exhibit an increase in mouth breathing and a loss of skin elasticity, which may be confused with dehydration.
  —Dependent edema may be caused by inactivity, not congestive heart failure.

14. Discuss the principles that should be employed when assessing and communicating with the elderly. pp. 145, 153, 155–160

To improve your skill at assessing and communicating with the elderly, keep in mind these principles.

- Always introduce yourself.
- Speak slowly, distinctly, and respectfully.
- Speak to the patient first, rather than to family members, caregivers, or bystanders.
- Speak face to face, at eye level with eye contact.
- Locate the patient's hearing aid or eyeglasses, if needed.
- DO NOT shout at the patient. This will not help if the patient is deaf, and it may distort sounds for the patient who has some level of hearing.
- Write notes, if necessary.
- Allow the patient to put on the stethoscope, while you speak into it like a microphone.
- Turn on the room lights.
- If a patient has forgotten to put in dentures, politely ask the person to do so.
- Display verbal and nonverbal signs of concern and empathy.
- Remain polite at all times.
- Preserve the person's dignity.
- Always explain what you are doing and why.
- Use your power of observation to recognize anxiety—tempo of speech, eye contact, tone of voice—during the telling of the history.

15. Compare the assessment of a young patient with that of an elderly patient. pp. 155–160

The assessment of the older person differs from that of a younger person in a number of ways. The elderly often have complicated medical histories that entail numerous chronic conditions. They also usually take multiple medications (both prescribed and nonprescribed), which in turn may produce a variety of physical and/or psychological side effects. As stated in previous objectives, remain sensitive to the special fears of an elderly patient, particularly the fear of increased dependency, and unique stresses of that age group, such as loss of long-term partners or friends. Allow for the extra time necessitated by communication challenges. DO NOT rush the elderly patient through an assessment unless it is absolutely necessary because of a life-threatening condition.

16. Discuss common complaints of elderly patients. pp. 151, 155, 168–196

Common complaints of elderly patients include fatigue and weakness, dizziness, vertigo or syncope, falls, headaches, insomnia, dysphagia, loss of appetite, inability to void, and constipation or

©2006 Pearson Education, Inc.
Paramedic Care: Principles & Practice, Vol. 5

diarrhea. Many of these complaints in and of themselves would not be too serious. However, given the context of complicated medical histories of the elderly, each of these complaints are important and should be followed up and taken very seriously.

17. Discuss the normal and abnormal changes of age in relation to the:

a. Pulmonary system   pp. 162–163

The effects of aging on the respiratory system begin as early as age 30. Without regular exercise and/or training, the lungs start to lose their ability to defend themselves and to carry out their prime function of ventilation. Age-related changes in the respiratory system include decreased chest wall compliance, loss of lung elasticity, increased air trapping due to collapse of the smaller airways, and reduced strength and endurance of the respiratory muscles. In addition, there is a decrease in an effective cough reflex and the activity of the cilia. The decline of these two defense mechanisms leave the lungs more susceptible to recurring infection. Other factors that may affect pulmonary function in the elderly are kyphosis (exaggeration of the normal posterior curvature of the spine), chronic exposure to pollutants, and long-term cigarette smoking.

b. Cardiovascular system   pp. 163–164

A number of variables unrelated to aging influence cardiovascular functions—diet, smoking and alcohol use, education, socioeconomic status, and even personality traits. Of particular importance is the level of physical activity.

This said, the cardiovascular system still experiences, in varying degrees, age-related deterioration. Changes include a loss of elasticity and hardening of the arteries, an increase in the size and bulk of the left ventricle (hypertrophy), development of fibrosis (formation of fiber-like connective/scar tissue), and changes in the rate, rhythm, and overall efficiency of the heart.

c. Nervous system   pp. 164–165

Unlike cells in other organ systems, cells in the central nervous system cannot reproduce. The brain can lose as much as 45 percent of its cells in certain areas of the cortex. Overall, there is an average 10 percent reduction in brain weight from age 20 to age 90. Keep in mind, however, that reductions in brain weight and ventricular size are not well correlated with intelligence, and elderly people may still be capable of highly creative and productive thought. In addition to shrinkage of brain tissue, the elderly may experience some memory loss, clinical depression, altered mental status, and impaired balance. Keep in mind that these changes vary greatly and may not be seen in all elderly patients, even at the close of very long lives.

d. Endocrine system   p. 165

The elderly experience a variety of age-related hormonal changes. Women, for example, experience menopause, the result of reductions in estrogen production. Men also experience a decline in levels of testosterone. In addition, the elderly commonly experience a decline in insulin sensitivity and/or an increase in insulin resistance. Finally, thyroid disorders, especially hypothyroidism and thyroid nodules, increase with age as well.

e. Gastrointestinal system   pp. 165–166

Age affects the gastrointestinal system in various ways. The volume of saliva may decrease by as much as 33 percent, leading to complaints of dry mouth, nutritional deficiencies, and a predisposition to choking. Gastric secretions may decrease to as little as 20 percent of the quantity present in younger people. Esophageal and intestinal motility also decrease, making swallowing more difficult and delaying digestive processes. The production of hydrochloric acid also declines, further disrupting digestion and, in some adults, contributing to nutritional anemia. Gums atrophy and the number of taste buds decrease, reducing even further the desire to eat.

Other conditions may also develop. Hiatal hernias are not age-related per se but can have serious consequences for the elderly. The hernias may incarcerate, strangulate, or, in the most severe cases, result in massive GI hemorrhage. A diminished liver function, which is associated with aging, can delay or impede detoxification. It also can reduce the production of clotting proteins, which in turn leads to bleeding abnormalities.

f. Thermoregulatory system   p. 166

As people age, the thermoregulatory system becomes altered or impaired. Aging seems to reduce the effectiveness of sweating in cooling the body. Older people tend to sweat at higher core temperatures and have less sweat output per gland than younger people. As people age, they also experience deterioration of the autonomic nervous system, including a decrease in shivering and lower resting peripheral blood flow. In addition, the elderly may have a diminished perception of the cold. Drugs and disease can further affect an elderly patient's response to temperature extremes, resulting in hyperthermia or accidental hypothermia.

g. Integumentary system   p. 166

As people age, the skin loses collagen, a connective tissue that gives elasticity and support to the skin. Without this support, the skin is subject to a great number of injuries from bumping or tearing. In addition, the skin thins as people age. Because cells reproduce more slowly, older patients often suffer more severe skin injuries than younger patients and healing takes a longer time. As a rule, the elderly are at a higher risk of secondary infections, skin tumors, drug-induced eruptions, and fungal or viral infections. Decades of exposure to the sun also makes the elderly vulnerable to melanoma and other sun-related carcinomas.

h. Musculoskeletal system   pp. 166–167

An aging person may lose as much as 2 to 3 inches of height from narrowing of the intervertebral disks and osteoporosis (softening of bone tissue due to the loss of essential minerals). This is especially evident in the vertebral bodies, thus causing a change in posture. The posture of the aged individual often reveals an increase in the curvature of the thoracic spine (kyphosis) and slight flexion of the knee and hip joints. The demineralization of bone makes the elderly patient much more susceptible to hip and other fractures.

In addition to skeletal changes, a decrease in skeletal muscle weight commonly occurs with age—especially with sedentary individuals. To compensate, elderly women develop a narrow, short gait, while older men develop a wide gait. These changes make the elderly more susceptible to falls.

18. Describe the incidence, morbidity/mortality, risk factors, prevention strategies, pathophysiology, assessment, need for intervention and transport, and management of the elderly medical patient with:

a. Pneumonia, chronic obstructive pulmonary disease, and pulmonary embolism   pp. 168–171

Pneumonia. Pneumonia is an infection of the lung, usually caused by a bacterium or virus. Aspiration pneumonia is also common in the elderly due to difficulty in swallowing.

Pneumonia is the fourth leading cause of death in people age 65 and older. Its incidence increases with age at a rate of 10 percent for each decade beyond age 20. It is found in up to 60 percent of autopsies performed on the elderly. Reasons for the high incidence of pneumonia among the elderly include decreased immune response, reduced pulmonary function, increased colonization of the pharynx by gram-negative bacteria, abnormal or ineffective cough reflex, and decreased effectiveness of mucociliary cells of the upper respiratory system. The elderly who are at the greatest risk for contracting pneumonia are frail adults and those with multiple chronic diseases or compromised immunity.

Common signs and symptoms of pneumonia include increasing dyspnea, congestion, fever, chills, tachypnea, sputum production, and altered mental status. Occasionally, abdominal pain may be the only symptom.

Prevention strategies include prophylactic treatment with antibiotics. Efforts should also be taken to reduce exposure to infectious patients and to promote patient mobility. Once a person has contracted the disease, treatment includes management of all life threats, maintenance of adequate oxygenation, and transport to the hospital for diagnosis and further management.
Chronic obstructive pulmonary disease (COPD). COPD is really a collection of diseases characterized by chronic airflow obstruction with reversible and/or irreversible components. Although each COPD has its own distinct features, elderly patients commonly have two or more types at the same time. COPD usually refers to some combination of emphysema, chronic bronchitis, and, to a lesser degree, asthma. Pneumonia, as well as other respiratory disorders, can further complicate chronic obstructive pulmonary disease in the elderly.

In the United States, COPD is among the ten leading causes of death. Its prevalence has been increasing over the past 20 years due to factors such as genetic predisposition, exposure to environmental pollutants, existence of a childhood respiratory disease, and cigarette smoking (a contributing factor in up to 80 percent of all COPD cases).

The physiology of COPD varies but may include inflammation of the air passages with increased mucus production or actual destruction of the alveoli. Usual signs and symptoms include a cough, increased sputum production, dyspnea, accessory muscle use, pursed-lip breathing, tripod positioning, exercise intolerance, wheezing, pleuritic chest pain, and tachypnea.

The most effective prevention involves elimination of tobacco products and reduced exposure to cigarette smoke. Once the disease is present, appropriate self-care measures include exercise, avoidance of infections, appropriate use of medications, avoidance of unnecessary stress, and, when necessary, calling EMS. When confronted with an elderly patient with COPD, treatment is essentially the same as for all age groups: supplemental oxygen and possibly drug therapy, usually for reducing dyspnea.

Pulmonary embolism (PE). Pulmonary embolism should always be considered as a possible cause of respiratory distress in the elderly. Although statistics for the elderly are unavailable, approximately 650,000 cases occur annually in the United States. Of this number, a pulmonary embolism is the primary cause of death in 100,000 people. Nearly 11 percent of PE deaths take place in the first hour, and another 38 percent in the second hour.

Blood clots are the most frequent cause of a PE. However, the condition may also be caused by fat, air, bone marrow, tumor cells, or foreign bodies. Risk factors for developing pulmonary embolism include deep venous thrombosis; prolonged immobility (common among the elderly); malignancy (tumors); paralysis; fractures of the pelvis, hip, or leg; obesity; trauma to the leg vessels; major surgery; presence of a venous catheter; use of estrogen (in women); and atrial fibrillation.

Definitive diagnosis of a PE takes place in a hospital setting. However, the condition should be suspected in a patient with the acute onset of dyspnea. Often, it is accompanied by pleuritic chest pain and right heart failure. If the PE is massive, you can expect severe dyspnea, cardiac dysrhythmias, and, ultimately, cardiovascular collapse.

The goals of field treatment are to manage and minimize complications of the condition. General treatment considerations include delivery of high-flow, high-concentration oxygen via mask, maintaining oxygen levels above an SaO_2 of 90 percent. Establishment of an IV for possible administration of medications, upon advice from medical direction, is appropriate. However, vigorous fluid therapy should be avoided, if possible. Rapid transport is essential. Position the patient in an upright position and avoid lifting the patient by the legs or knees, which may dislodge thrombi in the lower extremities. During transport, continue to monitor changes in skin color, pulse oximetry, and breathing rate and rhythm.

b. Angina pectoris myocardial infarction, heart failure, dysrhythmias, aneurysm, and hypertension pp. 172–175

The leading cause of death in the elderly is cardiovascular disease. Assessment and treatment of cardiovascular disease in the elderly patient is often complicated by non-age-related factors and disease processes in other organ systems. Commonly found cardiovascular disorders in the elderly include the following. (Additional disorders, including syncope, can be found in the text.)

Myocardial infarction (MI). Myocardial infarction involves actual death of muscle tissue due to a partial or complete occlusion of one or more of the coronary arteries. The greatest number of patients hospitalized for acute MI are older than age 65. The elderly patient with MI is less likely to present with classic symptoms, such as chest pain, than a younger counterpart. Atypical presentations that may be seen in the elderly include the absence of pain; exercise intolerance; confusion/dizziness; syncope; dyspnea (common in patients over age 85); neck, dental, and/or epigastric pain; and fatigue/weakness.

The mortality rate associated with MI doubles after age 70. Elderly patients are more likely to suffer a silent MI. They also tend to have larger MIs. The majority of the deaths that occur in the first few hours following a MI are due to dysrhythmias such as ventricular fibrillation.

Field management is the same as that listed for **angina pectoris**, except that the nitro often does not work and morphine may be necessary if the patient's blood pressure tolerates it. It may also be necessary to manage dysrhythmias and hypotension with medications. These patients need to be quickly evaluated and transported to a facility that can administer clot busters or provide emergency cardiac catheterization and angioplasty, if necessary.

Heart failure. Heart failure takes place when the cardiac output cannot meet the body's metabolic demands. The incidence rises exponentially after age 60 and is the most common diagnosis in hospitalized patients over the age of 65. The causes of heart failure fall in one of four categories—impairment to flow, inadequate cardiac filling, volume overload, and myocardial failure. Factors that place the elderly at risk for heart failure include prolonged myocardial contractions, noncompliance with drug therapy, anemia, ischemia, thermoregulatory disorders, hypoxia, infection, and use of nonsteroidal anti-inflammatory drugs.

Signs and symptoms of heart failure vary. In most patients, regardless of age, some form of edema exists. Assessment findings for the elderly may include musculoskeletal injury, fatigue (left failure), two-pillow orthopnea, dyspnea on exertion, dry hacking cough progressing to a productive cough, dependent edema (right failure), nocturia, anorexia, hepatomegaly (enlarged liver), and ascites.

Nonpharmacologic management of heart failure includes modifications in diet, exercise, and reduction in weight, if necessary. Pharmacologic management may include treatment with diuretics, vasodilators, antihypertensive agents, or inotropic agents. Check to see if the patient is already on any of these medications and if the patient is compliant with scheduled doses.

Dysrhythmias. Many cardiac dysrhythmias develop with age, but atrial fibrillation is the most common dysrhythmia encountered. Dysrhythmias occur primarily as a result of the degeneration of the patient's conductive system. Anything that decreases myocardial blood flow can produce a dysrhythmia. They may also be caused by electrolyte abnormalities.

To complicate matters further, the elderly do not tolerate extremes in heart rate as well as a younger person would. In addition, dysrhythmias can lead to falls due to cerebral hypoperfusion. They can also result in congestive heart failure (CHF) or a transient ischemic attack (TIA).

Treatment considerations depend upon the type of dysrhythmia. Patients may already have a pacemaker in place. In such cases, keep in mind that pacemakers have a low but significant rate of complications such as a failed battery, fibrosis around the catheter site, lead fracture, or electrode dislodgment. In a number of situations, drug therapy is indicated. Whenever you discover a dysrhythmia, remember that an abnormal or disordered heart rhythm may be the only clinical finding in an elderly patient suffering acute myocardial infarction. (For more on dysrhythmias, see *Paramedic Care: Principles & Practice,* Volume 4.)

Aneurysms. An aneurysm, or rupture of the vessel, often results from aortic dissection—a degeneration of the wall of the aorta, either in the thoracic or abdominal cavity. Approximately 80 percent of thoracic aneurysms are due to atherosclerosis combined with hypertension. The remaining cases occur secondary to other factors, including Marfan's syndrome or blunt trauma to the chest. Patients with dissections will often present with tearing chest pain radiating through to the back or, if a rupture/aneurysm occurs, cardiac arrest.

The distal portion of the aorta is the most common site for an abdominal aneurysm. Approximately 1 in 250 people over age 50 dies from a ruptured abdominal aneurysm. Patients may present with tearing abdominal pain or unexplained low back pain. Pulses in the legs are diminished or absent and the lower extremities feel cold to the touch. There may be sensory abnormalities such as numbness, tingling, or pain in the legs. The patient may fall when attempting to stand.

Treatment of the aneurysm depends on the size, location, and severity of the condition. In the case of thoracic aortic dissection, continuous IV infusion and/or administration of drug therapy to lower the arterial pressure and to diminish the velocity of left ventricle contraction may be indicated. Rapid transport is essential, especially for the older patient who most commonly requires care and observation in an intensive care unit.

Hypertension. Because hypertension is not widely seen in less-developed nations, experts believe that the condition is not a normal age-related change. Today more than 50 percent of Americans over age 65 have clinically diagnosed hypertension—defined as blood pressure greater than 140/90 mmHg. Prolonged elevated blood pressure will eventually damage the heart, brain, or kidneys. As a result of hypertension, elderly patients are at a greater risk for heart failure, stroke, blindness, renal failure, coronary heart disease, and peripheral vascular disease. In men with blood pressure greater than 160/95 mmHg, the risk of mortality nearly doubles.

Hypertension increases with atherosclerosis, which is more common in the elderly than other age groups. Other contributing factors include obesity and diabetes. The condition is often a "silent" disease because it produces no clinically obvious signs or symptoms. It may be associated with nonspecific complaints such as headache, tinnitus, epistaxis (nosebleed), slow tremors, and nausea or vomiting.

Hypertension can be prevented or controlled through diet, exercise, cessation of smoking, and compliance with medications. Management of the condition depends upon its severity and the existence of other conditions. For example, hypertension is often treated with beta-blockers—medications that are contraindicated in patients with chronic obstructive lung disease, asthma, or heart block greater than first degree. Diuretics, another common drug used for treating hypertension, should be prescribed with care for patients on digitalis. Keep in mind that centrally acting agents are more likely to produce negative side effects in the elderly. Unlike younger patients, the elderly may experience depression, forgetfulness, sleep problems, or vivid dreams and/or hallucinations.

c. **Cerebral vascular disease, delirium, dementia, Alzheimer's disease, and Parkinson's disease** pp. 176–180

Cerebral vascular disease (CVA). Cerebral vascular disease (stroke/brain attack) is the third leading cause of death in the United States. Annually, about 500,000 people suffer strokes and about 150,000 die. Incidence of stroke and the likelihood of dying from a stroke increases with age. Occlusive stroke is statistically more common in the elderly and relatively uncommon in younger individuals. Older patients are at higher risk of stroke because of atherosclerosis, hypertension, immobility, limb paralysis, congestive heart failure, and atrial fibrillation. Transient ischemic attacks (TIAs) are also more common in older patients, more than one third of whom will develop a major, permanent stroke.

Strokes fall into one of two categories. Brain ischemia—injury to brain tissue caused by an inadequate supply of oxygen and nutrients—accounts for about 80 percent of all strokes. Brain hemorrhage, the second major category, may be either subarachnoid hemorrhage or intracerebral hemorrhage. Because of the various kinds of strokes, signs and symptoms can present in many ways—altered mental status, coma, paralysis, slurred speech, a change in mood, and seizures. Stroke should be highly suspected in any elderly patient with a sudden change in mental status.

Keep two things in mind when treating stroke. One, complete the Glasgow coma scale for later comparison at the emergency department. Second, transport the patient as rapidly as possible. In the case of stroke, "time is brain tissue." By far the most preferred treatment is prevention. Preventive strategies include control of hypertension, treatment of cardiac disorders, treatment of blood disorders, cessation of smoking, cessation of recreational drugs, moderate use of alcohol, regular exercise, and good eating habits.

Delirium, dementia, and Alzheimer's disease. Approximately 15 percent of all Americans over age 65 have some degree of dementia or delirium. Dementia is chronic global cognitive impairment, often progressive or irreversible. The best-known form of dementia is Alzheimer's disease, a condition that affects an estimated 4 million Americans. Delirium is a global cognitive impairment of sudden onset and self-limited duration.

Possible causes of delirium include subdural hematoma, tumors and other mass lesions, drug-induced changes or alcohol intoxication, CNS infections, electrolyte abnormalities, cardiac failure, fever, metabolic disorders (including hypoglycemia), chronic endocrine abnormalities (including hypothyroidism and hyperthyroidism), and post-concussion syndrome. Common signs and symptoms include acute onset of anxiety, an inability to focus, disordered thinking, irritability, inappropriate behavior, fearfulness, excessive energy, or psychotic behavior such as hallucinations or paranoia. Aphasic or speaking errors and/or prominent slurring may be present.

Dementia is more prevalent in the elderly than delirium. Over 50 percent of all nursing home patients have dementia. The mental deterioration is often called *organic brain syndrome, senile dementia,* or *senility.* Causes of dementia include small strokes, atherosclerosis, age-related neurological changes, neurological diseases, certain hereditary diseases, and Alzheimer's disease. Signs and symptoms include progressive disorientation, shortened attention span, aphasia or nonsense talking, and hallucinations.

Alzheimer's disease, a particular type of dementia, is a chronic degenerative disorder that attacks the brain and results in impaired memory, thinking, and behavior. It goes through stages, each with different signs and symptoms, the culmination of which is death.

Parkinson's disease. Parkinson's disease is a degenerative disorder involving changes in muscle response, including tremors, loss of facial expressions, and gait disturbances. It usually appears in people over the age of 50 and peaks at age 70. The disease affects 1 million Americans, with 50,000 new cases each year. The causes include viral encephalitis, atherosclerosis of cerebral vessels, reaction to certain drugs or toxins (antipsychotics or carbon monoxide), metabolic disorders (anoxia), tumors, head trauma, and degenerative disorders (Shy-Drager syndrome).

There is no known cure for Parkinson's disease. In calls involving a Parkinson's patient, observe for conditions that may have involved the EMS system, such as a fall or the inability to move. Manage treatable conditions and transport as needed.

d. Diabetes and thyroid diseases   **pp. 180–181**

Diabetes. An estimated 20 percent of older adults have diabetes mellitus, primarily Type II diabetes. Almost 40 percent have some type of glucose intolerance. Reasons the elderly develop this disorder include poor diet, decreased physical activity, loss of lean body mass, impaired insulin production, and resistance by body cells to the actions of insulin. The condition may present, in the early stages, with vague symptoms as fatigue or weakness. Allowed to progress, diabetes can result in neuropathy and visual impairment.

Elderly patients on insulin risk hypoglycemia, especially if they accidentally take too much insulin or do not eat enough food following injection. The lack of good nutrition can be particularly troublesome to elderly diabetic patients. They often find it difficult to prepare meals, fail to enjoy food because of diminished taste, have trouble chewing food, or are unable to purchase adequate and/or enough food because of limited income.

Many diabetics use self-monitoring devices to monitor their glucose levels. Self-treatment involves diet, exercise, and the use of sulfonylurea agents and/or insulin. In EMS calls involving diabetic or hypoglycemic elderly patients, follow care steps similar to those taken with younger patients. However, remember that diabetes places the elderly at increased risk of other complications, including atherosclerosis, delayed healing, retinopathy (disorders of the retina), altered renal function, and severe peripheral vascular disease, leading to foot ulcers and even amputations. In the case of hypoglycemia, DO NOT rule out alcohol as a complicating factor.

Thyroid diseases. With normal aging, the thyroid gland undergoes moderate atrophy and changes in hormone production. An estimated 2 to 5 percent of the people over 65 experience hypothyroidism, a condition resulting from inadequate levels of thyroid hormones. It affects women in greater numbers than men, and the prevalence rises with age.

Less than 33 percent of the elderly present with typical signs and symptoms of hypothyroidism. When they do, their complaints are often attributed to aging. Common nonspecific complaints in the elderly include mental confusion, anorexia, falls, incontinence, decreased mobility, and muscle or joint pain. Treatment involves thyroid hormone replacement.

Hyperthyroidism is less common among the elderly but may result from medication errors such as an overdose of thyroid hormone replacement. The typical symptom of heat intolerance is often present. Otherwise, hyperthyroidism presents atypically in the elderly with nonspecific features or complaints such as atrial fibrillation, failure to thrive (weight loss and apathy combined), abdominal distress, diarrhea, exhaustion, and depression.

Diagnosis and treatment of thyroid disorders does not take place in the field. Elderly patients with known thyroid problems should be encouraged to go to the hospital for medical evaluation.

e. Gastrointestinal problems, GI hemorrhage, bowel obstruction   **pp. 181–183**

Gastrointestinal problems. Gastrointestinal emergencies are common among the elderly. The most frequent emergency is GI bleeding. However, older people will also describe a variety of other gastrointestinal complaints—nausea, poor appetite, diarrhea, and constipation, to name a few. Remember that, like other presenting complaints in the elderly, these conditions may be symptomatic of a more serious disease.

Prompt management of a GI emergency is essential for old and young alike. However, keep in mind that older patients are more intolerant of hypotension and anoxia than younger patients. The elderly also face a significant risk of hemorrhage and shock. Treatment of GI emergencies in the elderly includes airway management; support of breathing and circulation;

high-flow, high-concentration oxygen therapy; IV fluid replacement with a crystalloid solution; PASG placement (if indicated); and, above all else, rapid transport.

GI hemorrhage. Gastrointestinal hemorrhage falls into two general categories: upper GI bleed and lower GI bleed. Upper GI bleeds include peptic ulcer disease, gastritis, esophageal varices, and Mallory-Weiss tears. Lower GI bleeds include diverticulosis, tumors, ischemic colitis, and arterio-venous malformations.

Signs of significant gastrointestinal blood loss include the presence of "coffee ground" emesis, black tarlike stools (melena), obvious blood in the emesis or stool, orthostatic hypotension, pulse greater than 100 (unless on beta-blockers), and confusion. GI bleeding in the elderly is a true emergency and requires prompt transport to an appropriate medical facility.

Bowel obstruction. Bowel obstructions in the elderly typically involve the small bowel and may be caused by tumors, prior abdominal surgery, use of certain medications, and occasionally the presence of vertebral compression fractures. The patient will typically complain of diffuse abdominal pain, bloating, nausea, and vomiting. The abdomen may feel distended when palpated. Bowel sounds may be hypoactive or absent. If the obstruction has been present for a prolonged period, the patient may have fever, weakness, various electrolyte imbalances, and shock.

An even more serious condition arises with mesenteric infarct, which occurs when a portion of the bowel does not receive enough blood to survive. Certain age-related changes—atrial fibrillation or atherosclerosis—predispose the elderly to a clot lodging in one of the mesenteric arteries serving the bowel. In addition, age-related changes in the bowel itself can promote swelling that effectively cuts off blood flow. Primary signs and symptoms include pain out of proportion to the physical exam, bloody diarrhea, some tachycardia, and abdominal distention.

A mesenteric infarct, or dead bowel, attracts interstitial and intravascular fluids, thus removing them from use and increasing the likelihood of shock. Necrotic products are released to the peritoneal cavity, leading to massive infection. The prognosis is poor, due, in part, to decreased physiologic reserves on the part of older patients.

f. Skin diseases and pressure ulcers   pp. 183–184

Skin diseases. Age-related changes in the immune system make the elderly more prone to certain chronic skin diseases and infections. Elderly patients commonly complain about pruritus or itching. This condition can be caused by dermatitis or environmental conditions. Keep in mind that generalized itching can also be a sign of systemic diseases, particularly liver or renal disorders.

Slower healing and compromised tissue perfusion in the elderly make them more susceptible to bacterial infection of wounds, appearing as cellutitis, impetigo, and, in the case of immunocompromised adults, staphylococcal scalded skin. The elderly also experience a higher incidence of fungal infections and suffer higher rates of herpes zoster (shingles), which peaks between ages 50 and 70.

In treating skin disorders, remember that many conditions may be drug induced. For example, antihistamines and corticosteroids are two to three times more likely to provoke adverse reactions in the elderly than in younger adults. In most cases, encourage the patient to seek a medical evaluation to rule out drug complications or an underlying disease.

Pressure ulcers. Most pressure ulcers (bedsores) occur in people over age 70. Pressure ulcers typically develop from the waist down, usually over bony prominences, in bedridden patients. They most commonly result from tissue hypoxia and affect the skin, subcutaneous tissues, and muscle. Factors that can increase the risk of this condition include external compression of tissues, altered sensory perception, maceration (caused by excessive moisture), decreased activity or mobility, poor nutrition, and friction or shear.

To reduce the development of pressure ulcers or to alleviate their condition, assist the patient in changing position frequently, especially during extended transport. Use a pull sheet to move the patient, reducing the likelihood of tearing. Reduce the possibility of shearing by padding areas of skin prior to movement. Unless a life-threatening condition exists, take time to clean and dry areas of excessive moisture. Clean ulcers with normal saline solution and cover with hydrocolloid or hydrogel dressings, if available. With severe ulcers, pack with loosely woven gauze moistened with normal saline.

g. Osteoarthritis and osteoporosis   pp. 184–185

Osteoarthritis. Osteoarthritis is the leading cause of disability among people age 65 and older. Contributing factors to this disease include age-related wear and tear, loss of muscle mass, obesity, primary disorders of the joint (such as inflammatory arthritis), trauma, and congenital abnormalities (such as hip dysplasia).

Osteoarthritis initially presents as joint pain. As the disease progresses, pain may be accompanied by diminished mobility, joint deformity, and crepitus (grating sensations), and ultimately tenderness during passive motion or upon palpation. Prevention strategies include stretching exercises and activities that strengthen stress-absorbing ligaments. Immobilization, even for short periods, can accelerate the condition. Surgery—total joint replacement—is the last resort.

Osteoporosis. Osteoporosis affects an estimated 20 million Americans and is largely responsible for fractures of the hip, wrist, and vertebral bones following a fall or other injury. Risk factors include:

- *Age.* Bone mass usually starts to decline after the third decade of life, and decreased bone density generally becomes a treatment consideration at about age 50.
- *Gender.* Women are more than twice as likely as men to develop the disease, especially if they experience early menopause (before age 45) and do not take estrogen replacement therapy.
- *Race.* Whites and Asians are more likely to develop osteoporosis than African Americans and Latinos, who have higher bone mass at skeletal peak.
- *Body weight.* Increased skeletal weight is thought to promote bone density, putting thin people at greater risk of developing the disease than obese people. However, weight-bearing exercise can have the same effect.
- *Family history.* Genetic factors—peak mass attainment—may affect the occurrence of the disease.
- *Miscellaneous.* Late menarche, nulliparity, and use of caffeine, alcohol, and cigarettes are all thought to be important determinants of bone mass.

Unless a bone density test has been conducted, persons with osteoporosis are usually asymptotic until a fracture occurs. Management includes prevention of fractures through exercise and drug therapy, such as administration of calcium, vitamin D, estrogen, and other medications or minerals.

h. Hypothermia and hyperthermia pp. 187–188

Hypothermia. Thermoregulatory emergencies represent some of the most common EMS calls involving the elderly. As a group, the elderly are vulnerable to low temperatures, suffering about 750,000 winter deaths annually, primarily from hypothermia and "winter risks" such as pneumonia and influenza. Factors that predispose the elderly to hypothermia include accidental exposure to cold, CNS disorders, head trauma, stroke, endocrine disorders (particularly hypoglycemia and diabetes), drugs that interfere with heat production, malnutrition or starvation, chronic illness, forced inactivity as a result of a medical condition, low or fixed income (which discourages use of home heating), inflammatory dermatitis, and A-V shunts.

Hypothermic patients may exhibit slow speech, cold skin, confusion, and sleepiness. In early stages, patients will exhibit hypertension and an increased heart rate. As hypothermia progresses, however, blood pressure drops and the heart rate slows, sometimes to a barely detectable level. Keep in mind that the elderly patient with hypothermia often does not shiver. Check the abdomen and back to see if the skin is cool to the touch or, if your unit has a low-temperature thermometer, check the patient's core temperature.

Treatment is focused on rewarming the patient and rapid transport. Once elderly patients develop hypothermia, they become progressively impaired, with their condition worsening other chronic medical problems. Remain alert for complications, most commonly cardiac arrest or ventricular fibrillation.

Hyperthermia. Age-related changes in the sweat glands and increased incidence of heart disease place the elderly at risk of heat stress. They may develop heat cramps, heat exhaustion, or heat stroke. Risk factors for severe hyperthermia include altered sensory output, inadequate liquid intake, decreased functioning of the thermoregulatory center, commonly prescribed medications that inhibit sweating (such as antihistamines and tricyclic antidepressants), low or fixed incomes (which may result in a lack of fans or air conditioning), alcoholism, concomitant medical disorders, and use of diuretics (which increase fluid loss).

Early heatstroke may present with nonspecific signs and symptoms such as nausea, lightheadedness, dizziness, headache, and high fever. Prevention strategies include adequate fluid intake, reduced activity, shelter in an air-conditioned environment, and use of light clothing. If hyperthermia develops, however, rapid treatment and transport are necessary.

i. **Toxicological problems, including drug toxicity, substance abuse, alcohol abuse, and drug abuse**   **pp. 188–194**

Toxicological problems. Aging alters pharmacokinetics and pharmacodynamics in the elderly. Functional changes in the kidneys, liver, and GI system slow the absorption and elimination of many medications. In addition, the various compensatory mechanisms that help buffer against medication side effects are less effective in the elderly than in younger patients.

Approximately 30 percent of all hospital admissions are related to drug-induced illnesses. About 50 percent of all drug-related deaths occur in people over age 60. Accidental overdoses may occur more frequently in the aged due to confusion, vision impairment, self-selection of medications, forgetfulness, and concurrent drug use. Intentional drug overdose also occurs in attempts at self-destruction. Another complicating factor is the abuse of alcohol in the elderly.

In assessing the elderly patient, always take these steps:
- Obtain a full list of medications currently taken by the patient.
- Elicit any medications that are newly prescribed.
- Obtain a good past medical history, including prior renal or hepatic depression.
- Know your medications, their routes of elimination, and their potential side effects.
- If possible, always take all medications to the hospital along with the patient.

Some of the drugs or substances that have been identified as commonly causing toxicity in the elderly include:

- *Lidocaine.* Lidocaine is recommended for the treatment of ventricular dysrhythmias in the acute setting, especially in acute myocardial infarction and in dysrhythmias that arise from cardiac surgery or catheterization. Patients with liver or kidney problems will have problems metabolizing this drug. Lidocaine toxicity is characterized by vision disturbances, GI effects, tinnitus, trembling, breathing difficulties, dizziness or syncope, seizures, and bradycardiac dysrhythmias. Since the cardiac antidysrhythmics in general can cause a decrease in cardiac function and output, observe for shortness of breath, light-headedness, loss of consciousness, fatigue, chest discomfort, and palpitations.

- *Beta-blockers.* Beta-blockers are widely used to treat hypertension, angina pectoris, and cardiac dysrhythmias. Elderly patients, however, are susceptible to CNS side effects such as depression, lethargy, and sleep disorders. Because elderly patients often have preexisting cardiovascular problems that can cause decreased cardiac function and output, beta-blockers will limit the heart's ability to respond to postural changes, causing orthostatic hypotension. Beta-blockers also limit the heart's ability to increase contractile force and cardiac output whenever a sympathetic response is necessary in situations such as exercise or hypovolemia. This can be detrimental to the trauma patient who is hemorrhaging and cannot mount the sympathetic response necessary to maintain perfusion of vital organs.

  Treatment of beta-blocker overdoses includes general supportive measures, the removal of gastric contents, support of the ABCs, fluids, and administration of nonadrenergic inotropic agents such as glucagon for hypotension. Excessive bradycardia can be countered with atropine.

- *Antihypertensives/diuretics.* These medications act on the kidneys to increase urine flow and the excretion of water and sodium. They are used primarily in the treatment of hypertension and congestive heart failure. Of these drugs, furosemide is the most widely used diuretic in the elderly. The elimination half-life of furosemide is markedly prolonged in the patient with acute pulmonary edema and renal and hepatic failure. As a result, the geriatric patient is at risk for a drug buildup. Excessive urination caused by the drug may put the elderly at risk for postural hypotension, circulatory collapse, potassium depletion, and renal function impairment. To reduce this risk, a smaller dose is often prescribed and the patient usually takes a daily potassium supplement.

- *Angiotensin-converting enzyme (ACE) inhibitors.* ACE inhibitors are used for the management of hypertension and congestive heart failure. Geriatric patients generally respond well to treatment with ACE inhibitors. However, these drugs can cause chronic hypotension in patients with severe heart failure who are also taking high-dose loop diuretics. ACE inhibitors can also cause plasma volume reduction and hypotension with prolonged vomiting and diarrhea in the elderly patient. Some hemodialysis patients can experience anaphylactic reactions if treated with ACE inhibitors. Other side effects of ACE inhibitors include dizziness or light-headedness upon standing; presence of a rash; muscle cramps; swelling of the hands, face, or eyes; cough; headache; stomach upset; and fatigue.

- *Digitalis (digoxin, lanoxin).* Digoxin is the most widely used cardiac glycoside for the management of congestive heart failure, atrial fibrillation, atrial flutter, paroxysmal atrial tachycardia, and cardiogenic shock. The drug is unique in that it has a positive inotropic effect and a negative chronotropic effect. Because digoxin has a low margin of safety and a narrow therapeutic index, the amount of drug required to produce a desired effect is very close to the toxic range. Digoxin toxicity in the elderly can result from accidental or intentional ingestion. In the renally impaired elderly patient, any change in kidney function usually warrants an alteration in the dosing of digoxin. Diuretics, which are often given to patients with congestive heart failure, cause the loss of large amounts of potassium in the urine. If potassium is not adequately replenished in the patient taking digoxin, toxicity will develop.

  Signs and symptoms of digoxin toxicity include visual disturbances, fatigue, weakness, nausea, loss of appetite, abdominal discomfort, dizziness, abnormal dreams, headache, and vomiting. Low potassium (hypokalemia) is also common with chronic digoxin toxicity due to concurrent diuretic therapy. Dysrhythmias commonly associated with digoxin toxicity include sinoatrial (SA) exit block, SA arrest, second- or third-degree AV block, atrial fibrillation with a slow ventricular response, accelerated AV junctional rhythms, patterns of premature ventricular contractions, ventricular tachycardia, and atrial tachycardia with AV block.

  The management of digoxin toxicity includes gastric lavage with activated charcoal, correction of confirmed hypokalemia with potassium supplements, treatment of bradycardias with atropine or pacing, and the treatment of rapid ventricular rhythms with lidocaine. Digoxin-specific Fab fragment antibodies (Digibind), an antidote for digoxin toxicity, is used in the treatment of potentially life-threatening situations.

- *Antipsychotics/antidepressants.* Psychotropic medications comprise a variety of agents that affect mood, behavior, and other aspects of mental function. The elderly often experience a high incidence of psychiatric disorders and may take any number of medications, including antidepressants, antianxiety agents, sedative-hypnotic agents, and antipsychotics.

  Antidepressant use in the elderly may result in side effects such as sedation, lethargy, and muscle weakness. Some antidepressants tend to produce anticholinergic effects, including dry mouth, constipation, urinary retention, and confusion. Newly prescribed tricyclic antidepressants can also cause orthostatic hypotension, which can be compounded if the geriatric patient is taking diuretics or other antihypertensive medications. Side effects such as sedation and confusion may also impair the patient's cognitive abilities and possibly endanger the elderly patient who lives alone.

  Antipsychotic medications produce a number of minor side effects such as sedation and anticholinergic effects. Extrapyramidal side effects can also occur, including restlessness and involuntary muscle movements, particularly in the face, jaw, and extremities.

  Field treatment for overdose of antipsychotics and antidepressants is aimed primarily at the ABCs, with special emphasis on airway management.

- *Medications for Parkinson's disease.* Drug treatment for Parkinson's disease is aimed at restoring the balance of neurotransmitters in the basal ganglia. Toxicity of Parkinson's drugs commonly presents as dyskinesia (the inability to execute voluntary movements) and psychological disturbances such as visual hallucinations and nightmares. When these medications are first taken, orthostatic hypotension may also occur. The goal of field management is aimed at decreasing the patient's anxiety and providing a supportive environment. Remember that patients with gross involuntary motor movements are at risk for aspiration and choking.

- *Antiseizure medications.* Seizure disorders are not uncommon in the elderly, and the selection of antiseizure medication depends upon the type of seizure present in the patient.

The most common side effect of antiseizure medications is sedation. Other side effects include GI distress, headache, dizziness, lack of coordination, and dermatological reactions (rashes). Recommended treatment involves airway management and supportive therapy.

- *Analgesics and anti-inflammatory agents.* Treatment of pain and inflammation for chronic conditions such as rheumatoid arthritis and osteoarthritis includes narcotics and nonnarcotic analgesics and corticosteroids. Adverse side effects of these drugs include sedation, mood changes, nausea, vomiting, and constipation. Orthostatic hypotension and respiratory depression may also occur. Over long periods of time, patients may develop drug tolerance and physical dependence on narcotic agents. In the case of corticosteroids, side effects may include hypertension, peptic ulcer, aggravation of diabetes mellitus, glaucoma, increased risk of infection, and suppression of normally produced corticosteroids.

Substance abuse, drug abuse, alcohol abuse. In general, the factors that contribute to substance abuse among the elderly are different than those of younger people. They include age-related changes, loss of employment, loss of spouse or partner, malnutrition, loneliness, moving from a long-loved home, and multiple prescriptions.

The elderly who become physically and/or psychologically dependent upon drugs or alcohol are more likely to hide their dependence and less likely to seek help than other age groups. Common signs and symptoms of drug abuse include memory changes, drowsiness, decreased vision/hearing, orthostatic hypotension, poor dexterity, mood changes, falling, restlessness, and weight loss. Pertinent findings for alcohol abuse include mood swings, denial, and hostility (when questioned about alcohol); confusion; history of falls; anorexia; insomnia; visible anxiety; and nausea.

Treatment follows many of the same steps as for any other patient with a pattern of substance abuse. DO NOT judge the patient. Manage the ABCs and evaluate the need for fluid therapy or medications to accommodate withdrawal. Transport the patient to the hospital for further evaluation and referral.

j. Psychological disorders, including depression and suicide   pp. 194–196

Psychological disorders. When behavioral or psychological problems develop later in life, they are often dismissed as normal age-related changes. This attitude denies an elderly person the opportunity to correct a treatable condition and may overlook an underlying physical disorder. It is important to keep in mind the emotionally stressful situations facing many elderly people—isolation, loneliness, loss of self-dependence, loss of strength, and fear of the future. The elderly also face a higher incidence of secondary depression as a result of neuroleptic medications such as Haldol and Thorazine. Some of the common classifications of psychological disorders related to age include organic brain syndrome, affective disorders, personality disorders, and dissociative disorders.

Depression and suicide. Up to 15 percent of the noninstitutionalized elderly experience depression. Within institutions, that figure rises to about 30 percent. In general, depressed patients should receive supportive care, with caregivers delicately raising questions about suicidal thoughts. Keep in mind that the elderly account for 20 percent of all suicides even though they only represent 12 percent of the total population. In fact, suicide is the third leading cause of death among the elderly, following falls and car crashes.

In cases of seriously depressed patients, elicit behavior patterns from family, friends, or caregivers. Warning signs may include curtailing activities and self-care, breaking from medical or exercise regimens, grieving a personal loss, expressing feelings of uselessness, putting affairs in order, and stockpiling medications. Be particularly alert to suicide among the acutely ill, especially those in a home-care setting.

Your first priorities in the management of a suicidal elderly patient are to protect yourself and then to protect the patient from self-harm. Conduct a brief interview with the patient, if possible, to determine the need for further action. DO NOT leave the suicidal patient alone. Administer medications with caution, keeping in mind polypharmacy and drug interactions in the elderly. (Consult with medical direction.) *All suicidal elderly patients should be transported to the hospital.*

19. **Describe the incidence, morbidity/mortality, risk factors, prevention strategies, pathophysiology, assessment, need for intervention and transport, and management of the elderly trauma patient with:**

   a. **Orthopedic injuries**   pp. 198–200

   The elderly suffer the greatest mortality and greatest incidence of disability from falls. Approximately 33 percent of the falls in the elderly result in at least one fractured bone. The most common fall-related fracture is a fracture of the hip or pelvis. Falls also result in a variety of stress fractures in the elderly, including fractures of the proximal humerus, distal radius, proximal tibia, and thoracic and lumbar bodies. In treating orthopedic injuries, remember to ask questions aimed at detecting an underlying medical condition.

   b. **Burns**   p. 200

   People age 60 and older are more likely to suffer death from burns than any other age group except neonates and infants. Factors that help explain the high mortality rate among the elderly include age-related changes that slow reaction time, preexisting diseases that increase the risk of medical complications, age-related skin changes (thinning) that increase the severity of burns, immunological and metabolic changes that increase the risk of infection, and reductions in physiologic function and the reduced reserves of several organ systems that make the elderly more vulnerable to systemic stress.

   Management of the elderly burn patient follows the same general procedures as other patients. However, remember that the elderly are at increased risk of shock. Administration of fluids is important to prevent renal tubular damage. Assess hydration in the initial hours after the burn injury by blood pressure, pulse, and urine output. Keep in mind that complications in the elderly may manifest themselves in the days and weeks following the incident. For serious burns to heal, the body may use up to 20,000 calories a day. Elderly patients, with altered metabolisms and complications such as diabetes, may not be able to meet this demand, increasing the chances for infection and systemic failure. Part of your job may be to prepare the family for such a delayed response.

   c. **Head injuries**   pp. 200–201

   As people age, the brain decreases in size and weight. The skull, however, remains constant in size, allowing the brain more room to move, thus increasing the likelihood of brain injury. Because of this, the signs and symptoms of brain injury may develop more slowly in the elderly patient, sometimes over days or weeks. In fact, the patient may often have forgotten the offending incident.

   The cervical spine is also more susceptible to injury due to osteoporosis and spondylosis—a degeneration of the vertebral body. In addition, arthritic changes can gradually compress the nerve rootlets or spinal cord. Thus, injury to the spine in the elderly makes them much more susceptible to spinal cord injury. Therefore, it is important to provide older patients with suspected spinal cord injury, especially those involved in motor vehicle collisions, with immediate manual cervical stabilization at the time of initial assessment.

Skill Objective

20. **Given several preprogrammed simulated geriatric patients with various complaints, provide the appropriate assessment, management, and transport.**   pp. 142–201

During your classroom, clinical, and field training, you will assess real and simulated geriatric patients and develop a management plan for them. Use the information presented in this text chapter, the information on assessment of geriatric patients in the field presented by your instructors, and the guidance given by your clinical and field preceptors to develop good patient assessment and care skills. Continue to refine these skills once your training ends and you begin your career as a paramedic.

Case Study Review

Reread the case study on pages 140 to 142 in Paramedic Care: Special Considerations/Operations *and then read the following discussion.*

This case study draws attention to the importance of recognizing the vital lives led by elderly people and the need to take their complaints seriously, rather than dismissing them as normal age-related changes.

The case study puts you in the position of a paramedic who decides to mentor a student intern about the treatment of elderly patients. At the end of the call, the intern is asked: "So Andy, do you want to talk about what went right with this call and what we could have done better while we restock the ambulance?"

So let's discuss it! The complaint of abdominal pain can be caused by many different factors, most of which cannot not be resolved in a prehospital setting. Even so, after reading the text, you now know that the most frequent gastrointestinal emergency in the elderly is GI bleeding, a condition that can place the elderly at a significant risk of hypovolemia and shock. The elderly are also far more intolerant of hypotension and anoxia than younger patients. Any GI emergency should be aggressively managed.

In this case, the initial assessment ruled out an immediate life threat. The general impression was that of an elderly woman with severe abdominal pain. As noted, the pain was out of proportion to the physical exam—a symptom suggestive of mesenteric infarct. Care steps included administration of high-flow, high-concentration oxygen, IV fluid replacement therapy with a crystalloid solution, and, most importantly, rapid transport.

It was correct to place the patient on a cardiac monitor. An ECG of atrial fibrillation is common in elderly patients. Based on the patient's vital signs, Mrs. Hildegaard seemed to be tolerating the dysrhythmias. The monitor helped show that the pain was not cardiac related, though complications could result, depending on preexisting medical conditions.

It might have been helpful to inquire in more detail about any other GI distress experienced by the patient, such as diarrhea, vomiting, and nausea. Also, a pulse oximeter might have been useful to measure the patient's oxygen saturation en route to the hospital. However, considering the patient's presentation, she was managed appropriately.

Andy's quip about too many beers and a taco provided a "teachable moment" in that it corrected a mistaken attitude about the aging process—the idea that an elderly patient might not live like a younger counterpart. In fact, it would have been relevant to ask just what the patient ate—and drank—at dinner. It also highlighted the problem of alcohol abuse among the elderly. They are not only exposed to the stresses of aging, but age-related systemic changes and medical problems make it more difficult for them to metabolize alcohol or many other drugs. So it would have also been relevant to ask whether Mrs. Hildegaard consumed alcohol on a regular basis.

Content Self-Evaluation

MULTIPLE CHOICE

_____ 1. All of the following are responsible for the growing number of elderly people in the United States—and the projected increase in the number of elderly patients treated by EMS services—EXCEPT a(n):
A. increase in the mean survival rate of older persons.
B. increase in the birth rate.
C. absence of major wars.
D. improved health care.
E. higher standard of living.

_____ 2. The scientific study of the effects of aging and of age-related diseases on humans is known as:
A. geriatrics.
B. ageism.
C. gerontology.
D. eldercare.
E. gerontotherapeutics.

3. The elderly often do not reveal problems behind the chief complaints because they:
   A. fear the loss of their independence.
   B. consider the problems "normal" for their age.
   C. don't want to burden others with their problems.
   D. do not want to be treated as helpless human beings.
   E. all of the above.

4. A living arrangement in which the elderly live in, but do not own, individual apartments or rooms and receive selective services is known as:
   A. a nursing home.
   B. a life-care community.
   C. congregate care.
   D. a personal-care home.
   E. a hospice.

5. Drawbacks to living in an adult community or nursing home setting include all the following EXCEPT:
   A. loss of independence.
   B. exposure to illnesses found in the institutional setting.
   C. a lack of contact with young people.
   D. increased risk of criminal activities.
   E. poor or inadequate staff.

6. A deterioration in independence is a function of aging and should be treated as such by the paramedic.
   A. True   B. False

7. When confronted with multiple decision makers during the care of an elderly patient, you should usually honor the wishes of the:
   A. caregiver.   D. patient.
   B. family members.   E. spouse or partner.
   C. personal-care aide.

8. The largest share of public funding for long-term care of the elderly is provided by:
   A. the Veterans Administration.
   B. Medicaid.
   C. Medicare.
   D. private insurance.
   E. Health Maintenance Organizations.

9. Health care endeavors supported by many senior centers include:
   A. blood-pressure monitoring.
   B. transport to clinics.
   C. Meals on Wheels.
   D. flu shots.
   E. all of the above.

10. All of the following provide significant advocacy for the elderly EXCEPT:
    A. AA.
    B. AARP.
    C. Alzheimer's Association.
    D. Association for Senior Citizens.
    E. Department of Health.

11. The existence of multiple diseases in the elderly is known as:
    A. functional impairment.
    B. dysphagia.
    C. comorbidity.
    D. polypharmacy.
    E. senility.

_____ 12. Common complaints in the elderly include:
- A. falls, weakness, syncope.
- B. fractures, drowning, diabetes.
- C. GSW, croup, nausea.
- D. MVC, meningitis, poisoning.
- E. fever, epiglottitis, febrile seizures.

_____ 13. When compared to younger patients, the elderly experience fewer adverse drug reactions.
- A. True
- B. False

_____ 14. Drugs concentrate more readily in the plasma and tissues of elderly patients because of:
- A. diminished neurologic function.
- B. increased body fluid.
- C. atrophy of organs.
- D. more efficient compensatory mechanisms.
- E. increased renal function.

_____ 15. Factors that can decrease medication compliance in the elderly include all of the following EXCEPT:
- A. limited mobility.
- B. fear of toxicity.
- C. child-proof containers.
- D. multiple-compartment pill boxes.
- E. sensory impairment.

_____ 16. Factors that can increase medication compliance in the elderly include:
- A. compliance counseling.
- B. a belief that an illness is serious.
- C. clear, simple directions.
- D. blister-pack packaging.
- E. all of the above.

_____ 17. A lack of mobility can have detrimental physical and emotional effects on the elderly.
- A. True
- B. False

_____ 18. Which of the following is the leading cause of accidental deaths among the elderly?
- A. drownings
- B. fall-related injuries
- C. motor vehicle collisions
- D. gunshot wounds
- E. poisonings

_____ 19. Intrinsic factors that can cause an elderly person to fall include all of the following EXCEPT:
- A. dizziness.
- B. slippery floors.
- C. decreased mental status.
- D. impaired vision.
- E. CNS problems.

_____ 20. Extrinsic factors that can cause an elderly person to fall include:
- A. an altered gait.
- B. a sense of weakness.
- C. a lack of hand rails.
- D. use of certain medications.
- E. a history of repeated falls.

_____ 21. The inability to retain urine or feces because of loss of sphincter control or because of cerebral or spinal lesions is called:
  A. diarrhea.
  B. involuntary elimination.
  C. diuresis.
  D. incontinence.
  E. uremia.

_____ 22. In elderly people with cerebrovascular disease or impaired baroreceptor reflexes, efforts to force a bowel movement can lead to a transient ischemic attack.
  A. True   B. False

_____ 23. Possible causes of elimination problems in the elderly include:
  A. diverticular disease.
  B. constipation.
  C. colorectal cancer.
  D. use of opioids.
  E. all of the above.

_____ 24. One of the most common reasons that elderly patients underestimate the severity of a primary medical problem is that they have a(n):
  A. shrinkage of structures in the ear.
  B. clouding and thickening of lenses in the eyes.
  C. lowered sensitivity to pain.
  D. deterioration of the teeth and gums.
  E. altered sense of taste.

_____ 25. All of the following factors play a part in forming a general assessment of the elderly patient EXCEPT:
  A. average cost of rent.
  B. medication history.
  C. living situations.
  D. sleep patterns.
  E. level of activity.

_____ 26. Conditions that may discourage eating among the elderly include:
  A. breathing or respiratory problems.
  B. nausea or vomiting.
  C. poor dental care.
  D. alcohol or drug abuse.
  E. all of the above.

_____ 27. An eating disorder marked by excessive fasting found in the elderly and other age groups is called:
  A. diverticulitis.
  B. dysphagia.
  C. anorexia nervosa.
  D. bulimia.
  E. dehydration.

_____ 28. Which of the following is a byproduct of malnutrition?
  A. electrolyte abnormalities
  B. dehydration
  C. vitamin deficiencies
  D. hypoglycemia
  E. all of the above

_____ 29. The elderly are more prone to environmental thermal problems due to changes in the sweat glands.
  A. True   B. False

_____ **30.** A medical condition in which eye pressure increases and ultimately diminishes sight is known as:
- **A.** Meniere's disease.
- **B.** tinnitus.
- **C.** cataracts.
- **D.** glaucoma.
- **E.** retinitis.

_____ **31.** A disease of the inner ear characterized by vertigo, nerve deafness, and a roar or buzzing in the ear is called:
- **A.** Meniere's disease.
- **B.** tinnitus.
- **C.** cataracts.
- **D.** glaucoma.
- **E.** cerumen.

_____ **32.** To improve communication with an elderly patient, you should try to:
- **A.** display verbal and nonverbal signs of concern.
- **B.** dim the room lights.
- **C.** avoid looking directly into the patient's eyes.
- **D.** first talk to family members, then the patient.
- **E.** remain as quiet as possible.

_____ **33.** Both senility and organic brain syndrome may manifest themselves as:
- **A.** distractibility.
- **B.** excitability.
- **C.** hostility.
- **D.** restlessness.
- **E.** all of the above.

_____ **34.** When assessing an elderly person, if they are confused or disoriented, you can conclude that the patient is senile.
- **A.** True
- **B.** False

_____ **35.** Changes in mental status in the elderly patient may be due to which of the following?
- **A.** traumatic head injury
- **B.** dementia
- **C.** decreased sugar level
- **D.** infection
- **E.** all of the above

_____ **36.** To help reduce an elderly patient's fears, you should:
- **A.** downplay the patient's fears.
- **B.** ignore nonverbal messages.
- **C.** discourage the expression of feelings.
- **D.** confirm what the patient has said.
- **E.** instruct the patient to calm down.

_____ **37.** Compared to younger people, the skin of elderly people:
- **A.** is thicker and oilier.
- **B.** heals more quickly.
- **C.** tears less easily.
- **D.** is less subject to fungal infections.
- **E.** perspires less.

_____ **38.** The elderly have a greater risk of trauma-related complications due a decrease in blood volume.
- **A.** True
- **B.** False

_____ 39. Age-related changes to the respiratory system include all of the following EXCEPT:
   A. increased chest wall compliance.
   B. diminished breathing capacity.
   C. reduced strength and endurance.
   D. increased air trapping.
   E. reduced gag reflex.

_____ 40. The decrease of an effective cough reflex and the activity of the _____ make the elderly more prone to respiratory infection.
   A. gag reflex
   B. alveoli
   C. cilia
   D. bronchioles
   E. vagal response

_____ 41. In treating respiratory disorders in the elderly patient, do not fluid overload.
   A. True   B. False

_____ 42. An exaggeration of the normal posterior curvature of the spine is called:
   A. scoliosis.
   B. kyphosis.
   C. fibrosis.
   D. hypertrophy.
   E. spondylosis.

_____ 43. An increase in the size and bulk of the left ventricle wall in some elderly patients is an example of:
   A. kyphosis.
   B. anoxia hypoxemia.
   C. hypertrophy.
   D. fibrosis.
   E. Marfan's syndrome.

_____ 44. In managing elderly patients with complaints related to the cardiovascular system, take all of the following steps EXCEPT:
   A. monitor the ECG.
   B. provide high flow, high-concentration supplemental oxygen.
   C. walk the patient slowly to the rig.
   D. remain empathetic to the patient's fears.
   E. start an IV for medication administration.

_____ 45. All of the following are age-related changes to the nervous system EXCEPT:
   A. decreased reaction time.
   B. increased brain weight.
   C. impaired balance.
   D. shrinkage of brain tissue.
   E. recent memory loss.

_____ 46. The elderly are less susceptible to subdural hematomas than younger people.
   A. True   B. False

_____ 47. Age-related changes in the gastrointestinal system include all of the following EXCEPT:
   A. impaired swallowing.
   B. diminished digestive functions.
   C. decreased liver efficiency.
   D. a predisposition to choking.
   E. increased gastric secretions.

_____ 48. A protrusion of the stomach upward into the mediastinal cavity through the diaphragm is known as:
   A. a hiatal hernia.
   B. Marfan's syndrome.
   C. a diaphragmatic hernia.
   D. an inguinal hernia.
   E. an epigastric hernia.

_____ 49. Reasons that the elderly develop pneumonia more frequently than younger people include all of the following EXCEPT a(n):
   A. decreased immune response.
   B. increased pulmonary function.
   C. abnormal or ineffective cough reflex.
   D. decreased activity of mucociliary cells.
   E. decreased colonization of the pharynx by gram-negative bacteria.

_____ 50. An elderly patient in an institutional setting is up to 50 times more likely to contract pneumonia that an elderly patient receiving home care.
   A. True   B. False

_____ 51. The usual signs and symptoms of COPD include:
   A. cough and wheezing.
   B. dyspnea and tachypnea.
   C. exercise intolerance.
   D. pleuritic chest pain.
   E. all of the above.

_____ 52. The most effective prevention of COPD involves:
   A. elimination of smoking.
   B. lowering blood sugar.
   C. reducing physical activity.
   D. lowering blood pressure.
   E. use of supplemental oxygen.

_____ 53. Your elderly patient is complaining of acute onset of sharp chest pain and shortness of breath. The patient was recently released from the hospital for a leg fracture. What is the most likely suspected disorder?
   A. pneumonia
   B. pulmonary embolism
   C. heart attack
   D. COPD
   E. pulmonary edema

_____ 54. Although all of the following can contribute to a pulmonary embolism, the condition is most frequently caused by:
   A. fat.
   B. bone marrow.
   C. blood clots.
   D. tumor cells.
   E. air.

_____ 55. The leading cause of death in the elderly is:
   A. pneumonia.
   B. stroke.
   C. cardiovascular disease.
   D. Alzheimer's disease.
   E. COPD.

_____ 56. The heart sounds in an elderly patient are generally louder than those in a young patient.
   A. True   B. False

_____ 57. All of the following are atypical presentations of a myocardial infarction in the elderly EXCEPT:
   A. syncope.
   B. tearing chest pain.
   C. dyspnea.
   D. neck or dental pain.
   E. exercise intolerance.

_____ 58. Assessment findings specific to the elderly such as anorexia, nocturia, dependent edema, and hepatomegaly may be found in a patient with:
   A. a pulmonary embolism.
   B. heart failure.
   C. hypertension.
   D. an aneurysm.
   E. syncope.

_____ 59. An abnormal dilation of a blood vessel, usually an artery, due to a congenital defect or weakness in the wall of the vessel is called:
   A. an aneurysm.
   B. an infarct.
   C. thrombosis.
   D. an embolism.
   E. a hernia.

_____ 60. A series of symptoms resulting from decreased blood flow to the brain that are caused by a sudden decrease in cardiac output from a heart block are known as:
   A. autonomic dysfunction.
   B. Stokes-Adams syndrome.
   C. sick sinus syndrome.
   D. dying heart muscle.
   E. Marfan's syndrome.

_____ 61. Injury to or death of brain tissue resulting from interruption of cerebral blood flow and oxygenation is called a(n):
   A. subarachnoid hemorrhage.
   B. autonomic dysfunction.
   C. TIA.
   D. stroke.
   E. intracerebral hemorrhage.

_____ 62. Common causes of seizures in the elderly include all of the following EXCEPT:
   A. head trauma.
   B. alcohol withdrawal.
   C. spinal injury.
   D. stroke.
   E. hypoglycemia.

_____ 63. A progressive, degenerative disease that attacks the brain and results in impaired memory, thinking, and behavior is called:
   A. dementia.
   B. Parkinson's disease.
   C. delirium.
   D. Alzheimer's disease.
   E. aphasia.

_____ 64. A chronic, degenerative nervous disease characterized by tremors, muscular weakness and rigidity, and loss of postural reflexes is called:
A. Parkinson's disease.
B. Shy-Drager syndrome.
C. Alzheimer's disease.
D. sick sinus syndrome.
E. generalized tonic-clonic seizure.

_____ 65. All of the following are forms of upper GI bleeding EXCEPT:
A. peptic ulcer disease.
B. ischemic colitis.
C. esophageal varices.
D. gastritis.
E. peptic ulcer disease.

_____ 66. An example of a lower GI bleeding is:
A. a Mallory-Weiss tear.
B. diverticulosis.
C. peptic ulcer disease.
D. a bowel obstruction.
E. a mesenteric infarct.

_____ 67. An inflammation of the colon due to impaired or decreased blood supply is called:
A. diverticulosis.
B. ischemic colitis.
C. arterio-venous malformation.
D. colostomy.
E. gastritis.

_____ 68. An abnormal dilation of veins in the lower esophagus common in patients with cirrhosis of the liver is called esophageal varices.
A. True
B. False

_____ 69. The acute skin eruption caused by a reactivation of latent varicella virus that peaks between ages 50 and 70 is known as:
A. shingles.
B. pruritus.
C. maceration.
D. herpes zoster.
E. both A and D.

_____ 70. When transporting an elderly patient with pressure ulcers, you should encourage the patient to remain still.
A. True
B. False

_____ 71. Risk factors for osteoporosis include all of the following EXCEPT:
A. African or Latino ancestry.
B. low body weight.
C. early menopause.
D. family history of fractures.
E. use of caffeine, alcohol, and cigarettes.

_____ 72. In general, the kidney loses approximately one third of its weight between the ages of 30 and 80.
A. True
B. False

_____ 73. All of the following are signs and symptoms of hypothermia in an elderly patient EXCEPT:
A. confusion.
B. slow speech.
C. shivering.
D. skin cool to the touch.
E. sleepiness.

74. Elderly patients with hepatic impairment and decreased renal function should receive the normal dose of lidocaine.
    A. True   B. False

75. Dysrhythmias commonly associated with digoxin toxicity include all of the following EXCEPT:
    A. atrial fibrillation.
    B. third-degree heart block.
    C. sinoatrial exit block.
    D. ventricular fibrillation.
    E. sinoatrial arrest.

76. The most common adverse drug effect that occurs in the elderly is:
    A. lidocaine underdose.
    B. digoxin toxicity.
    C. furosemide overdose.
    D. lithium toxicity.
    E. morphine addiction.

77. Factors that contribute to substance abuse among the elderly include:
    A. multiple prescriptions.
    B. malnutrition.
    C. loneliness.
    D. age-related changes.
    E. all of the above.

78. The elderly who become physically and/or psychologically dependent upon drugs (or alcohol) are more likely to seek help than other age groups.
    A. True   B. False

79. The leading cause of suicide among the elderly is:
    A. chronic illness.
    B. unrelieved pain.
    C. living in a youth-oriented society.
    D. financial problems.
    E. depression.

80. One of the best indicators of shock in an elderly patient is:
    A. blood pressure.
    B. pulse rate.
    C. level of pain.
    D. mental status.
    E. both A and B.

MATCHING

Write the letter of the term in the space provided next to the appropriate description.

A. epistaxis

B. varicosities

C. sick sinus syndrome

D. autonomic dysfunction

E. transient ischemic attack

F. brain ischemia

G. urosepsis

H. nocturia

I. polycythemia

J. delirium

K. senile dementia

L. vertigo

M. mesenteric infarct

N. spondylosis

O. dysphoria

_____ 81. acute alteration in mental functioning that is often reversible

_____ 82. septicemia originating from the urinary tract

_____ 83. medical term for a nosebleed

_____ 84. excessive urination, usually at night

_____ 85. death of tissue in the peritoneal fold that encircles the small intestine

_____ 86. exaggerated feeling of depression or unrest

_____ 87. excess of red blood cells

_____ 88. abnormal dilation of a vein

_____ 89. group of disorders characterized by dysfunction of the sinoatrial node

_____ 90. sensation of faintness or dizziness causing loss of balance

_____ 91. general term used to describe an abnormal decline in mental function in the elderly

_____ 92. degeneration of the vertebral body

_____ 93. abnormality of the involuntary aspect of the nervous system

_____ 94. injury to the brain tissues caused by an inadequate supply of oxygen and nutrients

_____ 95. medical condition like a stroke but reversible and commonly involving syncope

Special Project

Common Age-Related Systemic Changes

Complete the chart on this page, showing the systemic changes that come with age and the clinical importance of these changes.

Body System	Changes with Age	Clinical Importance
Respiratory		
Cardiovascular		
Neurological		
Endocrine		
Gastrointestinal		
Thermoregulatory		
Integumentary (Skin)		
Musculoskeletal		
Renal		
Genitourinary		
Immune		
Hematological		

©2006 Pearson Education, Inc.
Paramedic Care: Principles & Practice, Vol. 5

4

Abuse and Assault

Review of Chapter Objectives

After reading this chapter, you should be able to:

1. Discuss the incidence of abuse and assault.   **p. 206**

Because of underreporting, it is difficult to provide accurate statistics on the incidence of abuse and assault in the United States today. That makes the available figures even more overwhelming in their seriousness. To grasp the magnitude of the problem, consider these facts:

- Nearly 3 million children suffer abuse each year and more than 1,000 die annually.
- Between 2 and 4 million women each year are battered by their partners or spouses.
- Elder abuse occurs at an incidence of between 700,000 and 1.1 million annually.

2. Describe the categories of abuse.   **pp. 206–216**

Partner abuse

Partner abuse results when a man or woman subjects a domestic partner to some form of physical or psychological violence. The victim may be a husband or wife, someone who shares a residence, or simply a boyfriend or girlfriend.

Elder abuse

There are basically two types of elder abuse—domestic and institutional. *Domestic elder abuse* takes place when an elder is being cared for in a home-based setting, usually by relatives. *Institutional elder abuse* occurs when an elder is being cared for by a person with a legal or contractual responsibility to provide care, such as paid caregivers, nursing home staff, or other professionals. Both types of abuse can be either acts of commission (acts of physical, sexual, or emotional violence) or acts of omission (neglect).

Child abuse

Child abuse may range from physical or emotional mistreatment to neglect of a child's most basic needs. It can occur from infancy to age 18 and can be inflicted by any number of caregivers—parents, foster parents, stepparents, babysitters, siblings, step-siblings, or other relatives or friends charged with a child's care.

Sexual abuse/assault

Sexual abuse, which is a form of physical abuse, can occur in almost any setting with a male or female of any age. It involves forced sexual contact and includes date rape and such contact within marriage. Although the legal definitions of sexual assault vary from state to state, courts generally interpret it as unwanted sexual contact, whether it be genital, oral, rectal, or manual. *Rape* is usually defined as penile penetration of the genitalia or rectum (however slight) without the consent of the victim. Both forms of sexual violence are prosecuted as crimes, with rape constituting a felony offense.

3. Discuss examples of spouse, elder, child, and sexual abuse.   pp. 206–220

Examples of spouse/partner abuse

Partner abuse can fall into several categories. The most obvious form is physical abuse, which involves the application of force in ways too numerous to list. In addition to direct injury, physical abuse may exacerbate existing medical conditions, such as hypertension, diabetes, or asthma. Verbal abuse, which consists of words chosen to control or harm a person, may leave no physical mark. However, it damages a person's self-esteem and can lead to depression, substance abuse, or other self-destructive behavior. As noted in objective 2, partner abuse can also take the form of sexual abuse—unwanted, forced sexual contact between two people.

Examples of elder abuse

Elder abuse can also be physical, verbal, or sexual. In some cases, signs of elder abuse are subtle, such as theft of the victim's belongings or loss of freedom. Other signs, such as wounds, untreated decubitus ulcers, or poor hygiene, are more obvious. (For other examples of elder abuse, see Chapter 3.)

Examples of child abuse

As pointed out in Chapters 1 and 2, abused children suffer every imaginable mistreatment. They can be shaken, thrown, burned or scalded, and battered with almost any kind of object. They can be denied food, clean clothing, medical care, or even access to a toilet. The damage done to a child can last a lifetime and perpetuate a cycle of violence for generations to come.

Examples of sexual abuse/assault

Sexual abuse/assault typically involves a male assailant and a female victim but not always. Forced sexual contact can range from exposure to fondling to rape to sexual torture. It may involve one assailant or multiple assailants. It can be an isolated act or an ongoing occurrence. Sexual abuse/assault can result in injuries, infections, sexually transmitted diseases, and unwanted pregnancies. The psychological damage is deep and long-lasting. Shame, anger, and a lack of trust may persist for years—or even a lifetime.

4. Describe the characteristics associated with the profile of a typical spouse, elder, or child abuser and the typical assailant of sexual abuse.   pp. 207–208, 211–212, 218

Profile of spouse/partner abusers

Partner abuse occurs in all demographic groups. However, abuse is more common in lower socioeconomic levels in which wage earners have trouble paying bills, holding down jobs, or keeping pace with technological changes. Typically the abuser does not like being out of control but at the same time feels powerless to change. A spouse or partner abuser usually exhibits an overly aggressive personality—an outgrowth of low self-esteem. They often feel insecure and jealous, flying into sudden and unpredictable rages. Use of alcohol or drugs increases the likelihood that the abuser will lose control and may not even remember his actions.

In the aftermath of an abusive incident, the abuser often feels a sense of remorse and shame. The person may seek to relieve his guilt by promising to change or even seeking help. For a time, the abuser may appear charming or loving, convincing an abused spouse or partner to think the pattern has finally been broken. All too often, however, the cycle of violence repeats itself in just a few days, weeks, or months.

Profile of elder abusers

Like partner abuse, elder abuse cuts across all demographic groups. As a result, it is difficult to profile the people who are most likely to abuse elders. However, there are several characteristics found in abusers of the elderly. Often, the perpetrators exhibit alcoholic behavior, drug addiction, or some mental impairment. The abuser may also be dependent upon the income or assistance of the elder—a situation that can cause resentment, anger, and, in some cases, violence. According to one study, in cases of domestic elder abuse, the most typical abusers are adult children who are overstressed by care of the elder and/or who were abused themselves.

Profile of child abusers

As with other types of abusers, you cannot relate child abuse to social class, income, or education. However, most child abusers share one common trait: They were physically or emotionally abused as children. They often would prefer to use other forms of discipline, but under stress they regress to the earliest and most familiar patterns. Once they have resorted to physical discipline, the punishments become more severe and more frequent.

In cases of reported physical abuse, perpetrators tend to be men. However, the statistics for men and women even out when neglect is taken into account. Although potential child abusers can include a wide variety of caregivers, one or both parents are the most likely abusers. Frequent behavioral traits include use or abuse of alcohol and/or drugs, immaturity, self-absorption, and an inability to emotionally identify with the child.

Typical assailants of sexual abuse

Once again, sexual assailants can come from almost any background. However, the violent victimizers of children are substantially more likely than the victimizers of adults to have been physically or sexually abused as children. Many assailants, particularly adolescents and abusive adults, think domination is part of any relationship. Such thinking can lead to date rape or marital rape. In a significant number of all cases, the assailants are under the influence of alcohol or drugs.

5. Identify the profile of the "at-risk" spouse, elder, and child.   pp. 208–209, 210, 212–213

At-risk spouses/partners

The primary risk factor for abuse is a family history of violence toward a spouse or partner. According to studies, pregnancy also appears to play a role, with 45 percent of abused women suffering some form of abuse during pregnancy. Substance abuse and emotional disorders play a role as well.

In identifying an abusive family situation, keep in mind the generic risk factors identified in "Domestic Violence: Cracking the Code of Silence," a source cited in the DOT's National Standard Curriculum. These factors, based on research of battered women, include:

- Male is unemployed.
- Male uses illegal drugs at least once a year.
- Partners have different religious backgrounds.
- Family income is below the poverty level.
- Partners are unmarried.
- Either partner is violent toward children at home.
- Male did not graduate from high school.
- Male is unemployed or has a blue-collar job.
- Male is between 18 and 30 years old.
- Male saw his father hit his mother.

At-risk elders

A number of factors place the elderly at risk of abuse. Some of these include increased dependency on others (as a result of longer life spans), decreased productivity in later years, physical and mental impairments (especially among the "old old"), limited resources for long-term care of the elderly, strained family resources, and stress on middle-aged caregivers responsible for two generations—children and parents.

In general, elder abuse occurs most frequently among people who are dependent upon others for their care, especially among those elders who are mentally or physically challenged. Elders in poor health are more likely to be abused than elders in good health. This situation results, in part, from their inability to report the abuse. Yet another risk factor is family history, or a cycle of violence among family members. Finally, the potential for elder abuse increases proportionately with the personal problems of the caregivers. Abusers of the elderly tend to have more difficulties, either financial or emotional, than nonabusers.

At-risk children

As indicated in Chapter 2, abused children share several characteristics. Often, the child is seen as "special" and different from others. Premature infants and twins stand a higher risk of abuse than other children. Many abused children are less than 5 years of age. Physically and mentally challenged children as well as those with special needs are at greater risk. So are uncommunicative (autistic) children. Boys are more often abused than girls. A child who is not what the parents wanted (e.g., the "wrong" gender) is at increased risk of abuse, too.

6. **Discuss the assessment and management of the abused patient.**   pp. 209–210, 213–216, 219

Your primary responsibility on a call involving an abusive situation is safety—both your own and that of the patient. You should never enter a scene if your safety is compromised, and you should leave the scene as soon as you feel unsafe.

You can expect the victims of abuse to feel threatened as a result of the violence they have suffered. One of your main duties is to provide a safe environment for an already traumatized patient. Sometimes you can provide safety merely by your official presence. Other times, you may have to move the patient to the ambulance so you can relocate to a different environment. In still other situations, you may have to summon additional personnel, such as law enforcement.

Specific assessment and management considerations will depend upon the type of abuse encountered. In cases of partner abuse, use direct questions, if possible, to convey an awareness that the person's partner may have contributed to the injury. In cases of suspected child abuse, examine the patient for identifiable patterns of physical mistreatment or neglect and record your objective observations. In cases of sexual abuse, use open-ended questions to reestablish a sense of control. If possible, allow a same-sex crew member to maintain contact with the victim.

Regardless of the situation, keep in mind that the patient has been harmed by another human being, in many cases a person that he or she knows intimately. Try to transport the patient to the hospital. If you cannot do so, either because of patient refusal or intervention by the suspected abuser, be sure to report your suspicions to the appropriate authorities or agencies.

7. **Discuss the legal aspects associated with abuse situations.**   pp. 206, 209, 216, 219–220

Abuse and assault constitute crimes. Although their nature and the extent of the crime often depends upon local laws, you have a responsibility to report suspected cases. Because the assailants may be detained only a short time, you also have an obligation to find out about the victim and witness protection programs available in your area.

Study the local laws and protocols regarding cases of abuse and assault. All 50 states require health care workers to report suspected cases of child abuse. Some states require EMS personnel to report even a suspicion of abuse or assault. Some states allow minors to seek medical care for sexual assault without parental consent. The Joint Commission of Accreditation of Healthcare Organizations (JCAHO) mandates that hospital personnel screen incoming patients for abuse. Regardless of where you live, take time to learn the rules and regulations that affect your practice, both for your sake and for the sake of your patient.

8. **Identify community resources that are able to assist victims of abuse and assault.**   pp. 206, 209, 211, 216, 219–220

Specialized resources include both private and state or federally funded programs. Make a point of learning about hospital units for the victims of sexual assault, public and private shelters for battered persons, and state agencies responsible for youth and their families. Also acquaint yourself with nurses trained as Sexual Assault Nurse Examiners (SANE). They have completed programs allowing them to perform the physical exam for sexual assaults.

9. **Discuss the documentation necessary when caring for abused and assaulted patients.**   pp. 206, 216, 219–220

It is important that you carefully and objectively document all your findings. Your actions can affect the outcome of a case or prosecution of a crime. If the patient tells you something about the abuser or assailant, mark it with quotation marks on the patient care report. In the case of rape, patients should not urinate, defecate, douche, bathe, eat, drink, or smoke. Some jurisdictions have specific rules for evidence protection, such as using paper bags to collect evidence or placing bags over the patient's hands to preserve trace evidence. Remember that any evidence you collect must remain in your custody until you can give it directly to a law enforcement official to preserve the *chain of evidence*. Regardless of the emotions evoked by the call, when documenting the incident, you must be completely factual and nonjudgmental.

Case Study Review

Reread the case study on page 205 in Paramedic Care: Special Considerations/Operations *and then read the following discussion.*

 The case study draws attention to the role of the paramedic on a call involving a female victim of sexual assault. It highlights the importance of emotional support for the victim and the legal ramifications of any documentation, particularly the narrative.

Fortunately, the patient in this case experienced no life-threatening injuries. Unfortunately, she has been psychologically scarred—perhaps for life—by this horrifying incident. Deciding to use the female crew member to conduct the assessment and most of the management was a wise decision. However, if a female crew member was unavailable, whoever cared for the patient should exhibit a compassionate and consoling attitude. The presence of a police officer ensured scene safety, but if the patient still felt vulnerable, it would have been appropriate (upon discussion with law enforcement) to move her to the ambulance.

 It was important for the crew to examine the patient carefully, while protecting her privacy as well as any evidence. Although it was not specifically stated in the case, it is essential to use nonjudgmental language and to remain conscious of all body language. In such instances, you should ask open-ended questions, encouraging the patient to talk and to regain a sense of control. Limiting unnecessary involvement by EMS responders would also be helpful for the patient. You may want to ask the patient who should be called or informed of the incident.

 Your actions toward a victim of abuse or assault can help begin the long road to psychological recovery. Furthermore, as pointed out in the case, your response may impact on the outcome of a case if you are called to testify at a later time.

Content Self-Evaluation

MULTIPLE CHOICE

_____ 1. Partner abuse is defined as physical or emotional violence from a man or woman toward a co-worker.
  A. True   B. False

_____ 2. The most widespread and best-known form of abuse involves the abuse of:
  A. women by men.
  B. children by their mothers.
  C. children by their fathers.
  D. elders by their children.
  E. same-sex partners.

_____ 3. Many victims of abuse hesitate or fail to report the problem because of a:
  A. fear of reprisal.
  B. lack of knowledge.
  C. fear of humiliation.
  D. lack of financial resources.
  E. all of the above.

_____ 4. By far the most common characteristic of abusers—whether they be partner abusers, child abusers, or elder abusers—is a:
  A. history of substance abuse.
  B. lack of employment.
  C. family history of violence.
  D. lack of education.
  E. mental impairment.

_____ 5. Forty-five percent of pregnant women suffer some form of battery during pregnancy.
  A. True   B. False

_____ 6. In assessing the battered patient, all of the following are appropriate actions EXCEPT:
  A. direct questioning.
  B. asking the victim why she or he doesn't leave.
  C. rehearsing the quickest way to leave the home.
  D. nonjudgmental questioning.
  E. reminding the patient that assault is a crime.

_____ 7. All of the following are causes of elder abuse EXCEPT:
  A. stress on middle-aged caregivers.
  B. decreased life expectancies.
  C. physical and mental impairments.
  D. limited resources for long-term care.
  E. decreased productivity in later years.

_____ 8. Which of the following are two main types of elder abuse?
  A. neglect and domestic
  B. emotional and financial
  C. domestic and institutional
  D. mental and institutional
  E. financial and domestic

_____ 9. The perpetrators of domestic elder abuse tend to be:
  A. paid caregivers.
  B. siblings.
  C. adult children.
  D. spouses.
  E. friends or neighbors.

_____ 10. In cases of child abuse, the most likely abusers are:
  A. babysitters.
  B. siblings.
  C. strangers.
  D. one or both parents.
  E. friends charged with the child's care.

_____ 11. All of the following are characteristics of abused children EXCEPT:
  A. sudden behavioral changes.
  B. neediness.
  C. absence of nearly all emotions.
  D. unusual wariness.
  E. concern over a parent's absence.

_____ 12. One of the signs of intentional scalding of a child is:
   A. staphylococcal scalded skin.
   B. hematological disorders.
   C. multiple splatter marks.
   D. multiple bruises.
   E. absence of splash burns.

_____ 13. Children rarely exhibit accidental fractures to the:
   A. head.
   B. ribs.
   C. legs.
   D. arms.
   E. hands or feet.

_____ 14. Which type of injury claims the largest number of lives among abused children?
   A. malnutrition
   B. head injuries
   C. burns
   D. chest injury
   E. abdominal injuries

_____ 15. The group most likely to be victims of sexual assault or rape are adolescent females under age 18.
   A. True   B. False

_____ 16. The victims of rape most commonly describe their assailant as a stranger.
   A. True   B. False

_____ 17. When talking to a rape victim, you can help the patient regain a sense of self-control by asking _____ questions.
   A. open-ended
   B. closed-ended
   C. indirect
   D. nonpersonal
   E. leading

_____ 18. Sexual Assault Nurse Examiners are specially trained health care workers who can:
   A. help with the prehospital care report.
   B. protect the patient against the assailant.
   C. provide information on the protection of evidence.
   D. protect EMS crews against legal suits.
   E. none of the above.

_____ 19. In managing a rape case, honor the patient's request to bathe or shower.
   A. True   B. False

_____ 20. All 50 states require health care workers to report suspected cases of:
   A. child abuse.
   B. rape.
   C. elder abuse.
   D. spousal abuse.
   E. partner abuse.

MATCHING

Write the letter of the term in the space provided next to the appropriate description.

A. partner abuse

B. sexual assault

C. rape

D. institutional elder abuse

E. JCAHO

F. domestic elder abuse

G. SANE

H. chain of evidence

I. battered

J. child abuse

_____ 21. patients who have been physically struck by an abuser

_____ 22. commission that mandates screening of incoming hospital patients for abuse

_____ 23. physical or emotional violence or neglect when an elder is being cared for in a home-based setting

_____ 24. penile penetration of the genitalia without the consent of the victim

_____ 25. physical or emotional violence or neglect toward a person from infancy to 18 years of age

_____ 26. physical or emotional violence or neglect when an elder is being cared for by a person paid to provide care

_____ 27. legally retaining and knowing the whereabouts of items pertinent to a rape or assault

_____ 28. nurses specially trained to examine the victims of sexual assault

_____ 29. physical or emotional violence toward a wife, husband, date, or live-in companion

_____ 30. unwanted oral, genital, or manual sexual contact

Special Project

Breaking the Cycle of Abuse: Support Services

Having the telephone numbers of the abuse hot lines and referral services within your state, region, or community can help the victim or the abuser take steps toward breaking the cycle of abuse before it is repeated or passed on to another generation. Take the time to investigate the contact numbers and the resources/services that can be provided for each of the following in your area:

Domestic Violence

Contact number: _____

Services provided: _____

_____

_____

_____

Child Abuse

Contact number: _____

Services provided: _____

_____

_____

_____

Elder Abuse

Contact number: _____

Services provided: _____

_____

_____

_____

Sexual Abuse

Contact number: _____

Services provided: _____

_____

_____

_____

Now take one more step. Make a copy of this information and carry it onboard the ambulance or write the phone numbers into the pocket reference that you carry in your uniform pocket!

The Challenged Patient

Review of Chapter Objectives

After reading this chapter, you should be able to:

1. Describe the various etiologies and types of hearing impairments. pp. 226–228

There are basically two types of deafness—**conductive deafness** and **sensorineural deafness**. Conductive deafness results from any condition that prevents sound waves from being transmitted from the external ear to the middle or inner ear. The condition may be temporary or permanent. If caught early, many forms of conductive deafness may be treated and cured. Sensorineural deafness, on the other hand, is often incurable. The condition arises from the inability of nerve impulses to reach the auditory center of the brain because of nerve damage either to the inner ear or to the brain. In the case of infants and children, sensorineural deafness often results from congenital defects or birth injuries.

2. Recognize the patient with a hearing impairment. p. 228

It is very important to detect deafness early in your assessment. A partially deaf person may ask questions repeatedly, misunderstand answers to questions, or respond inappropriately. Such reactions can easily be mistaken for head injury, leading to misdirected treatment.

The most obvious sign of deafness is a hearing aid. Unfortunately, hearing aids do not work for all types of deafness. Also, many people do not wear hearing aids, even when they have been prescribed. In addition, deaf people may have poor diction due to hearing loss. They might use their hands to gesture or use sign language. Deaf people may ask you to speak louder or they may speak excessively loud themselves. Finally, deaf people will commonly face you so that they can read your lips.

3. Anticipate accommodations that may be needed in order to properly manage the patient with a hearing impairment. pp. 228–229

When managing a patient with a hearing impairment, you can do several things to ease communications.

- Begin by identifying yourself and making sure the patient knows that you are speaking to him.
- Address deaf patients face to face, giving them the opportunity to read your lips and interpret your expression.
- Speak slowly in a normal voice. Never yell or use exaggerated gestures, which often distort your facial and body language.

- Keep in mind that nearly 80 percent of hearing loss is related to high-pitched sounds. As a result, you might use a low-pitched voice to speak directly into the patient's ear.
- Make sure background noise is reduced as much as possible.
- If necessary, find or adjust a hearing aid.
- Be innovative. Put the stethoscope on the patient and try speaking into it. Don't forget the most simple and effective means of communication—a pen and paper.
- If necessary and if time allows, draw pictures to illustrate procedures.
- If the patient knows sign language, usually American Sign Language (ASL), utilize an interpreter, documenting the name of the person who did the interpreting and the information received.

4. **Describe the various etiologies and types, recognize patients with, and anticipate accommodations that may be needed in order to properly manage each of the following conditions:**

a. **Visual impairments** pp. 229–231

When caring for the patient with a visual impairment, it is important to note if the impairment is a permanent disability or if it is a new symptom caused by the illness or injury for which you were called. Visual impairments have a number of etiologies—injury, disease, congenital conditions, infection (such as cytomegalovirus [CMV]), and degeneration of the retina, optic nerve, or nerve pathways.

Depending on the degree of impairment and a person's adjustment to the loss of vision, you may or may not recognize the condition right away. In cases of obvious blindness, identify yourself as you approach the patient so that the person knows you are there. Also describe everything you are doing. Take into account any special tools that assist a visually impaired person with daily living, most notably guide dogs and/or canes. Depending upon local protocols, arrange to transport the guide dog to the hospital with the patient. If the patient is ambulatory, have the person take your arm for guidance rather than taking the patient's arm.

b. **Speech impairments** pp. 231–232

When performing an assessment, you may come across a patient who is awake, alert, and oriented but cannot communicate with you due to a speech impairment. Possible miscommunication can hinder both the treatment administered and the information provided to the receiving facility. You may encounter four types of speech impairments. They include:

- **Language disorders.** A language disorder is an impaired ability to understand the spoken or written word. In children, language disorders result from a number of causes such as congenital learning disorders, cerebral palsy, hearing impairments, or inadequate language stimulation during the first year of life (delayed speaking ability). In adults, language disorders may result from a variety of illnesses or injuries—stroke, aneurysm, head injury, brain tumor, hearing loss, or some kind of emotional trauma. The loss of ability to communicate in speech, writing, or signs is known as aphasia. Aphasia can manifest itself in the following ways.

  Sensory aphasia—a person can no longer understand the spoken word. Patients with sensory aphasia will not respond to your questions because they cannot understand what you are saying.

  Motor aphasia—a person can no longer use the symbols of speech. Patients with motor aphasia, also known as expressive aphasia, will understand what you say but cannot clearly articulate a response.

  Global aphasia—occurs when a person has both sensory and motor aphasia. These patients can neither understand nor respond to your questions. A brain tumor in the Broca's region can cause this condition.

- **Articulation disorders.** Articulation disorders, also known as dysarthria, affect the way a person's speech is heard by others. These disorders occur when sounds are produced or put together incorrectly or in a way that makes it difficult to understand the spoken word. Articulation disorders may start at an early age, when the child learns to say words incorrectly or when a hearing impairment is involved. This type of disorder can occur in both children and adults when neural damage causes a disturbance in the nerve pathways leading from the brain to the larynx, mouth, or lips.

- **Voice production disorders.** When a patient has a voice production disorder, the quality of the person's voice is affected. This can be caused by trauma due to overuse of the vocal cords or infection. Cancer of the larynx can also cause a speech failure by impeding air from passing through the vocal cords. A patient with a production disorder will exhibit hoarseness, harshness, an inappropriate pitch, or abnormal nasal resonance.
- **Fluency disorders.** Fluency disorders present as stuttering. Although the cause of stuttering is not fully understood, the condition is found more often in men than in women. When speaking with patients who stutter, do not interrupt or finish their answers out of frustration and do not correct the way they speak.

When speaking to a patient with a speech impairment, never assume that the person lacks intelligence. Do not rush the patient or predict an answer. Try to form questions that require short, direct answers. When asking questions, look directly at the patient. If you cannot understand what the person has said, politely ask him to repeat it. Never pretend to understand when you don't. You might miss valuable information related to the call. If all else fails, give the patient the opportunity to write responses to your questions.

c. Obesity   pp. 232–234

Over 40 percent of the U.S. population are considered obese, while many more are heavier than their ideal body weight. Obesity occurs for a number of reasons. In many cases, diet, exercise, and lifestyle choices result in a caloric intake that exceeds daily energy needs. Genetic factors also predispose a person toward obesity. In rare cases, an obese patient may have a low basal metabolic rate, which causes the body to burn calories at a slower rate. In such cases, the condition may have been produced by an illness, such as hypothyroidism.

Managing an obese patient presents a number of challenges. Beside the obvious difficulty of lifting and moving these patients, excess weight can exacerbate the complaint for which you were called. Obesity can also lead to a number of serious medical conditions, including hypertension, heart disease, stroke, diabetes, and joint and muscle problems. In conducting a history, you will need to question patients carefully to make sure they are not mistakenly attributing signs and symptoms to their weight.

When doing your patient assessment, you may need to accommodate for the patient's weight. It may be necessary to auscultate lung sounds anteriorly on a patient who is too obese to lean forward. If the patient's adipose tissue presents an obstruction, you may need to place ECG monitoring electrodes on the arms and thighs instead of on the chest. Also be sure to have plenty of assistance for lifting and keep in mind that many of the lifters and stretchers are not rated for extremely large patients. Finally, alert the emergency department of the need for extra lifting assistance and special stretchers upon arrival.

d. Paraplegia/quadriplegia   p. 234

During your career, you may respond to a call and find that your patient is paralyzed from a previous traumatic or medical event. You will have to treat the chief complaint while taking into account the accommodations that must be made when treating a patient who cannot move some or all of his extremities.

A paralyzed patient may be paraplegic or quadriplegic. A paraplegic patient has been paralyzed from the waist down, while a quadriplegic patient has paralysis of all four extremities. In addition, spinal cord injuries in the area of C3 to C5 and above may also paralyze the patient's respiratory muscles and compromise the ability to breathe.

In managing a paraplegic or quadriplegic patient, be prepared for a number of common devices. These include a home ventilator, tracheostomy, halo traction, or colostomy. Be sure to make accommodations for these—and any other assisting devices—when you transport the patient. (For more on acute interventions for physically disabled and other chronic-care patients, see Chapter 6.)

e. Mental illness   p. 235

Mental and emotional illnesses or impairments present a special challenge to the EMS provider. The disorders may range from the psychoses caused by complex biochemical brain diseases, such as bipolar disorder (manic depression), to the personality disorders related to personality development, to a traumatic experience. Emotional impairments can include such conditions as hysteria, compulsive behavior, or anxiety. For a detailed discussion on the etiologies, assessment,

©2006 Pearson Education, Inc.
Paramedic Care: Principles & Practice, Vol. 5

management, and treatment of these patients, see Volume 3, Chapter 12, of *Paramedic Care: Principles & Practice.*

f. Developmentally disabled   **pp. 235, 236**

People with developmental disabilities are those individuals with impaired or insufficient development of the brain who are unable to learn at the usual rate. Developmental disabilities can occur for a variety of reasons. They can be genetic, such as Down syndrome, or they can be the product of a brain injury caused by some hypoxic or traumatic event. Such injuries can take place before birth, during birth, or anytime thereafter.

Except for patients with Down syndrome, it may be difficult to recognize someone with a developmental disability unless the person lives in a group home or other special residential setting. Remember that a person with a developmental disability can recognize body language, tone, and disrespect just like anyone else. Treat him as you would any other patient, listening to his/her answers, particularly if you suspect physical or emotional abuse.

If a patient has a severe cognitive disability, you may need to rely on others to obtain the chief complaint and history. Also, many children or young people with learning disabilities have been taught to be wary of strangers who may seek to touch them. You have to establish a basis of trust with the patient, perhaps by making it clear that you are a member of the medical community or by asking for the support of a person the patient does trust. Also, some people with developmental disabilities have been judged "stupid" or "bad" for behavior that results in an accident and they may try to cover up the events that led up to a call.

At all times, keep in mind that a person with a developmental disability may not understand what is happening. The ambulance, special equipment, and even your uniform may confuse or scare them. In cases of severe disabilities, it will be important to keep the primary caregivers with you at all times, even in the back of the ambulance.

g. Down syndrome   **p. 236**

Down syndrome results from an extra chromosome, usually on chromosome 21 or 22. Although the cause is unknown, the chromosomal abnormality increases with the age of the mother, especially after age 40. It also occurs at a higher rate in parents with a chromosomal abnormality, such as the translocation of chromosome 21 to chromosome 14.

Typically Down syndrome presents with easily recognized physical features. They include eyes sloped up at the outer corners, folds of skin on either side of the nose that cover the inner corner of the eye, small face and features, large and protruding tongue, flattening on the back of the head, and short and broad hands.

In addition to mild to moderate developmental disability, Down syndrome patients may have other physical ailments, such as heart defects, intestinal defects, and chronic lung problems. Down syndrome people are also at high risk of developing cataracts, blindness, and Alzheimer's disease at an early age.

When assessing the Down syndrome patient, consider the level of his developmental delay and follow the general guidelines mentioned in objective 4f. Transport to the hospital should be uneventful, especially if the caregiver comes along.

5. **Describe, identify possible presenting signs, and anticipate accommodations for the following diseases/illnesses:**

a. Arthritis   **pp. 237–238**

The three most common types of arthritis include:
- **Juvenile rheumatoid arthritis (JRA)** —a connective tissue disorder that strikes before age 16
- **Rheumatoid arthritis** —an autoimmune disorder
- **Osteoarthritis** —a degenerative joint disease, the most common arthritis seen in elderly people

All forms cause painful swelling and irritation of the joints, making everyday tasks sometimes impossible. Treatment of arthritis includes aspirin, nonsteroidal anti-inflammatory drugs (NSAIDs), and/or corticosteroids. It is important for you to recognize the side effects of these medications in case you have been called upon to treat a medication side effect rather than the disease. NSAIDs can cause stomach upset and vomiting, with or without bloody emesis. Corticosteroids, such as prednisone, can cause hyperglycemia, bloody emesis, and decreased immunity. You should also take note of all the patient's medications so that you do not administer a medication that can interact with the ones already taken by the patient.

When transporting arthritis patients, keep in mind their high level of discomfort. Use pillows to elevate affected extremities. The most comfortable position might not be the best position to start an IV, but try to make the patient as comfortable as possible.

b. Cancer
pp. 238–239

Cancer is caused by the abnormal growth of cells in normal tissue. The primary site of origin of the cancer determines the type of cancer the patient has. It may be difficult for you to recognize a cancer patient because the disease often has few obvious signs and symptoms. Rather, the treatments for the disease take on telltale signs, such as anorexia leading to weight loss or alopecia (hair loss). Tattoos may be left on the skin by radiation oncologists to mark positioning of radiation therapy equipment. In addition, physical changes, such as removal of a breast (mastectomy), may be obvious.

Management of the cancer patient can present a special challenge. Many patients undergoing chemotherapy treatments become neutropenic—a condition in which chemotherapy creates a dangerously low neutrophil (white blood cell) count. If patients have recently received chemotherapy, assume that they are neutropenic and take every precaution to protect them from infection. Keep a mask on the patient both during transport and during transfer at the emergency department.

In treating cancer patients, also keep in mind that their veins may have become scarred and difficult to access due to frequent IV starts, blood draws, and caustic chemotherapy transfusions. Cancer patients may also have an implanted infusion port, found just below the skin, with the catheter inserted into the subclavian vein or brachial artery. You need special training to access these ports and should not attempt to access them unless you have such training and the approval of medical direction.

Cancer patients may also have a peripheral access device such as a Groshong catheter or Hickman catheter. In this situation, it may simply be a matter of flushing the line and then hooking up your IV fluids to this external catheter. Whatever you decide to do, involve the patient, who has already lost a lot of control over his treatment, in the decision-making process.

c. Cerebral palsy
pp. 239–240

Cerebral palsy (CP) is a group of disorders caused by damage to the cerebrum in utero or by trauma during birth. There are three main types of cerebral palsy—spastic paralysis, athetosis, and ataxia. Prenatal exposure of the mother to German measles can cause cerebral palsy, as well as any condition leading to fetal hypoxia. Premature birth or brain damage from a difficult delivery can also lead to cerebral palsy. Other causes include encephalitis, meningitis, or head injury during a fall or abuse of an infant.

In treating patients with cerebral palsy, keep this fact in mind: Many people with atheotoid and diplegic cerebral palsy are highly intelligent. Do not assume that a person with cerebral palsy cannot communicate with you.

When transporting CP patients, make accommodations to prevent further injury. If they experience severe contractions, the patients may not rest comfortably on a stretcher. Use pillows and extra blankets to pad extremities that are not in proper alignment. Have suction available if a patient drools. If a patient has difficulty communicating, make sure that the caregiver helps in your assessment. Be alert for CP patients who sign. If you do not know how to sign, find somebody who does and alert the emergency department.

d. Cystic fibrosis
p. 240

Cystic fibrosis (CF) is an inherited disorder involving the exocrine glands primarily in the lungs and digestive system. Thick mucus forms in the lungs, causing bronchial obstruction and atelectasis in the small ducts of the alveoli. In addition, the thick mucus causes blockages in the small ducts of the pancreas, leading to decrease in the pancreatic enzymes needed to absorb nutrients.

Obtaining a complete medical history is important to the recognition of a cystic fibrosis patient. A unique characteristic of cystic fibrosis is the high concentration of chloride in the sweat, leading to the use of a diagnostic test known as the "sweat test." A CF patient may also complain of frequent lung infections, clay-colored stools, or clubbing of the fingers or toes.

Because of the high probability of respiratory distress in a CF patient, some form of oxygen therapy may be necessary. You may need to have a family member or caregiver hold blow-by oxygen (rather than use a mask) if this is all the patient will tolerate. Suctioning may be necessary to help the patient clear the thick secretions. If the patient is taking antibiotics to prevent infection and using inhalers or Mucomyst to thin secretions, bring these medications to the hospital. Above all else, keep in mind that these patients have been chronically ill for their entire lives. The last thing they or their loved ones want is another trip to the hospital.

Because of a poor prognosis, most of the CF patients that you see will be children or adolescents. A child with cystic fibrosis is still a child. So remember everything that you have learned about the treatment of pediatric patients and apply it to the developmental stage of the CF patient that you are treating.

e. Multiple sclerosis pp. 240–241

Multiple sclerosis (MS) is a disorder of the central nervous system that usually strikes between the ages of 20 and 40, affecting women more than men. The exact cause of multiple sclerosis is unknown, but it is considered to be an autoimmune disorder. Characteristically, repeated inflammation of the myelin sheath surrounding the nerves leads to scar tissue, which in turn blocks nerve impulses to the affected area.

The onset of MS is slow. It starts as a change in the strength of a muscle and a numbness or tingling in the affected muscle. Patients may develop problems with gait, slurred speech, and clumsiness. They may experience double vision due to weakness of the eye muscles or eye pain due to neuritis of the optic nerve. As symptoms progress, they become more permanent, leading the MS patient to become increasingly weak and more vulnerable to lung or urinary infections.

Transporting the MS patient to the hospital may require supportive care, such as oxygen therapy. Make sure the patient is comfortable and help position the patient as needed. Bring any assistive devices, such as a wheelchair or cane, so that the patient can maintain as much independence as possible.

f. Muscular dystrophy p. 241

Muscular dystrophy (MD) is a group of hereditary disorders characterized by progressive weakness and wasting of muscle tissue. It is a genetic disorder, leading to gradual degeneration of muscle fibers. The most common form of muscular dystrophy is Duchenne muscular dystrophy, which typically affects boys between the ages of 3 and 6. It leads to progressive muscle weakness in the legs and pelvis and to paralysis by age 12. Ultimately, the disease affects the respiratory muscles and heart, causing death. The other various MD disorders are classified by the age of the patient at onset of symptoms and by the muscles affected.

Since muscular dystrophy is a hereditary disease, you should obtain a complete family history. You should also note the particular muscle groups that the patient cannot move. Again, since MD patients are primarily children, choose age-appropriate language. Respiratory support may be needed, especially in later stages of the disease.

g. Myasthenia gravis pp. 242–243

Myasthenia gravis is an autoimmune disease characterized by chronic weakness of voluntary muscles and progressive fatigue. The condition results from a problem with the neurotransmitters, which causes a blocking of nerve signals to the muscles. It occurs most frequently in women between ages 20 and 50.

A patient with myasthenia gravis may complain of a complete lack of energy, especially in the evening. The disease commonly involves muscles in the face. You may note eyelid drooping or difficulty chewing or swallowing. The patient may also complain of double vision.

In severe cases of myasthenia gravis, a patient may experience paralysis of the respiratory muscles, leading to respiratory arrest. These patients may need assisted ventilations en route to the emergency facility.

h. Poliomyelitis pp. 241–242

Poliomyelitis is a communicable disease affecting the gray matter in the brain and spinal cord. Although it is highly contagious, immunization has made outbreaks of polio extremely rare in developed nations. However, it is important to be aware of the disease since many people born before development of the polio vaccine in the 1950s were affected by the disease.

Although most patients recover from polio, they are left with permanent paralysis of the affected muscles. You may recognize a polio victim by the use of assistive devices for ambulation or by the reduced size of the affected limb due to muscle atrophy. Some patients may have experienced paralysis of the respiratory muscles, requiring assisted ventilations. Patients on long-term ventilators will typically have tracheotomies.

Along with polio, you should know about a related disorder called post-polio syndrome. Post-polio syndrome affects those patients who suffered severely from polio more than 30 years ago. Patients with this condition quickly tire, especially after exercise, and develop an intolerance for cold in their extremities.

Many patients with polio or post-polio syndrome may insist on walking to the ambulance but should not be encouraged to do so. Because they may not have required hospitalization for polio since childhood, you will have to alleviate their anxiety, keeping in mind their fears of a renewed loss of independence.

i. Spina bifida
p. 242

Spina bifida is a congenital abnormality that falls under the category of a neural tube defect. It presents when there is a defect in the closure of the backbone and the spinal canal. In spina bifida occulta, the patient exhibits few outward signs of the deformity. In spina bifida cystica, the failure of the closure allows the spinal cord and covering membranes to protrude from the back, causing an obvious deformity.

Symptoms depend upon which part of the spinal cord is protruding through the back. The patient may have paralysis of both lower extremities and lack of bowel or bladder control. A large percentage of the children with this disease also have hydrocephalus, requiring a surgical shunt to help drain excess fluid from the brain.

When treating spina bifida patients, keep several things in mind. Recent research has shown that between 18 and 73 percent of children and adolescents with spina bifida have latex allergies. For safety, assume that all patients with spina bifida have this problem. In transporting spina bifida patients, be sure to bring along any devices that aid them. If you are called to treat an infant, safe transport to the hospital should be done in a car seat, unless contraindicated.

j. Patients with a previous head injury
p. 242

Patients with a previous head injury may not be easily recognized until they begin to speak. They may display similar symptoms to those of stroke, but without the hemiparesis (paralysis on one side of the body). Such patients may have aphasia, slurred speech, or loss of vision or hearing, or may develop a learning disability. They may also exhibit short-term memory loss and may not have any recollection of their original injury.

Obtaining a medical history from these patients will be extremely important, especially if you are responding to a traumatic event. Note any new symptoms the patient may be having or the recurrence of old ones. If the patient cannot speak, look for obvious physical signs of trauma or for facial expressions of pain. Treatment and transport considerations will depend upon the condition for which you were called.

6. Define, recognize, and anticipate accommodations needed to properly manage patients who:

a. Are culturally diverse
p. 243

Culturally diverse patients may speak a different language or have different traditions or religious beliefs from yours. What may make it difficult for you to treat culturally different patients may not be the differences per se, but your inability to understand them. Do not consider this a reason for refusing treatment. Rather, consider it a learning experience that will prepare you for a similar situation on another run.

As a paramedic, you are ethically required to take care of all patients in the same manner, regardless of their race, religion, gender, ethnic background, or living situation. Remember, the patient who has decision-making abilities has a right to self-determination and can refuse treatment. You should, however, obtain a signed document indicating informed refusal of consent. If your patient does not speak English, communication may be a problem. You may need to rely on a family member to act as an interpreter or on a translator device, such as a telephone language line for non–English-speaking people. In such cases, be sure to notify the receiving facility of the need for an interpreter.

©2006 Pearson Education, Inc.
Paramedic Care: Principles & Practice, Vol. 5

b. Are terminally ill p. 244

Caring for a terminally ill patient can be an emotional challenge. Many times, the patient will choose to die at home, but at the last minute the family compromises those wishes by calling for an ambulance. In other cases, the patient may call for an ambulance so that a newly developed condition can be treated or a medication adjusted. (For more on caring for the terminally ill, see Chapter 6.)

c. Have a communicable disease p. 244

When treating people with communicable diseases, you should withhold all personal judgment. Although you will need to take BSI precautions just as you would with any patient, keep in mind the heightened sensitivity of a person with a communicable disease. Although most of these patients are familiar with the health care setting, you should still explain that you take these measures with all patients who have a similar disease. Also, you do not need to take additional precautions beyond those required by departmental policy. The patient will generally spot these extra measures and react with feelings of shame, guilt, or anger. (For more on the etiologies and treatment of communicable diseases, see Volume 3, Chapter 11, of *Paramedic Care: Principles & Practice*.)

d. Have a financial impairment pp. 244–245

Patients who have financial impairments, such as the homeless, sometimes refuse care because they think they cannot afford to pay the medical bills. It is your job to help these patients understand that they can receive health care regardless of their financial situation. Become familiar with public hospitals and clinics that provide services for the needy. In providing care, keep this guideline in mind: Treat the patient, not the financial condition the patient is in!

7. Given several challenged patients, provide the appropriate assessment, management, and transportation. pp. 226–245

During your classroom, clinical, and field training, you will be presented with real and simulated challenged patients and develop management plans for them. Use the information presented in this text chapter, the information on assessing challenged patients provided by your instructors, and the guidance given by your clinical and field preceptors to develop good skills in caring for the special needs of these patients. Continue to refine newly learned skills once your training ends and you begin your career as a paramedic.

Case Study Review

Reread the case study on pages 225 and 226 in Paramedic Care: Special Considerations/Operations *and then read the following discussion.*

This case study draws attention to the effect of preexisting physical impairments—paralysis and weakness from polio and post-polio syndrome—on a call involving a fall. Although the medics were called to treat the patient for the fall, the physical impairments affected their assessment and management of the patient.

Preexisting impairments can complicate assessment. Mrs. Wade, for example, had lived with the effects of polio and post-polio syndrome for so long that she initially forgot to mention her paralyzed right leg and the weakness in her left arm. Fortunately, the patient was alert and could provide plenty of assistance. For example, she indicated that the pain in her hip and shoulder were new and in all likelihood fall related. When questioned about her leg, Mrs. Wade also could identify the cause, plus add further information on post-polio syndrome. However, not all calls involving challenged patients may be this clear-cut, especially in cases where the patient is not alert and/or is unable to communicate clearly. For this reason, it is important to be aware of the way in which common mental and physical impairments present themselves.

As with many challenged patients, Mrs. Wade had done some planning. She had hidden an extra key outside the house and carried a mobile phone with her. Some patients may also wear Lifeline® transmitter devices around their necks. These devices, which operate with the press of a button, are usually linked with either an answering service or a hospital, which in turn notifies an EMS dispatch agency to respond. Again, not all cases will be so well scripted. The patient may be locked inside a house or apartment, and you will have to gain access. Or a great deal of time may pass before the patient or somebody else summons help.

The impairments cited by Mrs. Wade—polio and post-polio syndrome—are not as commonly encountered as other impairments mentioned in this chapter. Never feel embarrassed about not knowing about every medical condition. Ask the patient for information. You will be surprised how much information the patient or caregiver can provide.

Finally, treatment was not confined to fall-related injuries. The weakness caused by post-polio syndrome was addressed by placing the patient's left arm in a sling. It relieved some of the pain related to the post-polio syndrome and made the patient more comfortable. During packaging and transport, it might have been helpful to use pillows and blankets to pad the scoop or stretcher to increase patient comfort even more.

Content Self-Evaluation

MULTIPLE CHOICE

_____ 1. The two main types of deafness are:
  A. tinnitus and Meniere's disease.
  B. conductive and sensorineural.
  C. partial and sudden.
  D. clinical and nonclinical.
  E. temporary and complete.

_____ 2. A middle ear infection frequently associated with upper respiratory infection is:
  A. labyrinthitis.
  B. otitis media.
  C. presbyacusis.
  D. otomycosis.
  E. cerumen.

_____ 3. During the patient interview and physical exam, hearing deficits may be mistaken for:
  A. head injury.
  B. intoxication.
  C. transducer infection.
  D. effusion syndrome.
  E. drug overdose.

_____ 4. When communicating with a deaf patient, consider all of the following strategies EXCEPT:
  A. speaking slowly in a normal voice.
  B. using a high-pitched voice to speak directly into the patient's ear.
  C. reducing background noise.
  D. using a pen and paper.
  E. putting a stethoscope on the patient and speaking into it.

_____ 5. The term for removal of the eyeball after trauma, such as a penetrating injury, or certain kinds of illnesses is:
  A. retinal detachment.
  B. enucleation.
  C. optic chiasm.
  D. orbitotomy.
  E. corneal abrasion.

_____ 6. Diabetes can slowly lead to a loss of a vision as a result of:
   A. degeneration of the optic nerve.
   B. disorders in the blood vessels leading to the retina.
   C. degeneration of the eyeball.
   D. cytomegalovirus (CMV).
   E. retinitis.

_____ 7. When approaching a patient with a seeing eye dog in a harness, pet the dog to show that you mean no harm to its owner.
   A. True   B. False

_____ 8. All of the following are types of speech impairments, except:
   A. congenital disorders.
   B. language disorders.
   C. fluency disorders.
   D. articulation disorders.
   E. voice production disorders.

_____ 9. A language disorder that can be caused by a stroke or brain injury is known as:
   A. amnesia.
   B. ataxia.
   C. aphagia.
   D. aphasia.
   E. aphonia.

_____ 10. Stuttering is an example of a(n):
   A. dyslexic disorder.
   B. fluency disorder.
   C. auditory disorder.
   D. vocal cord disorder.
   E. voice production disorder.

_____ 11. If the adipose tissue on an obese patient presents an obstruction, you may need to place ECG monitoring electrodes on the:
   A. chest and back.
   B. hands and feet.
   C. arms and back.
   D. neck and chest.
   E. arms and thighs.

_____ 12. A quadriplegic patient has been paralyzed from the waist down.
   A. True   B. False

_____ 13. Depression and psychoses are examples of:
   A. emotional and mental impairments.
   B. developmental disabilities.
   C. visual impairments.
   D. articulation disorders.
   E. pathological challenges.

_____ 14. People with Down syndrome are at risk of developing:
   A. cataracts.
   B. blindness.
   C. early Alzheimer's disease.
   D. heart defects.
   E. all of the above.

_____ 15. Fetal alcohol syndrome (FAS) is sometimes confused with Down syndrome because they both:
   A. produce similar facial characteristics.
   B. are caused by alcohol consumption during pregnancy.
   C. are preventable birth defects.
   D. cause death at an early age.
   E. produce hyperactivity.

_____ 16. It is not uncommon for children with juvenile rheumatoid arthritis (JRA) to suffer complications involving the spleen or liver.
   A. True   B. False

_____ 17. Cancer patients receiving chemotherapy are at high risk for:
   A. syncope.
   B. infection.
   C. altered mental status.
   D. weight gain.
   E. diminished sense of pain.

_____ 18. If a cancer patient has an implanted infusion port, you can generally hook up your IV fluids to this port.
   A. True   B. False

_____ 19. When caring for cerebral palsy patients, you may need to:
   A. treat them as if they have a spinal injury.
   B. change the order of the initial assessment.
   C. use pillows and blankets to pad unaligned extremities.
   D. anticipate brief periods of apnea.
   E. both A and D.

_____ 20. A group of hereditary disorders characterized by progressive weakness and wasting of muscle tissue is known as:
   A. poliomyelitis.
   B. spina bifida.
   C. multiple sclerosis.
   D. cystic fibrosis.
   E. muscular dystrophy.

_____ 21. Most of the cystic fibrosis patients that you see will be:
   A. adults in their 30s and 40s.
   B. elderly patients over age 60.
   C. infants 1 year old and younger.
   D. children and adolescents.
   E. women between the ages of 20 and 40.

_____ 22. A congenital abnormality in which a large percentage of children are born with hydrocephalus is:
   A. Down syndrome.
   B. cerebral palsy.
   C. spina bifida.
   D. fetal alcohol syndrome.
   E. cystic fibrosis.

_____ 23. A preventable disorder caused by alcohol consumption during pregnancy is:
  A. JRA.
  B. FAS.
  C. ACE.
  D. TIA.
  E. PE.

_____ 24. Research has shown that between 18 and 73 percent of children and adolescents with _____ have a latex allergy.
  A. cerebral palsy
  B. myasthenia gravis
  C. poliomyelitis
  D. spina bifida
  E. Down syndrome

_____ 25. A patient with spina bifida may have any of the following conditions EXCEPT:
  A. accumulation of fluid on the brain.
  B. loss of bladder control.
  C. paralysis of the lower extremities.
  D. loss of bowel control.
  E. paralysis on one side of the body.

_____ 26. Common complaints from a patient with myasthenia gravis include:
  A. chronic fatigue or lack of energy.
  B. nausea and headache.
  C. shortness of breath and heart palpitations.
  D. dizziness and loss of appetite.
  E. unsteady gait and double vision.

_____ 27. Accommodation of a culturally diverse population requires:
  A. patience.
  B. ingenuity.
  C. respect.
  D. use of translators.
  E. all of the above.

_____ 28. When a patient refuses treatment because of religious reasons, you should:
  A. call the police to intervene.
  B. administer treatment and document your reasons.
  C. ask the person to reconsider his religious views.
  D. obtain a signed refusal of treatment and transportation form.
  E. leave the scene.

_____ 29. When treating people with communicable diseases, you should take additional precautions beyond those required by departmental policy.
  A. True   B. False

_____ 30. If a homeless person is unable to afford medical bills, it is your job to help the patient get health care regardless of his financial situation.
  A. True   B. False

MATCHING

Write the letter of the term in the space provided next to the appropriate description.

A. labyrinthitis

B. conductive deafness

C. motor aphasia

D. deafness

E. diabetic retinopathy

F. sensorineural deafness

G. sensory aphasia

H. otitis media

I. neutropenic

J. enucleation

K. cerumen

L. colostomy

M. mucoviscidosis

N. presbyacusis

O. glaucoma

_____ 31. an inability to hear

_____ 32. progressive hearing loss that occurs with aging

_____ 33. middle ear infection

_____ 34. group of eye disorders that result in increased intraocular pressure on the optic nerve

_____ 35. ear wax

_____ 36. occurs when the patient cannot speak but can understand what is said

_____ 37. a surgical diversion of the large intestine through an opening in the skin where the fecal matter is collected in a pouch

_____ 38. a condition that results in an abnormally low white blood cell count

_____ 39. caused when there is a blocking of the transmission of the sound waves through the external ear canal to the middle or inner ear

_____ 40. slow loss of vision as a result of damage done by diabetes

_____ 41. occurs when a patient cannot understand the spoken word

_____ 42. inner-ear infection that causes vertigo, nausea, and an unsteady gait

_____ 43. removal of the eyeball after trauma or illness

_____ 44. caused by the inability of nerve impulses to reach the auditory center of the brain because of nerve damage either to the inner ear or to the brain

_____ 45. cystic fibrosis of the pancreas resulting in abnormally viscous mucoid secretion from the pancreas

Special Project

Continuing Education: Using the Internet

The Internet is a very useful source of information about many of the conditions and diseases discussed in this chapter. Take a moment to browse the Internet and locate the Websites for each of the following advocacy organizations. Record each URL, or Website address, in the space provided. Don't stop with this list. Expand your references, adding the Internet addresses for other organizations, including local chapters in your area.

1. American Cancer Society _____

2. American Foundation for the Blind _____

3. American Obesity Association _____

4. American Speech-Language-Hearing Association _____

5. Arthritis Foundation _____

6. Cystic Fibrosis Foundation _____

7. Down Syndrome Society _____

8. Multiple Sclerosis Association of America _____

9. Muscular Dystrophy Association _____

10. Myasthenia Gravis Foundation of America _____

11. National Health Care for the Homeless Council _____

12. National Organization on Fetal Alcohol Syndrome _____

13. Polio Experience Network _____

14. Spina Bifida Association of America _____

15. United Cerebral Palsy _____

6 Acute Interventions for the Chronic-Care Patient

Review of Chapter Objectives

After reading this chapter, you should be able to:

1. Compare and contrast the primary objectives of the paramedic and the home care provider. pp. 253, 258–259

The paramedic's primary role is to identify and treat any life-threatening problems and transport as necessary. Home care providers, on the other hand, assume responsibility, in varying degrees, for managing a chronic condition in the home setting and for helping the patient to live as normally as possible. A paramedic provides acute interventions; a home care provider provides ongoing care per medical directives, usually from a physician.

2. Identify the importance of home health care medicine as it relates to emergency medical services. pp. 251–254

The shift to home health care has important implications for emergency medical services. As patients assume greater responsibility for their own treatment and recovery, the likelihood of ALS intervention for the chronic-care patient increases. Calls may come from the patient, the patient's family, or a home health care provider.

In home care settings, you can expect to encounter a sometimes dizzying array of devices, machines, and equipment designed to provide anything from supportive to life-sustaining care. The failure or malfunction of this type of equipment has the potential to become a life-threatening or life-altering event.

In a call involving a home care patient, you are responding to a patient who is already sick or injured in some way. A previously manageable condition may have suddenly become unmanageable or more complicated. Unlike in a hospital, the patient or home care provider cannot push a button and summon immediate help. Instead, they often summon you, the ALS provider.

3. Differentiate between the role of the paramedic and the role of the home care provider. pp. 253–254, 258–259

As noted in objective 1, the paramedic provides acute interventions for the chronically ill patient who relies in some way on a home care provider who helps to manage his condition. Remember that the home care provider—whether it be a nurse, nurse's aide, family member, or friend—usually knows the patient better than anyone else. The provider will often spot subtle changes in the patient's condition that may seem insignificant to the outsider. In assessing the patient, it is crucial that you listen carefully to what this person says.

4. **Compare and contrast the primary objectives of acute care, home care, and hospice care.** pp. 252, 259, 285–288

- Acute care—focuses on short-term intervention aimed at identifying and managing any immediate life-threatening emergencies, using transport as needed.
- Home care—involves the ongoing care and supportive assistance required to help a patient manage an injury or a chronic condition, usually according to a physician's instructions or written orders; home care may be either short term or long term.
- Hospice care—provides a program of palliative care and support services that address the physical, social, economic, and spiritual needs of terminally ill patients and their families.

5. **Discuss aspects of home care that enhance the quality of patient care and aspects that have the potential to become detrimental.** pp. 254–257

Supporters of home health care offer several arguments in its favor. First, they point out that patients often recover faster in the familiar environments of their homes than in the hospital. They also emphasize the differences in the cost of home care versus hospital care. However, the technological devices required by many home care patients can—and do—fail. Family members may either willingly accept the responsibilities of home care or succumb to the pressure. Finally, as noted in objective 6, home care patients are susceptible to a wide variety of complications related to their particular treatments and/or conditions.

6. **List pathologies and complications in home care patients that commonly result in ALS intervention.** pp. 252–257, 265–285

A number of situations can involve you in the treatment of a home care patient—equipment failure, unexpected complications, absence of a caregiver, need for transport, the inability to operate a device, and more. Many of the medical problems that you will encounter in a home care setting are the same ones that you would encounter elsewhere in the field. Some of the typical responses involve airway complications, respiratory failure, cardiac decompensation, alterations in peripheral circulation, altered mental status, GI/GU crises, infections, and/or septic complications. (For specific information or examples of home care problems requiring acute interventions, see text pages 266–286.)

In providing ALS intervention, you must always keep in mind that the home care patient is in a more fragile state to begin with. A member of the medical community has already decided that the person needs extra help. A home care patient is more likely to decompensate and go into crisis more quickly than a member of the general population. As a result, you need to monitor the home care patient carefully and be ready to intervene at all times.

7. **Compare the cost, mortality, and quality of care for a given patient in the hospital versus the home care setting.** pp. 251–252

The steady rise in hospital charges and the cost of skilled nursing facilities prompted the growth of home health care, along with other factors such as the enactment of Medicare, advent of HMOs, increased medical acceptance, and improved medical technology. With total health expenditures expected to rise by an estimated 7.5 percent in the first decade of the 2000s, the savings promised by home health care continues to speed the dismissal of patients from hospitals and nursing homes. As indicated in objective 5, there are trade-offs to be made in treating a patient in the hospital versus a home care setting.

8. **Discuss the significance of palliative care programs as related to a patient in a home health care or hospice setting.** pp. 259, 285–288

A patient in the home care setting is usually receiving curative care aimed at healing the patient's illness or injury. If a patient's condition is terminal, treatment switches to palliative or comfort care. The goal is to relieve symptoms, manage pain, and give patients control over the end of their lives. Palliative care may be provided by hospice workers in the patient's home or in homes or apartments managed by hospices.

9. **Define hospice care, comfort care, and DNR/DNAR as they relate to local practice, law, and policy.**   pp. 253, 259, 265, 285–288

Hospice care provides a program of palliative or comfort care as well as support services that address the physical, social, economic, and spiritual needs of terminally ill patients and their families. The goal of hospice care is very different from the goal of most other branches of the health care professions, including EMS. For an ALS team, care is usually geared toward aggressive and lifesaving treatment. A hospice team, on the other hand, seeks to make the patient as comfortable as possible.

For the most part, patients in hospice situations have already exhausted or declined curative resources. As a rule, family members, caregivers, and health care workers have been instructed to call a hospice rather than EMS. However, you may be summoned for intervention, particularly in situations involving transport. In such cases, you should keep in mind that the hospice patient is in an end-stage disease and has already expressed wishes to withhold resuscitation. In all likelihood the patient will probably have a Do Not Resuscitate (DNR) or Do Not Attempt Resuscitation (DNAR) order in place. However, such orders should not prevent you from performing palliative or comfort care.

Local protocols may vary in respect to DNRs, DNARs, living wills, and durable power of attorney documents. Be sure that you are familiar with these legal statements and their implications for care of the terminally ill. (For more on this topic, see Volume 1, Chapter 6, "Medical/Legal Aspects of Advanced Prehospital Care.")

10. **List and describe the characteristics of typical home care devices related to airway maintenance, artificial and alveolar ventilation, vascular access, drug administration, and the GI/GU tract.**   pp. 257–258, 266–267, 270–282

You can expect to encounter a vast number of machines and devices in the home care situation—anything from a home dialysis unit to personal care items such as a long-handled shoehorn to wheelchairs, canes, and walkers. Examples of typical equipment aimed at airway maintenance and/or ventilation include portable suctioning devices, nebulized and aerosolized medication administrators, incentive spirometers, home ventilators, apnea monitors, tracheostomy tubes or collars, and oxygen delivery systems (oxygen concentrators, oxygen masks, liquid oxygen reservoirs, regulator-flow meters, nasal cannulas, tubing, and sterile water).

Patients may also have any variety of vascular access devices (VADs). Patients may have a peripherally inserted central catheter (PICC line) or a surgically implanted medication delivery system such as a Port-A-Cath or Medi-Port. Some VADs have been permanently implanted, such as a dialysis shunt or a Hickman, Broviac, or Groshong catheter.

Yet other patients may have various long-term devices to support gastrointestinal or genitourinary functions. These include urinary catheters (Texas/condom catheters or internal/Foley catheters), urostomies, nasogastric feeding tubes, or gastrostomy tubes (with a colostomy).

As these examples show, home care devices range from the simplicity of a nasal cannula to the complexity of a home ventilator. If you encounter an unfamiliar device—which may happen at some time in your career—don't panic. Find out what it's used for, and you will then have an idea how to proceed. Don't be afraid to look foolish by asking questions. You won't. You will be foolish, and endanger the patient, if you pretend to understand a device but don't.

11. **Discuss the complications of assessing each of the devices described in objective 10.**   pp. 272–273, 275–276, 278, 280, 281–282

Discussion of the complications for the various devices can be found on the pages indicated with this objective. However, in general, keep in mind these points.

Oxygen delivery systems
Very few problems arise from oxygen delivery systems themselves. When they do occur, patients or home care providers can usually correct the situation on their own. Some technical problems include impeded oxygen flow (faulty tubing/dirty or plugged humidifier), activation of the warning buzzer on the oxygen concentrator (unplugged unit or power failure), and hissing or rapidly depleted oxygen tank (leak). For corrective steps to each of these problems, see Table 6-4 on page 271.

©2006 Pearson Education, Inc.
Paramedic Care: Principles & Practice, Vol. 5

In terms of the oxygen therapy itself, follow these guidelines:

- Ensure the ability of the patient/home care provider to administer oxygen.
- Make sure the patient knows what to do in case of a power failure.
- Evaluate sterile conditions, especially disinfections of reusable equipment.
- Remain alert to signs and symptoms of hypoxemia.

Artificial airways/tracheostomies

The most common problems faced by tracheostomy patients include blockage of the airway by mucus and a dislodged cannula. Children can also have their stoma blocked by foreign objects that enter by accident or are put there by a sibling or playmate. Other complications include infection of the stoma, drying of the mucus leading to crusting or bleeding, and tracheal erosion from an overinflated cuff (causing necrosis).

If EMS is called, it means that neither the patient nor the caregiver has been able to solve the problem. If the tracheostomy patient is on a ventilator, you must rapidly determine if the problem is with the ventilator or with the airway itself. If the problem is simply a loose fitting or disconnected tube, fix it. If the problem is not immediately apparent, do not waste time trying to troubleshoot the machine—unless you are qualified to do so. Your bag-valve device will connect directly to where the ventilator tubing connects. Remove the tubing, connect the bag-valve device to the trach connector, and ventilate.

If the problem is with the patient's airway, you will need to clear it. If the patient is hypoxic, always hyperventilate before suctioning. Remember to ensure that ventilations are directed downward toward the lungs. If you are unable to ventilate, clearing the airway is your first priority. If it appears that the inner cannula is blocked or dislodged, you may remove it. If necessary, you may intubate the stoma. Once the airway is secure, you may proceed with the rest of your assessment. It is inappropriate to proceed until you have protected the airway.

Ventilators

Ventilatory problems are traditionally easy to remedy, such as in the case of unplugged power cords or a temporary loss of electricity. If you are familiar with the ventilator, you can remedy other problems by adjusting the settings to restore or improve ventilations. However, if you are unfamiliar with the ventilator, play it safe and support ventilations with your own equipment. Remember—if a home ventilator fails, begin manual positive-pressure ventilation immediately. Whatever interventions you choose, you will have to make arrangements for home devices to be transported with you to the hospital.

Vascular access devices

In the case of patients with VADs, the most common complications result from various types of obstructions. A thrombus may form at the catheter site, or an embolus may lodge elsewhere in the body. Other obstructive problems include catheter kinking or catheter tip embolus. With central venous access devices, always be aware of the potential for an air embolus. Of course, any device implanted in the body has a risk for infection. Because these catheters provide a channel into the central circulation, patients may quickly become septic, especially if they are weakened or immunosuppressed.

Urinary tract devices

Most complications related to urinary tract support devices result from infection or device malfunctions. Infection is a very common problem with urinary tract devices because the area is rich with pathogens and because the catheter provides a pathway directly into the body. Remain alert to foul-smelling urine or altered urine color, such as tea-colored, cloudy, or blood-tinged urine. Also look for signs and symptoms of systemic infection, or urosepsis, as urinary infections can quickly spread in the immunocompromised patient.

Device malfunctions typically include accidental displacement of the device, obstruction, balloon ruptures in devices that use a balloon as an anchor, or leaking collection devices. Changes in the patient's anatomy, such as a shortened urinary tract or tissue necrosis, can also cause malfunctions. Ensure that the collection device is empty and record the amount of urine output. Look for kinks or other obstructions in the device and make sure the collection bag is placed below the patient.

Gastrointestinal tract devices

Complications from GI tract devices include tube misplacement, obstruction, or infection. Because misplaced tubes can obstruct the airway or GI system, you should always ensure device patency if you have any doubts about placement of the tube. First, have the patient speak to you. If he cannot speak, the tube may be in the airway and need to be removed. Second, to assure patency of an NG tube, use a 60-mL syringe to insert air into the stomach. Use your stethoscope to listen over the epigastrium for air movement within the stomach. A low-pitched rumbling should be heard. You may also note stomach contents spontaneously moving up the tube or they may be aspirated with a 60-cc syringe. In such cases, patients may be repositioned to return patency, or the device reinserted.

Tubes are also prone to obstruction. Colostomies may become clogged or otherwise obstructed. Feeding tubes can become clogged due to the thick consistency of supplemental feedings or pill fragments. As a result, the tubes may require irrigation with water. In addition, the thick consistency of food may cause bowel obstructions or constipation.

As might be expected, ostomies can become infected or lose skin integrity from pressure. Look for signs and symptoms of skin or systemic infection. In addition, remember that digestive enzymes may leak from various ostomies and begin to digest the skin and abdominal contents.

12. Describe indications, contraindications, and techniques for urinary catheter insertion in the male and female patient in a prehospital setting.   **p. 279**

There are various medical devices designed to support patients with urinary tract dysfunction. External devices, such as Texas catheters or condom catheters, attach to the male external genitalia to collect urine. Because these devices are not inserted into the urethra, they reduce the risk of infection. However, they do not collect urine in a sterile manner, nor are they adequate for long-term use.

Internal catheters, such as Foley or indwelling catheters, are the most commonly used devices for urinary tract dysfunction. They are long catheters with a balloon tip that is inserted through the urethra into the urinary bladder. The balloon is then inflated with saline to keep the device in place. Internal catheters are well tolerated for long-term use and are frequently found in hospitals, skilled nursing facilities, or home care situations.

Suprapubic catheters are similar in purpose to internal catheters. However, they are inserted directly through the abdominal wall into the urinary bladder. Suprapubic catheters may be used instead of indwelling catheters in the event of surgery or other problems with the genitalia or bladder.

In nearly all cases, insertion of urinary catheters is performed in a medical setting.

13. Identify failure of GI/GU, ventilatory, vascular access, and drain devices found in the home care setting.   **pp. 272–273, 276, 278, 280, 281–282**

See appropriate portions of points listed in objective 11.

14. Discuss the relationship between local home care treatment protocols/SOPs and local EMS protocols/SOPs.   **pp. 258–259**

In responding to a call involving a home care patient, remember that you may not be the first person to provide intervention. If home care patients have a good relationship with their home health care practitioner or physician, they may contact this person first. If in fact, they may be required to do so in order to receive reimbursement for medical services. As a result, be sure to ask whether a patient has called another health care professional. If so, find out what instructions or medications have been issued. Also inquire about written orders from the physician or the physician-approved health care plan. Health care agencies resubmit these plans to physicians at least every 62 days. So check the date to see when the plan was last revised.

If the call involved a hospice patient, the situation will almost always require intervention by specially trained health care professionals. Find out the names of these people as quickly as possible and determine the advisability of consultations versus rapid transport.

©2006 Pearson Education, Inc.
Paramedic Care: Principles & Practice, Vol. 5

15. Discuss differences in the ability of individuals to accept and cope with their own impending death.   p. 288

Each patient deals with his impending death in a different manner. Some can come to grips with it, while others refuse to believe they are going to die. Remember that while hospice prepares patients for their death, patients without hospice may be ill-prepared for the end stages of life. Don't assume that all terminally ill patients are under hospice care. A simple question to determine the presence of hospice may alter your course of treatment and approach to the patient.

16. List the stages of the grief process and relate them to an individual in hospice care.   p. 288

Regardless of whether a patient is in hospice or not, keep in mind the stages of the grief process—denial, anger, depression, bargaining, and acceptance. Remember that both the patient and the family will go through these stages, and, in the case of the terminally ill, the patient may have reached acceptance well ahead of those who will remain behind.

17. Discuss the rights of the terminally ill patient.   pp. 285–288

In treating a terminally ill patient, you need to establish communication with the home care worker as quickly as possible. Your inclination may be to intubate, start a line, or administer medications. However, palliative care supersedes curative care. A hospice worker, when faced with the end stage of a disease, may do nothing in accordance with the patient's wishes, whether those wishes are expressed through a family member or a written document. If you are called to the house, it is your responsibility to respect the wishes of the patient and the ideas of hospice care. (See Table 6-6 on page 285 for a list of the National Hospice Organization standards of care for the terminally ill.)

18. Summarize the types of home health care available in your area and the services provided.   pp. 252, 258–260

There is a wide variety of home health care services provided in every community, ranging from professional home care agencies to unpaid volunteers. Find out what services operate in your area, using sources such as local hospitals (which arrange referrals) or county health departments (which certify and/or regulate many agencies).

19. Given a series of home care scenarios, determine which patients should receive follow-up home care and which should be transported to an emergency care facility.   pp. 252–288

During your classroom, clinical, and field training, you will assess real and simulated patients and decide which patients should be transported to the hospital and which should receive additional care in the prehospital setting. Use the information in this text chapter, the information on chronic home care patients presented by your instructors, and the guidance given by your clinical and field preceptors to develop good assessment and decision-making skills in regard to patient transport. Continue to refine these skills once your training ends and you begin your career as a paramedic.

20. Given a series of scenarios, demonstrate interaction and support with the family members/support persons for a patient who has died.   pp. 287–288

Approaching the family members/support persons left behind after a patient has died is never easy, even if they have had the help of hospice. As noted in the text, many times the terminally ill patients are more prepared for their impending death than their family or caregivers. However, they, too, must go through the stages of grieving—denial, anger, depression, bargaining, and acceptance. Use practice scenarios to draw upon the information in this text chapter and suggestions presented by your instructors and clinical and field preceptors to develop the communication skills needed to manage this difficult situation. Continue to refine these skills once your training ends and you begin your career as a paramedic. Also find out about stress management programs provided by your agency so that you can get support after such a call has ended.

Case Study Review

Reread the case study on pages 249 and 250 in Paramedic Care: Special Considerations/Operations *and then read the following discussion.*

    The case study draws attention to the assessment and management of a chronic condition commonly found in a prehospital setting—chronic obstructive pulmonary disease (COPD), an illness that is subject to acute exacerbation during the end stage.

Patient assessment in the case begins as soon as the paramedics arrive on-scene. A quick survey of the room reveals the presence of several oxygen bottles on the floor and a patient on a nasal cannula. The EMS team immediately knows that their patient has already been treated on a home care basis for some kind of respiratory disorder, which conforms with the description supplied by the dispatcher ("elderly male, short of breath").

    Signs and symptoms clearly point to severe respiratory distress: use of the accessory muscles for breathing, anxiety, dyspnea, prolonged expiration with pursed lips, and the inability to speak in full sentences. Auscultation of lung sounds (diminished breathing in all fields with inspiratory and expiratory wheezes), vital signs, and patient history confirm this suspicion.

    Mr. Casey—who is in end-stage COPD—has a valid prehospital DNR, which he shows the paramedic. This document affects the actions taken by the prehospital care providers. As indicated in the case study, the DNR precludes intubation, so they continue with pharmacological interventions only. Because local protocols vary on advanced directives, it is important for you to become familiar with these well ahead of facing a real-life situation such as the one in this case.

Content Self-Evaluation

MULTIPLE CHOICE

_____ 1. All of the following factors have promoted the growth of home care in recent years EXCEPT:
    A. enactment of Medicare.
    B. the advent of HMOs.
    C. an increase in malpractice lawsuits.
    D. changes in the attitudes of doctors and patients toward hospital care.
    E. improved medical technology.

_____ 2. As patients assume greater responsibility for their own treatment and recovery, the likelihood of ALS intervention for the chronic-care patient increases.
    A. True   B. False

_____ 3. Common reasons for ALS intervention in the treatment of a home care patient include all of the following EXCEPT:
    A. inability to operate a device.
    B. absence of a caregiver.
    C. equipment failure.
    D. need for transport.
    E. pain management.

_____ 4. Home care providers can be of great assistance to EMS crews because they:
    A. have more experience in the field of prehospital medicine.
    B. will often spot subtle changes in the patient's condition.
    C. will easily grasp technical medical language.
    D. have legal authority to speak for the patient.
    E. both C and D.

_____ 5. A home care patient is less likely to decompensate and will go into crisis less quickly than the general population.
   A. True   B. False

_____ 6. Common causes of cardiac decompensation—a true medical emergency leading to shock—include all of the following EXCEPT:
   A. acute myocardial infarction.   D. sepsis.
   B. stroke.   E. heart transplant.
   C. cardiac hypertrophy.

_____ 7. One reason that diabetics get gangrene is due to slowed circulation to the extremities.
   A. True   B. False

_____ 8. Signs and symptoms of sepsis in a patient with an indwelling device can include:
   A. cyanosis at the infection site.
   B. fever.
   C. increased urination.
   D. cool skin at the insertion site.
   E. all of the above.

_____ 9. Home interventions such as peritoneal dialysis can alter electrolytes.
   A. True   B. False

_____ 10. The ability of the skin to return to normal appearance after being subjected to pressure is called:
   A. capillary refill.   D. diaphoresis.
   B. tenting.   E. hypertrophy.
   C. turgor.

_____ 11. Conditions that may be treated in a home care setting include:
   A. brain or spinal trauma.   D. both B and C.
   B. arthritis.   E. all of the above.
   C. AIDS.

_____ 12. Examples of commonly used medical devices in the home care setting includes all of the following EXCEPT:
   A. glucometers.   D. heart/lung machines.
   B. tracheostomies.   E. dialysis units.
   C. apnea monitors.

_____ 13. The matrix for injury prevention developed by William Haddon include all of the following steps EXCEPT:
   A. prevent the creation of the hazard in the first place.
   B. counter the damage done by the hazard.
   C. increase the release of an already existing hazard.
   D. modify the basic qualities of the hazard.
   E. separate the hazard and that which is to be protected by a barrier.

_____ 14. It is a serious mistake to arrive on the scene with a "take-over" mentality that all but eliminates the home care provider.
   A. True   B. False

_____ 15. In responding to any home care situation, you should remember that:
   A. any bed-bound patient may have pressure sores.
   B. hospital beds, wheelchairs, or walkers may be contaminated by body fluid.
   C. medical wastes may not be properly contained.
   D. sharps may be present.
   E. all of the above.

_____ 16. In assessing home care patients, the focus of your physical exam should be on the patient's chronic condition.
  A. True   B. False

_____ 17. Of the following acute home care situations, the one LEAST commonly encountered by paramedics is:
  A. respiratory disorders.   D. GI/GU disorders.
  B. end stages of a hospice patient. E. use of vascular access devices.
  C. cardiac problems.

_____ 18. When providing intervention to home care patients with chronic respiratory diseases, remember that they usually have a low-dosing regimen, which may make them more responsive to their medications.
  A. True   B. False

_____ 19. In treating home care patients with cystic fibrosis (CF), the patient will probably be:
  A. over age 65.   D. under age 40.
  B. between 40 and 60 years old.   E. an infant.
  C. of almost any age.

_____ 20. Which of the following is an advantage of oxygen therapy for the home care patient?
  A. It is relatively easy to manage.
  B. Most patients tolerate it easily.
  C. Oxygen therapy adds to the quality of life.
  D. Oxygen prevents hypoxic states.
  E. All of the above.

_____ 21. If a buzzer goes off on an oxygen concentrator, you would mostly likely suspect:
  A. faulty tubing.   D. power failure.
  B. a leak in the tank.   E. either A or C.
  C. a dirty or plugged humidifier.

_____ 22. Routine care of a tracheostomy includes all of the following EXCEPT:
  A. keeping the stoma clean and dry.
  B. removing the device daily.
  C. frequent suctioning.
  D. changing the ventilator hose routinely.
  E. periodically changing/cleaning of the inner cannula.

_____ 23. Which of the following ventilatory options are you LEAST likely to find in a home care setting?
  A. PEEP   D. poncho-wrap
  B. CPAP   E. both A and C.
  C. BIPAP

_____ 24. Patients with VADs will be much more prone to bleeding disorders than the general population.
  A. True   B. False

_____ 25. The most common complication found in patients with VADs results from:
  A. an embolus.   D. hypertension.
  B. dehydration.   E. both A and C.
  C. a thrombus.

_____ 26. The most commonly used device for urinary tract dysfunction is a(n):
  A. Texas catheter.   D. suprapubic catheter.
  B. urostomy.   E. condom catheter.
  C. Foley catheter.

_____ 27. The most common complications related to urinary tract support devices result from:
   A. obstructions.
   B. device malfunctions.
   C. infections.
   D. misplacement of devices.
   E. both B and C.

_____ 28. If you have any doubts about the placement of a nasogastric feeding tube, your first step should be to:
   A. listen for air movement within the stomach.
   B. use a 60-mL syringe to insert air into the stomach.
   C. have the patient speak to you.
   D. irrigate the tube with water.
   E. immediately remove the tube.

_____ 29. In terms of providing care, the goal of hospices closely resembles the goal of EMS services.
   A. True
   B. False

_____ 30. The stages in the grief process for both the patient and those left behind are:
   A. depression, bargaining, guilt, anger, acceptance.
   B. anger, denial, bargaining, guilt, acceptance.
   C. denial, bargaining, anger, acceptance, guilt.
   D. bargaining, denial, anger, guilt, acceptance.
   E. denial, anger, depression, bargaining, acceptance.

MATCHING

Write the letter of the term in the space provided next to the appropriate description.

A. hypertrophy   F. cellulitis

B. hemoptysis   G. gangrene

C. exocrine   H. turgor

D. demylenation   I. cor pulmonale

E. emesis   J. sensorium

_____ 31. destruction or removal of the myelin sheath of nerve tissue; found in Guillain-Barré syndrome

_____ 32. death of tissue or bone, usually from an insufficient blood supply

_____ 33. disorder involving external secretions

_____ 34. an increase in the size of an organ or structure caused by growth rather than by tumor

_____ 35. ability of the skin to return to normal appearance after being subjected to pressure

_____ 36. sensory apparatus of the body as a whole; also that portion of the brain that functions as a center of sensations

_____ 37. inflammation of cellular or connective tissue

_____ 38. expectoration of blood arising from the oral cavity, larynx, trachea, bronchi, or lungs

_____ 39. vomitus

_____ 40. congestive heart failure secondary to pulmonary hypertension

SHORT ANSWER

Write out the terms that each of the following abbreviations/acronyms stands for in the space provided.

41. PEEP _____

42. CPAP _____

43. BIPAP _____

44. COPD _____

45. ARDS _____

46. PPV _____

47. VAD _____

48. PICC _____

49. DNAR _____

50. CHF _____

Special Project

Find out the names and telephone numbers of home care agencies and hospices in your area. Inquire about the resources/services that they provide and record the information in the following spaces.

Home Care Agency

Name of agency: _____

Contact number: _____

Services provided: _____

_____

_____

_____

Home Care Agency

Name of agency: _____

Contact number: _____

Services provided: _____

_____

_____

_____

©2006 Pearson Education, Inc.
Paramedic Care: Principles & Practice, Vol. 5

Home Care Agency

Name of agency: _____

Contact number: _____

Services provided: _____

_____

_____

_____

Hospice

Name of agency: _____

Contact number: _____

Services provided: _____

_____

_____

_____

Hospice

Name of agency: _____

Contact number: _____

Services provided: _____

_____

_____

_____

Hospice

Name of agency: _____

Contact number: _____

Services provided: _____

_____

_____

_____

Now take one more step. Make a copy of this information and carry it aboard the ambulance or write the phone numbers in the pocket reference that you carry in your uniform pocket!

7 Assessment-Based Management

Review of Chapter Objectives

After reading this chapter, you should be able to:

1. Explain how effective assessment is critical to clinical decision making. pp. 296–297

Assessment forms the foundation for patient care. You can't treat or report a problem that is not found or identified. To find a problem, you must gather, evaluate, and synthesize information. Based on this process, you can then make a decision and take the appropriate actions to formulate a management plan and determine the priorities for patient care.

A paramedic is entrusted with a great deal of independent judgment and responsibility for performing the correct actions for each individual patient, including such advanced skills as ECG interpretation, rapid sequence intubation, and medication administration. Additionally, the medical director and hospital staff must rely on your experience and expertise as you describe the patient's condition and your conclusions about it. Consequently, the ability to reason and to reach a field diagnosis is critical to paramedic practice.

2. Explain how the paramedic's attitude and uncooperative patients affect assessment and decision making. p. 298

Attitude

Your attitude is one of the most critical factors in performing an effective assessment. You must be as nonjudgmental as possible to avoid "short-circuiting" accurate data collection and pattern recognition by leaping to conclusions before completing a thorough assessment. Remember the popular computer mnemonic GIGO—garbage in/garbage out. You can't reach valid conclusions about your patient based on hasty or incomplete assessment. Seek to identify any preconceived notions that you may have about a group and then work to eliminate them.

Uncooperative patients

Admittedly, uncooperative patients make it difficult to perform good assessments. However, you must remember that there are many possible causes for patient belligerence. Whenever you assess an uncooperative or a restless patient, consider medical causes for the behavior—hypoxia, hypovolemia, hypoglycemia, or a head injury. Be careful not to jump to the conclusion that the patient is "just another drunk" or a "frequent flyer." The frequent flier that you have transported for alcoholic behavior in the past may, this time, be suffering from trauma or a medical emergency.

In addition, cultural and ethnic barriers—as well as prior negative experiences—may cause a patient to lack confidence in the rescuers. Such situations make it difficult for you to be effective at the scene, and the patient in fact may refuse to provide expressed consent for treatment or transport. However, it is your job to increase patient confidence. Become familiar with the cultural customs of any large ethnic populations in your area. Find out about available translation services. Above all, don't permit yourself to make snap judgments about the patient.

3. Explain strategies to prevent labeling and tunnel vision, and to decrease environmental distractions.   pp. 296–300

A number of factors—both internal (for example, your personal attitudes) and external (for example, the patient's attitude, distracting injuries, or environmental factors at the scene)—can affect your assessment of the patient and ultimately your decisions on how to manage treatment.

Labeling and tunnel vision
The dangers of labeling have been discussed in objective 2. However, another internal factor that can negatively affect your assessment is tunnel vision. Do not focus on distracting injuries, such as a scalp laceration, that look worse than they really are. Instead, resist the temptation to form a field diagnosis too early. Always take a systematic approach to patient assessment to avoid distractions and to find and prioritize care for all of the patient's injuries and conditions. In general, follow an inverted pyramid format that progresses from a differential diagnosis to a narrowing process to your field diagnosis. (For more information on the inverted pyramid format, see the diagram on page 295 of your textbook.)

Environmental distractions
You've probably already experienced some of the environmental factors that can affect patient assessment and care—scene chaos, violent or dangerous situations, high noise levels, crowds of bystanders, or even crowds of responders. Limit these distractions through the careful staging of personnel (see objectives 4 and 5). In the case of a large number of rescuers, you might assign crowd control tasks to some of them or stage them nearby. They can then be brought to the scene when and if necessary. Finally, you might change environments completely. Sometimes the best way to deal with excessive environmental noise and distractions is to rapidly load the patient into the ambulance and leave the scene. You can always pull over for further assessment in a quieter environment.

4. Describe how personnel considerations and staffing configurations affect assessment and decision making.   pp. 299–300

As a rule, assessment is best achieved by one rescuer. A single paramedic can gather information and provide treatment sequentially. In the case of two paramedics, one paramedic can assess the patient, while the other provides simultaneous treatment. With multiple responders, however, assessment and history may take place entirely by "committee," which often leads to disorganized management. It can also be difficult to manage a patient if the responders are all at the same professional level and have no clear direction. Therefore, it is important to plan for these events so that personnel can have predesignated roles. These roles may be rotated among team members so no one is left out, but there must be a plan to avoid "freelancing." If there is only one paramedic, then that person must assume all ALS roles.

5. Synthesize and apply concepts of scene management and choreography to simulated emergency calls.   p. 300

Points in the textbook and direction by your instructors and clinical or field preceptors will help you to manage and choreograph simulated emergency calls. When approaching these practice sessions, remember the importance of an effective preplan. In the case of a two-person team, the roles of team care leader and patient care provider can be assigned on an alternating basis. Paramedics who work together regularly may develop their own plan, but a universally understood plan allows for other rescuers to participate in a rescue without interrupting the flow. While the dynamics of field situations may necessitate changes in plans, a general "game plan" can go a long way toward preventing chaos. If field dynamics dictate a change in the preplanned roles, you are still working from a solid base.

6. Explain the roles of the team leader and the patient care person.   **p. 300**

In setting up a two-person team, keep in mind the general tasks performed by the team leader and patient care provider as outlined below.

Roles of Team Leader	*Roles of Patient Care Provider*
Establishes patient contact	Provides "scene cover"
Obtains history	Gathers scene information
Performs physical exam	Talks to relatives/bystanders
Presents patient	Obtains vital signs
Handles documentation	Performs interventions
Acts as EMS commander	Acts as triage group leader

7. List and explain the rationale for bringing the essential care items to the patient.   **pp. 301–302**

Having the right equipment at the patient's side is essential. As a paramedic, you must be prepared to manage many conditions and injuries or changes in the patient's condition. Assessment and management must usually be done simultaneously. If you do not have the right equipment readily available, then you have compromised patient care and, in fact, the patient may die.

8. When given a simulated call, list the appropriate equipment to be taken to the patient.   **pp. 301–302**

Think of your equipment as items in a backpack. Just like backpacking, you must downsize your equipment to minimum weight and bulk to facilitate rapid movement. At the same time, you need certain essential items to ensure survival—in this case, patient survival. The following is a list of the essential equipment for paramedic management of life-threatening conditions. You must bring these items to the side of every patient, regardless of what you initially think you may need.

- Infection Control
  —Infection control supplies—e.g., gloves, eye shields
- Airway Control
  —Oral airways
  —Nasal airways
  —Suction (electric or manual)
  —Rigid tonsil-tip and flexible suction catheters
  —Laryngoscope and blades
  —Endotracheal tubes, stylettes, syringes, tape
- Breathing
  —Pocket mask
  —Manual ventilation bag-valve mask
  —Spare masks in various sizes
  —Oxygen masks, cannulas, and extension tubing
  —Occlusive dressings
  —Large-bore IV catheter for thoracic decompression
- Circulation
  —Dressings
  —Bandages and tape
  —Sphygmomanometer, stethoscope
  —Note pad and pen or pencil
- Disability
  —Rigid collars
  —Flashlights
- Dysrhythmia
  —Cardiac monitor/defibrillator

- Exposure and Protection
  —Scissors
  —Space blankets or something to cover the patient

You may also pack some optional "take in" equipment, such as drug therapy and venous access supplies. The method by which these supplies are carried may depend upon how your system is designed—e.g., paramedic ambulances versus paramedics in nontransporting vehicles. It may also depend upon local protocols, flexibility of standing orders, the number of paramedic responders in your area, and the difficulty of accessing patients because of terrain or some other problem.

9. Explain the general approach to the emergency patient. pp. 302–305

In addition to having the right equipment, you need to have the essential demeanor to calm or reassure the patient. You must look and act the professional, while exhibiting the compassion and understanding associated with an effective "bedside manner." While patients may not have the ability to rate your medical performance, they can certainly rate your people skills and service. Be aware of your body language and the messages it sends, either intentionally or unintentionally. Think carefully about what you say and how you say it—this includes your conversations with other members of the ALS team and anyone else on the scene.

Once again, it helps to preplan your general approach to the patient. This will prevent confusion and improve the accuracy of your assessment. One team member should engage in an active, concerned dialogue with the patient. This same person should also demonstrate the listening skills needed to collect information and to convey a caring attitude. Taking notes may prevent asking the same question repeatedly, as well as ensuring that you acquire and pass on accurate data.

10. Explain the general approach, patient assessment differentials, and management priorities for patients with various types of emergencies that may be experienced in prehospital care. pp. 305, 308, 309–317

Scene size-up

Before approaching the patient (see objective 9), you must carefully size up the scene. The scene size-up has the following components: body substance isolation, ensuring scene safety, locating all patients, and identifying the mechanism of injury or the nature of the illness.

Initial assessment

After you size up the scene, you quickly begin the initial assessment for the purpose of detecting and treating immediate life threats. The components of the initial assessment are:

- Forming a general impression
- Determining mental status (AVPU)
- Assessing airway, breathing, and circulation
- Determining the patient's priority for further on-scene care or immediate transport

Depending upon your findings during initial assessment, you might take either the contemplative or the resuscitative approach to patient care. You might also decide to immediately transport the patient.

Contemplative approach. In general, use the contemplative approach when immediate intervention is not necessary. In such situations, the focused history and physical exam, followed by any required interventions, can be performed at the scene, before transport to the hospital.

Resuscitative approach. Use the resuscitative approach whenever you suspect a life-threatening problem, including:

- Cardiac or respiratory arrest
- Respiratory distress or failure
- Unstable dysrhythmias
- Status epilepticus

- Coma or altered mental status
- Shock or hypotension
- Major trauma
- Possible C-spine injury

In these cases, you must take immediate resuscitative action (such as CPR, defibrillation, or ventilation) or other critical action (such as supplemental oxygen, control of major bleeding, or C-spine immobilization). Additional assessment and care can be performed after resuscitation and the rapid trauma assessment and/or en route to the hospital.

Immediate evacuation. In some cases, you will need to immediately evacuate the patient to the ambulance. For example, a patient with severe internal bleeding requires lifesaving interventions beyond a paramedic's skills. You might also resort to immediate evacuation if the scene is too chaotic for rational assessment or if it is too unsafe or unstable.

Focused history and physical exam

Following the initial assessment, you will perform the focused history and physical exam. Based on the patient's chief complaint and the information gathered during the initial assessment, you should consider your patient to belong to one of the following four categories:

- Trauma patient with a significant mechanism of injury or altered mental status
- Trauma patient with an isolated injury
- Medical patient who is unresponsive
- Medical patient who is responsive

For a trauma patient with a significant mechanism of injury or altered mental status or for an unresponsive medical patient, perform a complete head-to-toe physical examination (rapid trauma assessment for the trauma patient, rapid medical assessment for the medical patient). For a trauma patient with an isolated injury or for a responsive medical patient, perform a physical exam focused on body systems related to the chief complaint.

Ongoing assessment and detailed physical exam

The ongoing assessment must be performed on all patients to monitor and to observe trends in the patient's condition—every 5 minutes if the patient is unstable, every 15 minutes if the patient is stable. Ongoing assessments must be performed until the patient is transferred to the care of hospital personnel. The ongoing assessment includes evaluation of the following:

- Mental status
- Airway, breathing, and circulation (ABCs)
- Transport priorities
- Vital signs
- Focused assessment of any problem areas or conditions
- Effectiveness of interventions
- Management plans

The detailed physical exam is similar to but more thorough than the rapid trauma assessment. It is generally performed only on trauma patients and only if time and the patient's condition permit.

Identification of life-threatening problems

At all stages of the assessment, from initial assessment through ongoing assessments, from the scene—to the ambulance—to arrival at the hospital, you must actively and continuously look for and manage any life-threatening problems. Basically your role as a paramedic is to rapidly and accurately assess the patient and then to treat for the worst-case scenario. This is the underlying principle of assessment-based management—your guide to providing effective medical care. (For sample scenarios, see pages 309–317 in your textbook.)

11. Describe how to effectively communicate patient information face to face, over the telephone, by radio, and in writing. pp. 305–307

The ability to communicate effectively is the key to transferring patient information, whether in a prehospital setting or within the hospital itself. Although neither basic nor advanced life-support interventions may be required for every patient, a skill that will be used on every single patient is that of presentation, whether it is over the radio or telephone, in writing, or in face-to-face transfers at the receiving facility.

Effective presentation and communication skills help establish a paramedic's credibility. They also inspire trust and confidence in patients. If you present your assessment, your findings, and your treatment in a clear, concise manner, you give the impression of a job well done. A poor presentation, on the other hand, implies poor assessment and poor patient care. The most effective oral presentations usually meet these guidelines:

- Last less than 1 minute
- Are very concise and clear
- Avoid excessive use of medical jargon
- Follow a basic format, usually the SOAP format or some variation
- Include both pertinent findings and pertinent negatives
- Conclude with specific actions, requests, or questions related to the plan

An ideal presentation should include the following:

- Patient identification, age, sex, and degree of distress
- Chief complaint
- Present illness/injury
    —Pertinent details about the present problem
    —Pertinent negatives
- Past medical history
    —Allergies
    —Medications
    —Pertinent medical history
- Physical signs
    —Vital signs
    —Pertinent positive findings
    —Pertinent negative findings
- Assessment
    —Paramedic impression
- Plan
    —What has been done
    —Orders requested

12. Given various preprogrammed and moulaged patients, provide the appropriate scene size-up, initial assessment, focused assessment, and detailed assessment, then provide the appropriate care, ongoing assessments, and patient transport. pp. 295–317

In order to develop as an entry-level practitioner at the paramedic level, it is important to participate in scenario-based reviews of commonly encountered complaints. Laboratory-based simulations require you to assess a preprogrammed patient or mannequin. Use the information presented in the textbook, the information on assessment-based management provided by your instructors, and the guidance given by your clinical and field preceptors to develop good assessment-based management skills. Remember—the chance to practice does not stop at the classroom. While a paramedic student or the new member of a team, take advantage of every opportunity to practice your new skills.

Case Study Review

Reread the case study on pages 293 and 294 in Paramedic Care: Special Considerations/Operations *and then read the following discussion.*

This case study leads you through the thought process of a paramedic who uses "inverted reasoning"—the foundation of assessment-based management—to choreograph a call involving a patient injured in a single-vehicle crash.

The paramedic starts planning the call from the moment of dispatch, listing possible medical conditions and injuries that might be found upon arrival and reviewing the equipment that should be taken to the patient's side. Upon arrival, the paramedic determines scene safety—the most important concern on any run—before determining the approach. Paramount on the paramedic's mind is quick identification and treatment of any life-threatening injuries. Before even reaching the patient, the paramedic has formed a general impression of a seriously injured patient—one who will in all likelihood require a resuscitative approach.

The importance of having the right equipment becomes clear as the paramedic conducts the initial assessment. The paramedic also illustrates the role of a team leader, quickly assigning additional personnel as they arrive on the scene. Ignoring distracting injuries, the paramedic identifies immediate life threats, prioritizes care, and prepares the patient for immediate transport.

Despite obvious trauma, the paramedic does not forget to rule out medical complications that may have led to the crash. Because of the seriousness of the injury, the ALS team stays with the patient in the back of the ambulance, while an EMT from another crew volunteers to drive.

In the end, it is all those little things—the right equipment at the patient's side, good scene choreography, use of inverted reasoning, good presentation skills, and more—that can save a life.

(For more on this case study, see the analysis of reasoning skills on page 295 of the textbook.)

Content Self-Evaluation

MULTIPLE CHOICE

_____ 1. Which of the following gives the correct order of steps in the clinical decision making of the inverted pyramid?
  A. field diagnosis, differential diagnosis, narrowing process
  B. differential diagnosis, narrowing process, field diagnosis
  C. narrowing process, field diagnosis, differential diagnosis
  D. differential diagnosis, field diagnosis, narrowing process
  E. field diagnosis, narrowing process, differential diagnosis

_____ 2. The foundation of patient care is:
  A. the detailed physical exam.   D. medication administration.
  B. BLS protocols.   E. ALS protocols.
  C. assessment.

_____ 3. In a medical patient, the physical exam takes precedence over the history.
  A. True   B. False

_____ 4. All of the following are examples of external factors that can affect assessment EXCEPT:
  A. the attitudes of family members.   D. scene chaos.
  B. an uncooperative patient.   E. personal attitudes.
  C. distracting injuries.

_____ 5. Protocols and standing orders do not replace:
  A. good history taking.   D. the team approach.
  B. a good attitude.   E. pattern recognition.
  C. good judgment.

_____ 6. A paramedic can do something to correct or lessen obstacles to performing a good assessment such as reducing:
   A. tunnel vision.
   B. labeling.
   C. cultural and ethnic barriers.
   D. preconceived notions.
   E. all of the above.

_____ 7. You should treat a "frequent flier" just like you would any other patient.
   A. True
   B. False

_____ 8. A team leader's roles include all of the following EXCEPT:
   A. obtaining a history.
   B. performing the physical exam.
   C. handling documentation.
   D. triageing patients.
   E. performing a detailed exam.

_____ 9. Roles of a patient care provider include:
   A. talking to bystanders.
   B. obtaining vital signs.
   C. gathering scene information.
   D. providing scene cover.
   E. all of the above

_____ 10. Patient assessment is best performed by two paramedics rather than just one.
   A. True
   B. False

_____ 11. Which of the following is probably optional "take in" equipment carried by paramedics?
   A. rigid collars
   B. infection control supplies
   C. drug therapy
   D. space blankets
   E. sphygmomanometer

_____ 12. Components of the initial assessment include all of the following EXCEPT:
   A. forming a general impression.
   B. assessing ABCs.
   C. assessing the scene.
   D. determining the patient's priority.
   E. assessing mental status.

_____ 13. A patient with severe internal bleeding is a candidate for:
   A. the resuscitative approach.
   B. the contemplative approach.
   C. immediate evacuation.
   D. a detailed physical exam.
   E. both B and D.

_____ 14. In critical patients, a detailed physical exam is more important than continuing ongoing assessments.
   A. True
   B. False

_____ 15. The most effective patient presentations will:
   A. use medical jargon.
   B. follow the SOAP format.
   C. be done in writing.
   D. last 5 to 10 minutes.
   E. exclude subjective findings.

Special Project

Developing Effective Presentation Skills

Part I: Completion
Fill in the missing items in the following incomplete outline of an ideal patient presentation. Try not to look back at information in the chapter objectives; see what you can remember on your own.

   A. Patient identification, _____, _____, and _____

B. Chief complaint

C. Present illness/injury

   1. _____

   2. _____

D. _____

   1. Allergies

   2. Medications

   3. Pertinent medical history

E. Physical signs

   1. _____

   2. Pertinent positive findings

   3. _____

F. _____

   1. Paramedic impression

G. Plan

   1. _____

   2. _____

Part II: Sample Presentation

Pick one of the three scenarios on textbook pages 309–317 and develop a presentation that includes items in your completed outline. If possible, use one of the preprinted forms from the EMS service where you serve. Deliver your presentation verbally to one of your classmates for practice and review.

Ambulance Operations

Review of Chapter Objectives

After reading this chapter, you should be able to:

1. Identify current local and state standards that influence ambulance design, equipment requirements, and staffing of ambulances.　　pp. 322–324

Various standards, as well as administrative rules and regulations, influence the design of ambulances and the medical equipment carried on each unit. Similar guidelines determine staffing levels and deployment of EMS agencies.

　　Because the oversight for EMS usually falls to state governments, many of the requirements for ambulance services are written in state statutes or regulations. However, national standards and trends do have an influence on the development of these laws. Typically, state laws are broad, while corresponding regulations provide more specific guidelines or rules. For example, a public health law may authorize the state department of health to issue regulations through its EMS bureau. These regulations, known as the "state EMS code," might then handle such matters as the essential equipment to be carried on every ambulance.

　　In most cases, government standards tend to be generic enough so that they are "palatable," affordable, and politically feasible to all EMS agencies in the state. State standards usually set minimum standards, rather than the "gold standard," for operation. In other words, they establish the lowest level at which units will be allowed to operate. When local and/or regional EMS systems get involved in regulation, their lists tend to be much more detailed and often approach a gold standard, which is the goal when ample resources are provided.

2. Identify the elements of a vehicle, equipment, and supply checklist.　　pp. 324–326

The components of a typical vehicle/equipment checklist include the following:

- Patient infection control, comfort, and protection supplies
- Initial and focused assessment equipment
- Equipment for the transfer of the patient
- Equipment for airway maintenance, ventilation, and resuscitation
- Oxygen therapy and suction equipment
- Equipment for assisting with cardiac resuscitation
- Supplies and equipment for immobilization of suspected bone injuries
- Supplies for wound care and treatment of shock
- Supplies for childbirth

- Supplies, equipment, and medications for the treatment of acute poisoning, snakebite, chemical burns, and diabetic emergencies
- Advanced life support equipment, medications, and supplies
- Safety and miscellaneous equipment
- Information on the operation and inspection of the ambulance itself

3. Describe the process for reporting vehicle or equipment problems/failure to the director of operations. p. 325

If the ambulance or any equipment is found inoperable or in need of repair, it is your responsibility to report the failure to your supervisor in a manner prescribed by the SOPs for your service.

4. Identify the EMS equipment that needs routine service to assure proper field operation. pp. 325–326

Items that should be regularly checked include:

- Automated external defibrillator (AED)
- Glucometer
- Cardiac monitor
- Oxygen systems
- Automated transport ventilator (ATV)
- Pulse oximeter
- Suction units
- Laryngoscope blades
- Lighted stylets
- Penlights
- Any other battery-operated equipment

5. Discuss OSHA standards and other federal requirements for vehicle and equipment cleaning. p. 325

To meet OSHA requirements, you must make sure that the ambulance has been properly disinfected after the transport of any patients with potentially communicable diseases. Most services routinely clean the ambulance after every call, and some agencies document the procedure. All services are required, either by OSHA or the state equivalent of OSHA, to have an exposure control plan that specifies cleaning requirements and the methods of cleaning up blood spills in the ambulance. If there is no specific SOP in your agency, you should document cleaning and disinfecting on your shift checklist.

6. Discuss the importance of completing an ambulance equipment/supply checklist. pp. 324–326

Routine, detailed shift checks of the ambulance can minimize the issues associated with risk management. Many services, for example, hold a "stretcher day" once a week. By performing and documenting preventative maintenance on stretchers, it is less likely that a faulty stretcher will cause a patient to be dropped or EMS personnel to injure their backs. Medications carried on the paramedic unit expire. Therefore, expiration dates should be checked each shift, and the older unexpired drugs marked appropriately so that they will be used first. In services that utilize scheduled medications such as narcotics, the paramedics should sign for these medications at the beginning and at the end of each shift. In addition, the vehicle itself should be regularly checked so that it always in safe working order.

7. **Discuss factors used to determine ambulance stationing and staffing within a community** pp. 326–327

Deployment

The strategy used by an EMS agency to maneuver its ambulances and crews in order to reduce response times is referred to as deployment. Deployment is based upon a number of factors: location of the facilities to house ambulances, location of hospitals, anticipated volume of calls, and the specific geography and traffic congestion in your area.

The ideal deployment decisions must take into account two sets of data: past community responses and projected demographic changes. The highest volume of calls, or peak load, should be described both in terms of the day of the week and the time of day.

In communities that do not have multiple strategically located stations, services often deploy ambulances to wait for calls at specific high-volume locations. Such stationing locations are known as primary areas of responsibility (PAR).

Some technologically sophisticated systems use computers to assist the dispatch center in relocating ambulances. Vehicle tracking systems tell the computer exactly where each ambulance is located at a given time.

Operational staffing

In general, ambulance staffing should take into account the peak load of the system. Some services vary shift times to ensure ample coverage for the busiest days of the week and the busiest times of day. Services should also take into account the need for reserve capacity—the ability to muster additional crews when all ambulances are on call or when a system's resources are taxed by a multiple casualty incident. Some services fulfill this need by asking off-duty personnel to carry pagers or to volunteer for backup.

Whatever plan is adopted, each system must consider how they will deal with assigning paramedics. Clearly, an ambulance with two paramedics onboard is limited in the amount of care these two highly trained personnel can provide if they are the only available responders to cardiac arrests (meaning no backup for simultaneous additional emergencies). As a result, some communities prefer to combine an EMT-Intermediate with a paramedic to make an ALS unit. Other communities, such as New York City, specify that an ALS unit must have two paramedics so that they can back each other up in making scene decisions.

Finally, each service needs to determine standards for ambulance operators and for driving the vehicle itself. As a rule, these standards are usually spelled out at the local service level.

8. **Describe the advantages and disadvantages of air medical transport.** pp. 336–337

Advantages of air medical transport include:

- Rapid transport in situations where the time required for ground transport poses a threat to the patient's survival or recovery
- Access to rural or remote areas
- Access to specialty units—e.g., neonatal intensive care units, replantation units, transplant centers, burn centers, and so on
- Access to personnel with specialized skills—e.g., surgical airway, thoracotomy, rapid sequence intubation, critical care, and more
- Access to special supplies—e.g., aortic balloon pumps

Disadvantages of air medical transport include:

- Weather and environmental restrictions to flying
- Altitude limitations
- Airspeed limitations
- Cabin sizes that sometimes restrict the number of crew members, the amount of on-board equipment, stretcher configuration, and the procedures that can be performed

- Lack of normal temperature control, especially in helicopters with their thin-walled fuselages
- Limited lighting (to prevent glare from entering the pilot's compartment)
- High cost of equipment, maintenance, and downtime, which puts air medical transport (especially helicopters) beyond the reach of some communities

9. Identify conditions/situations that merit air medical transport. pp. 336–337

Indications for patient transport by helicopter include medical emergencies, trauma emergencies, and search and rescue missions. Anatomic or physiologic compromising factors that may warrant the need for air medical transport include:

Clinical Criteria*

General and mechanism considerations:

- Trauma score < 12
- Unstable vital signs (e.g., hypotension or tachypnea)
- Significant trauma to patients < 12 years old, > 55 years old, or pregnant patients
- Multisystem injuries (e.g., long-bone fracture in different extremities; injury to more than two body regions)
- Ejection from vehicle
- Pedestrian or cyclist struck by motor vehicle
- Death in same passenger compartment as patient
- Ground provider perception of significant damage to patient's passenger compartment
- Penetrating trauma to the abdomen, pelvis, chest, neck, or head
- Crush injury to the abdomen, chest, or head

Neurological considerations:

- Glasgow coma scale score < 10
- Deteriorating mental status
- Skull fracture
- Neurological presentation suggestive of spinal cord injury

Thoracic considerations:

- Major chest wall injury (e.g., flail chest)
- Pneumothorax/hemothorax
- Suspected cardiac history

Abdominal/pelvic considerations:

- Significant abdominal pain after trauma
- Presence of a "seatbelt" sign or other abdominal wall contusion
- Obvious rib fractures below the nipple line
- Major pelvic fracture (e.g., unstable pelvic ring disruption, open pelvic fracture, or pelvic fracture with hypotension)

Orthopedic/extremity considerations:

- Partial or total amputation of a limb (exclusive of digits)
- Finger/thumb amputation when emergent surgical evaluation (i.e., for replantation consideration) is indicated and rapid surface transportation is not available
- Fracture or dislocation with vascular compromise
- Extremity ischemia
- Open long-bone fractures
- Two or more long-bone fractures

Major burns:

- > 20 percent body surface area
- Involvement of face, head, hands, feet, or genitalia
- Inhalational injury
- Electrical or chemical burns
- Burns with associated injuries

Immersion injuries:

- Patients with near-drowning injuries

* Source: National Association of EMS Physicians Position Paper, Guidelines for Air Medical Dispatch, *Prehospital Emergency Care*, 7(2)(2003):265–271.

10. Discuss strategies to help assure safe operation of ambulances when responding to or at an emergency.   **pp. 327–334**

The first step in any proactive program to help assure safe ambulance operation is the recognition and definition of the problem. Ambulance collisions exact a physical and emotional toll on patients, EMS providers, motorists, and family members of the injured patients. In addition to personal injuries, ambulance collisions are costly in terms of vehicle repair or replacement, lawsuits, downtime from work, increased insurance premiums, and damage to your agency's reputation.

Reducing collisions

If you have the opportunity to develop programs to reduce ambulance collisions, consider implementing the following actions or standards.

- Routine use of driver qualification checklists and driver's license checks, either through the local police or the Department of Motor Vehicles
- Demonstrated driver understanding of preventive mechanical maintenance, including a vehicle operator checklist and a procedure for reporting any problems found during the check or while driving the vehicle
- Provision of plenty of hands-on driver training, using experienced and qualified field officers
- Implementation of a slow-speed course to ensure that operators know how to use mirrors, and back up, park, and handle ambulance-size vehicles—including accurate estimation of braking distance and turn radius
- Training that ensures that operators know how to react to emergency situations such as the loss of brakes, loss of power steering, a stuck accelerator, a blown-out tire, or vehicle breakdown
- Demonstrated driver understanding of the rules, regulations, and laws that your Department of Motor Vehicles has established, both for drivers in general and for ambulance drivers in particular

Standard operating procedures

Each EMS agency should have standard operating procedures (SOPs) pertaining to the operation of the vehicles. At a minimum there should be SOPs that clearly spell out the following:

- Procedure for qualifying as an ambulance operator
- Procedure for handling and reporting an ambulance collision
- Process for investigating and reviewing each collision
- Process for implementing quality assurance in the aftermath of a collision
- Method for using a spotter when backing up a vehicle
- Use of seat belts in the ambulance, and the procedure for transporting a child passenger under 40 pounds
- Guidelines on what constitutes an emergency response and the exemptions that may be taken under state law

- Guidelines on prudent speed; proper travel in, and the circumstances for using, oncoming lanes; and safe negotiation of intersections
- Circumstances and procedures for use of escorts
- A policy of zero tolerance for driving the vehicle under the influence of alcohol or any drugs

Case Study Review

Reread the case study on page 321 in Paramedic Care: Special Considerations/Operations *and then read the following discussion.*

  This case study draws attention to the importance of well-stocked ambulances to provide effective patient care.

As indicated in the closing paragraph of the case study, some services do not value the importance of having the right equipment and supplies available at all times for every patient. Eventually that attitude catches up with them and someone gets hurt.

  Most quality services are very strict about restocking ambulances. A rig check should be the first order of business upon arrival for each shift. This helps to ensure that the last crew did its job correctly. It is also a good practice to restock after each call as well as to refuel the vehicle. In this way, you will not run short of any essential item—and you will experience a smooth and uneventful run, like the dedicated service described in the case study.

Content Self-Evaluation

MULTIPLE CHOICE

_____ 1. What type of ambulance standards are usually set by states?
  A. minimum standards
  B. maximum standards
  C. gold standards
  D. essential-equipment standards
  E. DOT KKK standards

_____ 2. A conventional truck cab-chassis with a modular ambulance body is a _____ ambulance design.
  A. Type I   D. medium-duty
  B. Type II   E. heavy-duty
  C. Type III

_____ 3. A specialty van with a forward control integral cab-body is a _____ ambulance design.
  A. Type I   D. medium-duty
  B. Type II   E. heavy-duty
  C. Type III

_____ 4. Which of the following agencies or organizations influence ambulance standards?
  A. Department of Transportation (DOT)
  B. National Flight Nurses Association (NFNA)
  C. National Flight Paramedics Association (NFPA)
  D. Federal Communications Commission (FCC)
  E. all of the above

_____ 5. The agency that has helped ensure equipment lists calling for disinfecting agents, sharps containers, and other protective items onboard ambulances is:
A. NIOSH.
B. NFPA.
C. OSHA.
D. CDC.
E. NFPA.

_____ 6. The agency that provides a "gold standard" for the EMS community to follow, including a list of "essential equipment" to be carried on ambulances is:
A. ACS.
B. CAAS.
C. NFPA.
D. NIOSH.
E. OSHA.

_____ 7. The expiration dates on medications carried on the paramedic unit should be checked:
A. once a day.
B. once a week.
C. at the start of every shift.
D. at the start of every month.
E. every other day.

_____ 8. An EMS agency uses deployment based on all of the following factors EXCEPT:
A. anticipated call volume.
B. local geographic and traffic conditions.
C. location of hospitals.
D. projected ethnic makeup of the population.
E. location of facilities to house ambulances.

_____ 9. A deployment strategy that uses a computerized personnel and ambulance deployment system is known as:
A. a peak load system.
B. a primary area of responsibility.
C. system status management.
D. primary deploy management.
E. none of the above.

_____ 10. A system that allows multiple vehicles to arrive at an EMS call at different times is called a _____ system.
A. multiple response
B. tiered response
C. primary response
D. reserve capacity
E. peak load

_____ 11. Almost all communities in the United States require two paramedics aboard an ALS unit.
A. True
B. False

_____ 12. According to one study, the majority of ambulance collisions occur:
A. in patients' driveways.
B. at intersections.
C. backing into ambulance bays.
D. at night.
E. during inclement weather.

_____ 13. A legal term found in the motor vehicle laws of most states that sets up a higher standard for the operators of emergency vehicles is called:
A. _res ispa loquitur._
B. exempt rights.
C. emergency power.
D. due regard.
E. special status.

_____ 14. State laws typically exempt ambulance drivers who are operating in an emergency from all of the following traffic situations EXCEPT:
A. posted speed limits.
B. crossing railroad tracks with the gates down.
C. posted directions of travel.
D. parking regulations.
E. requirements to wait for red lights.

_____ 15. Nowhere in the motor vehicle laws are drivers other than emergency vehicle operators held accountable for the safety of all other motorists.
A. True   B. False

_____ 16. Which of the following is NOT true about the use of lights and sirens?
A. Motorists are less inclined to yield to an ambulance when the siren is continually sounded.
B. Many motorists feel that the right-of-way privileges given to ambulances are abused when sirens are sounded.
C. Inexperienced motorists tend to decrease their driving speed by 10 to 15 miles per hour when a siren is sounded.
D. The continuous sound of a siren can possibly worsen the condition of patients by increasing their anxiety.
E. Ambulance drivers may develop anxiety from using sirens on long runs.

_____ 17. Why do most EMS agencies no longer suggest the use of a police escort for ambulances?
A. Ambulances and police cars have different braking distances.
B. Motorists are often confused by escorts going through intersections.
C. Motorists often will not see the second vehicle and pull out in front of it.
D. Ambulance drivers may have trouble keeping up with police cars.
E. All of the above.

_____ 18. When your ambulance is the first to arrive at the scene of a motor vehicle collision, you should park:
A. behind the wreckage.
B. in front of the wreckage.
C. in a staging area.
D. next to the wreckage on the side.
E. across the road from the wreckage.

_____ 19. Always go around cars stopped at an intersection on their right (passenger's) side.
A. True   B. False

_____ 20. The type of air transport that you will most likely encounter as a paramedic is fixed-wing aircraft.
A. True   B. False

_____ 21. The use of helicopters for medical rescue grew out of their proven benefit during:
A. the Vietnam War.   D. World War II.
B. Operation Desert Storm.   E. both A and C.
C. the Korean War.

_____ 22. All of the following are advantages of air transport EXCEPT:
A. cost efficiency.
B. access to remote areas.
C. access to specialty units.
D. rapid transport when distance is a consideration.
E. access to specialty supplies.

©2006 Pearson Education, Inc.
Paramedic Care: Principles & Practice, Vol. 5

_____ 23. Neurologic considerations for air medical service include GCS < 10, deteriorating mental status, and indications of spinal injury.
  A. True   B. False

_____ 24. A piece of equipment that can be affected by pressure changes during a flight is a(n):
  A. IV bag.   D. mobile radio.
  B. capnograph.   E. both A and C.
  C. PASG.

_____ 25. As a rule, a helicopter requires a landing zone of approximately:
  A. 100 by 100 feet.   D. 75 by 75 feet.
  B. 100 by 100 yards.   E. 15 large steps on each side.
  C. 75 by 75 yards.

MATCHING

Write the letter of the term in the space provided next to the appropriate description.

A. peak load   F. gold standard

B. primary area of responsibility   G. spotter

C. tiered response system   H. reportable collisions

D. deployment   I. minimum standard

E. demographic   J. reserve capacity

_____ 26. strategy used by an EMS agency to maneuver its ambulances and crews in an effort to reduce response times

_____ 27. ultimate standard of excellence

_____ 28. lowest or least allowable standards

_____ 29. the highest volume of calls at a given time

_____ 30. pertaining to population makeup or changes

_____ 31. stationing of ambulances at specific high-volume locations

_____ 32. allows multiple vehicles to arrive at an EMS call at different times, often providing different levels of care or transport

_____ 33. the ability of an EMS agency to respond to calls beyond those handled by the on-duty crews

_____ 34. collisions that involve over $1,000 in damage or a personal injury

_____ 35. the person behind the left rear side of the ambulance who assists the operator in backing up the vehicle

Special Project

The motor vehicle laws differ slightly from state to state. Ask your chief or EMS director for a copy of the laws in your state and review them very closely. List below the exemptions that you may take when responding to an emergency in your ambulance:

_____

_____

_____

_____

_____

_____

_____

_____

Now review the standard operating procedures for negotiating an intersection. Write the key elements of the policy below:

_____

_____

_____

_____

_____

_____

_____

_____

_____

_____

Medical Incident Management

Review of Chapter Objectives

After reading this chapter, you should be able to:

1. Explain the need for the Incident Management System (IMS)/Incident Command System (ICS) in managing emergency medical services incidents.   pp. 349–352

Traditional paramedic education focuses on the relationship between one or two patient-care providers and a single patient. In this setting, a paramedic has the ability to concentrate on the assessment and treatment of the patient. Occasionally, however, paramedics are called upon to treat more than one patient at a time. The multipatient incident may result from a motor vehicle collision (MVC), an apartment fire, a gang fight, or any number of other scenarios.

    Based on the need for overall scene and resource management recognized at a number of major fires and other large-scale incidents in the 1970s, the fire service took the lead in organizing responses to large-scale emergencies. The result was the beginning of the modern-day Incident Command System (ICS)—a management program designed for controlling, directing, and coordinating emergency response resources. In the time since the events of September 11, 2001, and the increased potential for large-scale terrorist incidents, the ICS continues to evolve into a comprehensive, standardized National Incident Management System (NIMS). NIMS is a national system used for the management of multiple-casualty incidents, involving assumption of responsibility for command and designation and coordination of such elements as triage, treatment, transport, and staging.

2. Describe the functional components (Command, finance, logistics, operations, and planning) of the Incident Management System.   pp. 352–361

To familiarize yourself with the components of the Incident Management System, use the mnemonic **C-FLOP**, which stands for the first letter in each of the following functions or roles:

- **Command**—individual or group responsible for coordinating all activities and who makes final decisions on the emergency scene; often referred to as the Incident Commander (IC).
- **Finance/Administration**—section responsible for maintaining records for personnel, time, and costs of resources/procurement; reports directly to the IC; rarely operates on small-scale incidents.
- **Logistics**—section that supports incident operations, coordinating procurement and distribution of all medical and other resources.
- **Operations**—section that fulfills directions from command and does the action work at an incident.

- **Planning**—section that provides past, present, and future information about an incident; operates on the principle of "anything that can go wrong, will go wrong," thus ensuring the necessary strategic support.

3. **Differentiate between Singular and Unified Command and identify when each is most applicable.** pp. 354–355

There are at least two different types of command: Singular and Unified Command. To distinguish between these two types of command, keep these definitions in mind:

- **Singular Command**—process where a single individual is responsible for coordinating an incident.
- **Unified Command**—process in which managers from different jurisdictions—law enforcement agencies, fire, EMS—coordinate their activities and share responsibility for command.

At small incidents with limited jurisdictions, Singular Command usually works best. Such incidents have a smaller scope and usually do not involve outside agencies. In many incidents, however, a Singular Command will not be feasible because of overlapping responsibilities or jurisdictions. Instead, a Unified Command will be established. Examples of such incidents include terrorist attacks, explosions, sniper or hostage situations, and large-scale disasters. In each of these examples, the managers from several jurisdictions, law enforcement, fire, and EMS will coordinate their activities.

4. **Describe the role of command, the need for command transfer, and procedures for transferring it.** pp. 352–353, 356–357

The most important functional area in the Incident Management System is command. The Incident Commander is the individual who essentially oversees and controls the incident. The ultimate authority for decision making rests with the Incident Commander. Most agencies have a chain of authority that defines the highest-ranking official at a scene. However, establishing command at a multiagency, multijurisdictional incident can be complicated. State or local agencies often decide the issue in such situations. Otherwise, the decision should be reached by a preexisting disaster plan.

The criteria for determining when to establish command and when to declare a multiple casualty incident (MCI) varies from agency to agency. As a rule, the first arriving public safety unit usually establishes command. Sometimes this unit is an ambulance and then you and your partner will most likely fill the roles of Incident Commander and Triage Officer—until other units arrive. If, or when, higher-ranking officers do arrive, command will be transferred. However, a higher-ranking officer does not become IC simply by his or her arrival. Command is only transferred face-to-face, with the current Incident Commander conducting a short but complete briefing on the incident status.

5. **List and describe the functions of the following groups and leaders in ICS as it pertains to EMS incidents:**

The functions differ depending on which vest is being worn at a MCI. The following are examples of the Sectors for which you, the paramedic, may be responsible for at the next MCI:

a. **Safety** p. 358

The Safety Officer may hold the most important role at a MCI. This person—or, in some cases, team of people—monitors all on-scene actions and ensures that they do not create any potentially harmful conditions.

b. **Logistics** p. 360

The Logistics Section supports incident operations. One of its most critical functions is overseeing the Medical Supply Unit. In general, logistics coordinates the procurement and distribution of equipment and supplies at a MCI or disaster.

c. **Rehabilitation (rehab)** pp. 369–370

Medical personnel operating in the rehabilitation section assume responsibility for monitoring the well-being of rescuers. They assure food and water are available, rescuers take rest breaks, take vital signs, and watch for signs of fatigue or incident stress. A predetermined threshold should be established so that rescuers with abnormal vitals or signs of fatigue or stress are removed from operation. This is especially important during extremely hot or cold conditions.

©2006 Pearson Education, Inc.
Paramedic Care: Principles & Practice, Vol. 5

d. Staging   **p. 368**

The Staging Officer supervises the Staging Area—the location where ambulances, personnel, and equipment are kept in reserve—and guards against premature commitment of resources. The Staging Officer makes every effort to prevent "freelancing" by EMS personnel.

e. Treatment   **pp. 366–368**

When the number of patients exceeds the number of ambulances available for support, you will need to collect patients in a treatment Sector comprised of a red treatment unit, a yellow treatment unit, and a green treatment unit. Each of these units is supervised by a Treatment Unit Leader, who reports to the Treatment Group Supervisor—the person who controls all actions in the Treatment Group Sector.

The unit leader's job requires extreme flexibility to ensure that patients receive adequate care. Patient conditions can change and responders, equipment, or supplies may not be available in the subarea. As a result, communications must be carefully coordinated. The Treatment Group Supervisor must be apprised of activities in each subarea. He or she must also help coordinate operations with other functional areas, particularly command, triage, and transport.

f. Triage   **pp. 362–366**

Because triage will drive subsequent incident operations, it is one of the first functions performed at a MCI. As a result, all personnel should be trained in triage techniques and all response units should carry triage equipment. At small incidents, you or your partner may assume the role of triage. Larger incidents may require a Triage Group Supervisor, who may either act independently or supervise the Triage Group or Sector.

g. Transportation   **pp. 368–369**

The Transportation Unit Supervisor coordinates operations with the Staging Officer and the Treatment Supervisor. His or her job is to get patients into the ambulances and routed to hospitals. If you are assigned to this role, you will need to be flexible in determining the order in which patients are packaged and loaded. You may, for example, elect to place two critical patients in one ambulance for transport to a trauma center. If you decide that the ambulance provider cannot adequately care for two critical patients, you may instead decide to transport one critical and one noncritical patient.

The routing of patients to hospitals is as important as getting them into the ambulance. Communication with local hospitals is essential to avoid overloading the resources of any one unit.

h. Extrication/rescue   **p. 369**

In general, the Extrication/Rescue Group removes patients from entanglements at the incident and arranges for them to be carried to treatment areas. The operation has many facets and may require specialized personnel and equipment.

i. Disposition of deceased (morgue)   **p. 366**

The Morgue Officer supervises the morgue—the area where the expectant victims of an incident are collected. This person may report to the Triage Officer or to the Treatment Officer. In many cases, these supervisors will in fact assist in selection and securing of an area for the morgue.

j. Communications   **pp. 355, 370**

At large-scale incidents, the Incident Management System provides for an EMS Communications Officer, also known as the EMS COM or the MED COM. This person works closely with the Transportation Unit Supervisor to notify hospitals of incoming patients. A dedicated radio channel works best for this purpose. The EMS COM will not deliver complete patient reports, which would increase communications traffic. Instead, he or she will transmit the basic information collected by the Transportation Supervisor, such as the number of Priority one patients en route to the hospital, the expected arrival time, and so on.

6. Describe the methods and rationale for identifying specific functions and leaders for the functions in the ICS.   **pp. 352–370**

The rationale for dividing tasks at a MCI has already been discussed in previous objectives. However, it is equally important that everybody knows who is in charge of the various functions.

For an Incident Commander to manage a MCI, all personnel must be able to recognize the IC. At smaller, single-agency events, everyone may know the IC simply by his or her voice over the radio. However, at medium- or large-scale incidents, such recognition is often impossible. As a result, the Incident Management System calls for the IC and other officers to wear special reflective vests. The vests can be color-coded to functional areas and may have the officer's title on the front and back. Such vests should be worn whenever IMS is utilized, even at smaller incidents. By making a basic set of vests, especially command and triage, available on every response unit, personnel will get in the habit of wearing and/or recognizing the vests prior to a major incident.

7. **Describe essential elements of the scene size-up when arriving at a potential MCI.** pp. 353–354

The first few minutes at a MCI can set the course of the next 60 minutes. The scene size-up is very important and should include three main priorities: life safety, incident stabilization, and property conservation.

Life Safety
Life safety is always the top priority. If you arrive first on the scene of a high-impact incident, you must observe and protect all rescuers, including yourself, from hazards. Then, and only then, will you attend to patients who are in immediately life-threatening situations. Keep in mind, however, that the needs of the many usually outweigh the needs of the few. If you commit to caring for the first patient that you encounter, you may neglect the other critical patients lying nearby.

Incident Stabilization
To achieve incident stabilization, quickly identify whether the situation is an open incident or a closed incident. Because an open incident can generate more patients at any time, it's better to call too many resources than to call too few.

In the case of a closed incident, the injuries have usually already occurred by the time you arrive on-scene. Yet even a so-called closed incident carries the potential for additional hazards—an undetected gas leak, a distraught family member who rushes into traffic, or further injury to patients wandering about the scene. As a result, it only makes sense for an Incident Commander to expend effort stabilizing the incident. Preventing further injuries—either of patients or rescue personnel—helps to ensure a smoother and more successful management of a MCI.

Property Conservation
At no time during an operation should rescue personnel damage property unless it is absolutely necessary for achieving the first two priorities—life safety and incident stabilization. Property conservation includes protection of the environment where operations are staged.

8. **Define the terms *multiple casualty incident (MCI), disaster management, open* or *uncontained incident,* and *closed* or *contained incident.*** pp. 348, 353, 371

- **Multiple casualty incident (MCI)**—incident that generates large numbers of patients and that often makes traditional EMS response ineffective because of special circumstances surrounding the event; also known as a mass casualty incident.
- **Disaster management**—management of incidents that generate large numbers of patients, often overwhelming resources and damaging parts of the infrastructure.
- **Open (uncontained) incident**—an incident that has the potential to generate additional patients; also known as an unstable incident.
- **Closed (contained) incident**—an incident that is not likely to generate any further patients; also known as a stable incident.

9. **Describe the role of the paramedics and EMS system in planning for MCIs and disasters.** pp. 349–351, 361, 371

The first step you can take in planning for MCIs and disasters is to familiarize yourself with the various laws, regulations, protocols, and standards that apply to EMS operations at a MCI. In the aftermath of September 11, 2001, the federal government is moving to assure that incident

©2006 Pearson Education, Inc.
Paramedic Care: Principles & Practice, Vol. 5

management is uniform throughout the country. Research the current NICS standards and assure your EMS policies and protocols conform.

With this information in mind, you can more effectively take part in developing a plan before a MCI or disaster actually occurs. Conduct a hazard analysis and then rate these hazards according to their likelihood. Anticipate any problems that could occur and work toward removing them. Anything that can be planned in advance should be planned in advance.

Once you have assessed potential hazards and any complicating problems, your agency should develop a plan that outlines the SOPs and protocols for the incidents that you have identified. Develop contingency plans for worst-case scenarios. Then, after you have completed your preplan, test it. Make sure that all personnel who could show up at any MCI or disaster are familiar with the preplan and, if possible, take part in practice drills. Start out small. Use local drills within your department to help familiarize personnel with the system. Then, aim for large-scale drills that involve outside agencies.

10. Explain the local/regional threshold for establishing command and implementation of the Incident Management System including MCI declaration. pp. 348–349, 352

The threshold for establishing command and implementation of the IMS may differ from agency to agency, depending on the resources available at any given time. An example, as taken from the sample Incident Tactical Worksheet in Figure 9–5 of the textbook, would be as follows:

Level 1: 3 to 10 patients
Level 2: 11 to 25 patients
Level 3: over 25 patients

11. Describe the role of both Command Posts and Emergency Operations Centers in MCI and disaster management. pp. 351, 352–353, 356–357, 371

A Command Post (CP) provides a place where representatives and officers from various agencies can meet with each other and make relevant decisions. Because a Command Post may operate for weeks, the site should be selected carefully. Access to telephones, restrooms, and shelters should be taken into account. Also, the Command Post should be close enough to the scene so that officers can monitor operations, but far enough away so that they are outside the direct operational area. Persons operating on the scene, members of the media, and bystanders should not have routine access to the CP.

The Emergency Operations Center (EOC) is where governmental officials (municipal, county, state, and/or federal) exercise oversight of a large emergency or disaster. It is often a predesignated secure site with communications capability and informational resources to permit remote tracking, resource management, and control of the incident and the response.

12. Describe the role of the on-scene physician at multiple casualty incidents. p. 368

At some high-impact or long-term incidents, physicians may be used outside the hospital to support EMS. Physicians may use their advanced medical knowledge and skills in several ways at a MCI. For example, they may be better able to make difficult triage decisions, perform advanced triage and treatment in the treatment area, or perform emergency surgery to extricate a patient as a last resort. Physicians also provide direct supervision and medical direction over paramedics in the treatment area, removing the need to operate under standing orders or radio contact. A contingency plan should be established outlining when and how physicians respond to and operate at a MCI.

13. Define triage and describe the principles of triage. pp. 362–366

Triage is the act of sorting patients based upon the severity of their injuries. The objective of emergency medical services at a MCI is to do the most good for the most people. For this reason, you need to determine which patients need immediate care to live, which patients will live despite delays in care, and which patients will die despite receiving medical attention. Because triage will drive the EMS response, it is one of the first functions provided at the MCI.

14. Describe the START (simple triage and rapid transport) method of initial triage. pp. 363–365

The most widely used triage system is START, an acronym standing for simple triage and rapid transport. START's easy-to-use procedures allow for rapid sorting of patients into the categories in objective 15. START does not require a specific diagnosis on the part of the responder. Instead it focuses on four criteria:

Ability to walk
    Able to walk—minimal (green)
Respiratory effort (if not able to walk)
    Not breathing with airway positioning—expectant—(black)
    Breathe once airway is positioned—immediate—(red)
    Spontaneous respirations > 30/minute—immediate—(red)
Pulses/perfusion (if breathing is spontaneous and < 30/minute)
    Absent radial pulse—immediate—(red)
Neurological status (if radial pulse is present)
    On command, grips both your hands—delayed—(yellow)
    On command does not grip both your hands—immediate—(red)

15. Given color-coded tags and numerical priorities, assign the following terms to each:
a. Immediate Patients in need of immediate treatment receive a red tag, indicating Priority–1 (P–1). **b. Delayed** Patients whose treatment can be delayed (i.e., they do not have an immediately life-threatening injury or condition) receive a yellow tag, indicating Priority–2 (P–2).
c. Minimal Patients who do not exhibit the signs and symptoms of START can have treatment withheld, even if they are injured, until a later time. They receive a green tag, indicating Priority–3 (P–3). **d. Expectant** Patients who have mortal injuries or have died receive a black tag, indicating Priority–0 (P–0). p. 363

16. Define primary, secondary, and ongoing triage and their implimentation techniques. pp. 363–366

- **Primary triage**—the initial and immediate evaluation of a patient (using the START system) at a MCI.
- **Secondary triage**—a more in-depth and ongoing triage of the patient during the MCI. Also called ongoing triage.

17. Describe techniques used to allocate patients to hospitals and track them. pp. 368–369

The Transportation Unit Supervisor is responsible for assessing the ability of local health care facilities (hospitals and other facilities) to care for the injured. He or she then identifies patient injury severity and special needs (such as burn care) and then distributes patients to assure an appropriate distribution of patients to the health care facilities available.

18. Describe the techniques used in tracking patients during multiple casualty incidents and the need for such techniques. pp. 365–366, 368–369

Triage helps the Transportation Unit Supervisor to assign priorities for transport and to determine the types of treatment facilities to which patients should be sent. As you might suspect, the Transportation Supervisor needs to implement some type of tracking system or designation log. Ideally, the tracking sheet or log should include the following data:

- Triage tag number
- Triage priority
- Patient's age, gender, and major injuries
- Transporting unit
- Hospital destination

- Departure time
- Patient's name, if possible

The tracking sheet not only helps to organize activities at a MCI but it also proves invaluable in reconstructing the incident at a later time. In addition, this record will help document on-scene patient care.

19. Describe modification of telecommunications procedures during multiple casualty incidents. pp. 355, 370

Modified Telecommunications

Communication forms the cornerstone of the Incident Management System. Once command is established, the Incident Commander has a responsibility to relay this information to dispatch. After a MCI has been declared, further communication should be moved to a secondary, or tactical, channel. The Incident Commander must be able to supply the information necessary to coordinate resources. That is the whole purpose of the Incident Management System. Use of a secondary channel will also prevent an Incident Commander from interfacing with the communications by other jurisdictions or from overwhelming the primary EMS channel.

When acting as an Incident Commander, remember that communication will involve units from different jurisdictions and perhaps different districts. One of the foundations of incident management is the use of a common terminology. When communicating, you should eliminate all radio codes and use only plain English. A radio code may have different meanings in different places. As an Incident Commander, you must eliminate any unnecessary confusion in an already complicated situation. In fact, it may be preferable to avoid radio codes even in routine operations. Then there will be no need to even think about switching to plain English when you assume command of a MCI.

Alternative Means of Communication

Also keep in mind the possibility of communications failure. Things can—and do—go wrong. Your primary radio system might not always work at a MCI. Disasters can knock out radio towers and power. Frequencies can be overwhelmed. Telephone lines can be down. Radio batteries can fail. As a result, alternative means of communication should be included in every MCI preplan and should be practiced regularly. You might use cellular phones, mobile data terminals, alphanumeric pages, fax machines, or other technology to overcome the failure of your primary radio system. When all else fails, runners can be used to hand deliver messages around the incident scene. Although there are obvious limitations, it may be your last resort. So know how to use it.

20. List and describe the essential equipment to provide logistical support to MCI operations to include: p. 367

The treatment Sector(s) of a MCI often requires large quantities of basic EMS equipment. Such equipment may be stored in a trailer for quick movement to the scene and includes materials for:

a. **Airway, respiratory, and hemorrhage control**
Oxygen masks and additional oxygen cylinders and regulator/flow-meters, oral and nasal airways, bag-valve-masks, and dressing and bandage materials.

b. **Burn management**
Clean burn sheets and dressings and intravenous fluids.

c. **Patient packaging/immobilization**
Short and long spine boards, cervical collars, cravats, padded board and air splints, and straps.

21. Describe the role of mental health support in MCIs. pp. 359–360, 369–370, 373

Research has begun to demonstrate that critical incident stress debriefing has not had the intended effect on rescuers that was once thought. In fact, it may actually be detrimental. However, there is an important role for mental health personnel to provide psychological first aid to those affected by an event.

22. **Describe the role of the following exercises in preparation for MCIs:**　　pp. 372–373

   a. **Tabletop exercises**

   For any MCI preplan to be effective, it must be tested and practiced. Tabletop drills are a good place to begin. Once you have worked out the wrinkles, distribute the plan to everyone in your department, the surrounding departments, local police, fire departments, hospitals—in short, to anyone who could be involved in the IMS in your area.

   b. **Small and large MCI drills**

   The next step is to make sure that all the personnel who could show up at a MCI have received training in the use of the IMS. Run or take part in drills so that you gain practice in MCI operations and large-scale use of the IMS. Start out small. Use local drills within your department and then plan large-scale, multiagency drills. Never say "It will never happen here." Experience has proven time and again that multicasualty incidents and disasters can occur almost anywhere and at any time.

23. **Given several incident scenarios with preprogrammed patients, provide the appropriate triage, treatment, and transport options for MCI operations based on local resources and protocols.**　　pp. 348–373

   During your classroom, clinical, and field training, you will have the opportunity to practice the skills required for the various roles and Sectors at a MCI. Use the information presented in this text chapter, the information on MCIs presented by your instructors, and the guidance given by your clinical and field preceptors to develop skills needed to implement the Incident Management System in the unit where you serve. Continue to refine these skills once your training ends and you begin your career as a paramedic.

Case Study Review

Reread the case study on pages 346 and 347 in Paramedic Care: Special Considerations/Operations *and then read the following discussion.*

   This case study shows how, when used properly, the IMS enables EMS units to handle a multipatient incident without unreasonably compromising response time on other calls within the system.

In this case, the first arriving ambulance crew locked their unit and defined their individual responsibilities as Incident Commander and Triage Officer. While the Triage Officer counted and tagged patients using the START system, the IC surveyed the scene for potential rescue problems, scene hazards, resource needs, and staging areas for arriving vehicles. After the Triage Officer reported the patient count, the IC called the dispatch center, relaying pertinent information and declaring a MCI. The call immediately activated the regional MCI plan, proving the importance of having a plan in the first place.

   Upon arrival of the Field Supervisor, command was transferred in a face-to-face fashion. The new IC then began setting up the various functional components required to manage the event.

   Although not every community can muster 20 ambulances quickly, EMS units can still implement an IMS. Again preplanning is the key. Mutual aid agreements or broader regional plans should be in place in anticipation of worst-case scenarios. If the necessary ambulances are not readily available, operations will expand their activities in the Treatment Sector, while the Transportation Officer carefully prioritizes the routing of patients based upon available resources.

   A few things that were not spelled out in the case should come to mind as you reread it. The Incident Commander should establish a location for a Command Post, if one is used, and mark it. Command vests are very helpful in identifying the Command Officers and should be used at the incident. Before establishing a staging area, command should talk with the police, especially when on a highway. The police will be responsible for traffic control as well as investigations and scene security. They will need to be involved in the plan to stage and move ambulances.

   Reread the final paragraph carefully. During this event, other calls were going on in the district, including another small MCI. This underscores the need for major incidents to be handled on a separate tactical communications channel—TAC-1. Because of the smooth operation of the IMS, patient care was not at any time compromised—fulfilling the rationale behind adhering to a standardized IMS plan.

Content Self-Evaluation

MULTIPLE CHOICE

_____ 1. An emergency event that involves more patients than paramedics to provide care or ambulances to transport may be called a(n):
   A. disaster.
   B. critical incident.
   C. multiple casualty incident.
   D. mutual aid situation.
   E. command situation

_____ 2. Standards being merged into a Uniform Command system for use at MCIs is being developed by:
   A. the Department of Homeland Security.
   B. the Environmental Protection Agency.
   C. OSHA.
   D. the National Fire Protection Association.
   E. Firescope.

_____ 3. The most important functional area in the Incident Management System is:
   A. logistics.
   B. planning.
   C. command.
   D. triage.
   E. operations.

_____ 4. On average the span of control at a MCI is around:
   A. 5.
   B. 10.
   C. 15.
   D. 20.
   E. 25.

_____ 5. Singular Command, in many incidents, is not feasible because of overlapping responsibilities or jurisdictions.
   A. True
   B. False

_____ 6. A place where officers from various agencies can meet with each other and select a Management Staff is called a(n):
   A. Command Post.
   B. coordination post.
   C. incident post.
   D. Incident Management System.
   E. direct operational area.

_____ 7. At a MCI, the needs of the many usually outweigh the needs of the few.
   A. True
   B. False

_____ 8. An incident that has the potential to generate additional patients is known as a(n):
   A. open incident.
   B. MCI.
   C. closed incident.
   D. ICS.
   E. contained incident.

_____ 9. The cornerstone of the Incident Command System (ICS) is:
   A. leadership.
   B. utilizing Singular Command.
   C. having enough resources.
   D. practice and drilling.
   E. communication.

_____ 10. The primary role of the Incident Commander is:
   A. recognizing Unified Command.
   B. identifying a staging area.
   C. using common terminology.
   D. the strategic deployment of all resources.
   E. directing the efficient movement of patients to the ED.

_____ 11. To ensure flexibility, an Incident Commander should radio a brief progress report every 10 minutes until the event has been stabilized.
   A. True   B. False

_____ 12. Before command can be transferred to another leader, it is necessary to report:
   A. face-to-face.
   B. via radio.
   C. in writing at the Command Post.
   D. via an indirect contact.
   E. none of the above—a higher-ranking officer automatically takes command upon arrival.

_____ 13. The management, or command, staff handles all of the following EXCEPT:
   A. public information.   D. outside liaisons.
   B. safety.   E. mental health support services.
   C. triage.

_____ 14. Under the Incident Management System, the Safety Officer has the authority to stop any action that is deemed as life threatening.
   A. True   B. False

_____ 15. The person or group responsible for fulfilling the Medical Supply Unit is the:
   A. Facilities Unit.   D. Logistics Sector.
   B. Liaison Officer.   E. Planning Officer.
   C. Finance/Administration Sector.

_____ 16. Which of the following is the most task-specific section at a MCI?
   A. Branch   D. unit
   B. Group   E. Sector
   C. Division

_____ 17. The term _Sector_ is interchangeable for a functional or geographical area.
   A. True   B. False

_____ 18. Triage that takes place after patients are moved to a treatment area to determine any changes in their status is referred to as:
   A. secondary triage.   D. delayed triage.
   B. supplemental triage.   E. primary triage.
   C. sector triage.

_____ 19. Under the START system, a Triage Officer would focus on all of the following signs and symptoms EXCEPT:
   A. ability to walk.   D. ability to talk.
   B. respiration.   E. neurological status.
   C. pulses/perfusion.

_____ 20. Patients with absent radial pulses should be tagged:
   A. red.   D. white.
   B. yellow.   E. black.
   C. green.

_____ **21.** Color-coded tags that are placed on patients that have been sorted serve to:
   A. track the patient.
   B. prevent retriage of the patient.
   C. alert care providers to patient priorities.
   D. record treatment information.
   E. all of the above.

_____ **22.** One efficient way to speed up the triage process is to:
   A. add extra personnel to triage.
   B. not use triage tags.
   C. skip the primary triage.
   D. not triage the walking wounded.
   E. ask the IC to assist in triage.

_____ **23.** An ambulance crew who is dedicated to stand by in case a rescuer becomes ill or injured is called a _____ Team.
   A. Rescue Response   **D.** Rapid Intervention
   B. Rehabilitation   **E.** TIP
   C. Extrication

_____ **24.** As a general rule, disaster management occurs in which four stages?
   A. mitigation, planning, response, recovery
   B. request, response, react, recover
   C. mitigation, react, recovery, recall
   D. activation, planning, mitigation, recall
   E. planning, response, react, reassess

_____ **25.** Mental health personnel should circulate around the scene of a high-impact incident to help meet the emotional needs of those affected by the incident.
   A. True   **B.** False

MATCHING

Write the letter of the term in the space provided next to the appropriate description.

A. Public Information Officer   **F.** scene-authority law

B. closed incident   **G.** demobilized

C. planning   **H.** span of control

D. C-FLOP   **I.** Liaison Officer

E. Command Post   **J.** Staff Functions

_____ **26.** mnemonic for the main functional areas within the NIMS

_____ **27.** supervisory roles in the NIMS

_____ **28.** coordinates all incident operations that involve outside agencies

_____ **29.** the number of people a single individual can monitor

_____ **30.** collects data about the incident and releases it to the media

_____ **31.** an incident that is not likely to generate additional patients

_____ **32.** release of resources no longer needed at an incident

_____ **33.** provides past, present, and future information about the incident

_____ **34.** state or local statute specifying who has authority at a MCI

_____ **35.** place where command officers from various agencies can meet

SHORT ANSWER

Write out the terms that each of the following acronyms stands for in the spaces provided.

36. MCI _____

37. C-FLOP _____

38. EOC _____

39. IMS _____

40. START _____

Special Project

Using the EMS response units in your community, design a preplan and the administrative flowchart for a Level 1, Level 2, and Level 3 incident. If the levels have not been described in your local MCI plan, use the following patient counts:

Level 1: 3 to 10 patients
Level 2: 11 to 25 patients
Level 3: over 25 patients

Be sure to consider normal coverage of calls in your community as well as the need for mutual aid, if necessary.

10 Rescue Awareness and Operations

Review of Chapter Objectives

After reading this chapter, you should be able to:

1. Define the term rescue, and explain the medical and mechanical aspects of rescue operations.   pp. 381–382

According to the dictionary, rescue is "the act of delivering from danger or imprisonment." In the case of EMS, rescue means extricating and/or disentangling the victims who will become your patients.

Rescue involves a combination of medical and mechanical skills with the correct amount of each applied at the appropriate time. The medical aspects of rescue involve assessment and treatment of the patient. Mechanical aspects involve the tools and skills to disentangle the victim.

2. Describe the phases of a rescue operation and the role of the paramedic at each phase.   pp. 388–395

There are basically seven phases in a rescue operation. They include:

Arrival and size-up. Key to the success of any rescue operation is the prompt recognition of a rescue situation and the quick identification of the specific type of rescue required. You can then quickly notify dispatch of the magnitude of the event and summon the necessary resources. Now is the time to implement the IMS, any mutual-aid agreements, and the procedures for contacting off-duty personnel or backup ALS units. In calling for support, follow this precaution: "Don't undersell overkill."

Hazard control. On-scene hazards must be identified with speed and clarity. You must often deal with these hazards before even attempting to reach the patient. To do otherwise would place you and other personnel at risk. Control as many of the hazards as possible, but don't attempt to manage any conditions beyond your training or skills. Individual acts of courage may be called for, but safety comes first. If in doubt, err on the side of safety.

Patient access. After controlling hazards, you will then attempt to gain access to the patient or patients. Begin by formulating a plan. Determine the best method to gain access and deploy the necessary personnel. Make sure that you take steps to stabilize the physical location of the patient.

As you know, access triggers the technical beginning of the rescue. While gaining access, you must use appropriate safety equipment and procedures. This is the point when you and/or the Command and Safety Officer must honestly evaluate the training and skills needed to access the patient. During this phase, key medical, technical, and command personnel must confer with the Safety Officer on the strategy they will use to accomplish the rescue.

Medical treatment. After devising a rescue plan, medical personnel can begin to make patient contact. No personnel should enter an area to provide patient care unless they are physically fit, protected from hazards, and have the technical skills to reach, manage, and remove patients safely. In general, a paramedic has three responsibilities during this phase of operation. They are:

- Initiation of patient assessment and care as soon as possible
- Maintenance of patient care procedures during disentanglement
- Accompaniment of the patient during removal and transport

See pages 390–393 of the textbook for more details on the decisions involved in this all-important phase and for the guidelines to implement these decisions.

Disentanglement. Disentanglement involves the actual release from the cause of entrapment. This phase may be the most technical and time-consuming portion of the rescue. If assigned to patient care during this phase of the rescue, you have three responsibilities. They are:

- Personal and professional confidence in the technical expertise and gear needed to function effectively in the active rescue zone
- Readiness to provide prolonged patient care
- Ability to call for and/or use special rescue resources

If you or another member of the rescue team cannot fulfill these requirements, reassess available rescue personnel and call for backup.

Patient packaging. After disentanglement, a patient must be appropriately packaged to ensure that all medical needs are addressed. Some forms of packaging can be more complex than others, depending upon the specialized rescue techniques required to extricate the patient—for example, being lifted out of a hole in a Stokes basket by a ladder truck. In situations where the patient may be vertical or suspended in a Stokes basket, it is paramount that the rescuer know how to properly package the patient to prevent additional injury.

Removal/transport. Removal of the patient may be one of the most difficult tasks to accomplish or it may be as easy as placing the person on a stretcher and wheeling it to a nearby ambulance. Activities involved in the removal of a patient will require the coordinated effort of all personnel. Transportation to a medical facility should be planned well in advance, especially if you anticipate any delays. Decisions regarding patient transport—whether it be by ground vehicle, by aircraft, or by physical carry-out—should be coordinated based on advice from medical direction. En route to the hospital, perform the ongoing assessment and treatment per the patient's condition.

3. **List and describe the personal protective equipment needed to safely operate in the rescue environment, to include:**

   a. **Head, eye, and hand protection** p. 383

   Head. To protect the head, every unit should carry helmets, preferably ones with a four-point, nonelastic suspension system. A compact firefighting helmet that meets NFPA standards is adequate for most vehicle and structural applications. However, climbing helmets may work better for confined space and technical rescues, while padded rafting or kayaking helmets are more appropriate for water rescues.

   Eye. Two essential pieces of eye gear include goggles, vented to prevent fogging, and industrial safety glasses. These should be ANSI approved. Do not rely on the face shields found in fire helmets. They usually provide inadequate eye protection.

   Hand. Leather gloves usually protect against cuts and punctures. They allow free movement of the fingers and ample dexterity. As a rule, heavy gauntlet-style gloves are too awkward for most rescue work.

   b. **Personal flotation devices** p. 385

   All PFDs should meet the U.S. Coast Guard standards for flotation and should be worn whenever operating on or around water. The Type III PFD is preferred for rescue work. You should also attach a knife, strobe light, and whistle to the PFD so that they can be easily accessed.

   c. **Thermal protection/layering systems** p. 384

   Appropriate clothing and gear should be worn for both flame/flash protection and insulation against extreme cold. Turnout gear, coveralls, or jumpsuits all offer some arm and leg protection. However, for limited flame protection, select gear made from Nomex, PBI, or flame-retardant cotton. For protection in cold or wet situations, such as remote wilderness areas, layer your clothing. Avoid cotton and choose synthetic materials that wipe away moisture. Outer layers should be made from water- and wind-resistant fabrics such as Gore-Tex or nylon. Although insulated gear or jumpsuits are helpful in cold environments, they can also increase heat stress during heavy work or in high ambient temperatures.

d. High-visibility clothing p. 383

For high visibility, pick bright colors such as orange or lime and reflective trim or symbols. Some services, for example, have an SOP calling for highly visible gear and/or orange safety vests at all highway operations—both day and night.

4. Explain the risks and complications associated with rescues involving moving water, low head dams, flat water, trenches, motor vehicles, and confined spaces. pp. 397–411

Moving water. The force of moving water can be very deceptive. The hydraulics of moving water change with a number of variables, including water depth, velocity, obstructions to flow, changing tides, and more. Four swift-water rescue scenarios present a special challenge and danger to rescuers. They include:

- **Recirculating currents**—movement of currents over a uniform obstruction; also known as a "drowning machine"
- **Strainers**—a partial obstruction that filters, or strains, the water, such as downed trees or wire mesh; causes an unequal force on two sides
- **Pins**—entrapped foot or extremity that exposes a person to the force and weight of moving water
- **Low head dams/hydroelectric intakes**—structures that create the risk of recirculating currents (dams) and strainers (hydroelectric intakes)

Flat water. The greatest problem with flat water is that it looks so calm. Yet a large proportion of drowning or near-drowning incidents take place in flat or slow-moving water. Entry into the water exposes the rescuer to some of the same risks as the patient, such as hypothermia, exhaustion, and so on. Remember: REACH-THROW-ROW-GO, with "go" being absolutely the last resort.

Trenches. If a collapse has caused burial, a secondary collapse is likely. Therefore, your initial actions should be geared toward safety. While waiting for a rescue team to arrive, do not allow entry in the area surrounding the trench or cave-in. Safe access can take place only when proper shoring is in place.

Motor vehicles. Traffic flow is the largest single hazard associated with EMS highway operations. Studies have shown that drivers who are tired, drunk, or drugged actually drive right into the emergency lights. Spectators can worsen the situation by getting out of their cars to watch or even "help." Other hazards besides traffic flow include:

- fire and fuel
- alternative fuel systems
- sharp objects
- electric power (downed lines or underground feeds)
- energy-absorbing bumpers
- supplemental restraint systems
- hazardous cargoes
- rolling vehicles
- unstable vehicles

Confined spaces. Confined spaces present a wide range of risks. Some of the most common ones include:

- oxygen-deficient atmospheres
- toxic or explosive chemicals
- engulfment
- machinery entrapment
- electricity
- structural complications

5. **Explain the effects of immersion hypothermia on the ability to survive sudden immersion and self rescue.** pp. 397–411

Immersion can rapidly lead to hypothermia. As a rule, people cannot maintain body heat in water that is less than 92° F. The colder the water, the faster the loss of heat. In fact, water causes heat loss 25 times faster than the air. Immersion in 35° F water for 15 to 20 minutes is likely to kill a person. Factors contributing to the demise of a hypothermic patient include:

- Incapacitation and an inability to self-rescue
- Inability to follow simple directions
- Inability to grasp a line or flotation device
- Laryngospasm (caused by sudden immersion) and greater likelihood of drowning

6. **Explain the benefits and disadvantages of water-entry or "go" techniques versus the reach-throw-row-go approach to water rescue.** p. 397

The water rescue model is REACH-THROW-ROW-GO. All paramedics should be trained in reach-and-throw techniques. You should become proficient with a water-throw bag for shore-based operations. Remember: Boat-based techniques require specialized rescue training. Water entry ("go") is only the last resort—and is an action best left to specialized water rescuers. In all instances, a PFD should be worn in case you or another rescuer are pulled into the water, accidentally slip, and so on.

7. **Explain the self-rescue position if unexpectedly immersed in moving water.** p. 397

If people suddenly become submerged, they can assume the Heat Escape Lessening Position (HELP). This position involves floating with the head out of the water and the body in a fetal tuck. Researchers estimate that someone who has practiced with HELP can reduce heat loss by almost 60 percent, as compared to the heat expended when treading water.

8. **Describe the use of apparatus placement, headlights and emergency vehicle lighting, cones and flare placement, and reflective and high-visibility clothing to reduce scene risk at highway incidents.** p. 409

Apparatus placement. When apparatus arrives, ensure that it causes the minimum reduction of traffic flow. As much as possible, apparatus should be positioned to protect the scene. The ambulance loading area should NOT be directly exposed to traffic.
Headlights and emergency vehicle lighting. DO NOT rely solely on ambulance lights to warn traffic away. These lights are often obstructed when medics open the doors for loading. When deciding upon emergency lighting, use only a minimum amount of warning lights to alert traffic of a hazard and to define the actual size of your vehicle. Too many lights can confuse or blind drivers, causing yet other accidents. Experts strongly advise that you turn off all headlights when parked at the scene and rely instead on amber scene lighting.
Cones and flare placement. Be sure traffic cones and flares are placed early in the incident. If the police are not already on scene, this is your responsibility. As a first responder, you must redirect traffic away from the collision and away from all emergency workers. In other words, you need to create a safety zone. Make sure that you do not place lighted flares too near any sources of fuel or brush; otherwise you risk an explosion or fire. Once you light the flares, allow them to burn out. DO NOT try to extinguish them. Attempting to pick up a flare can cause a very serious thermal burn.
Reflective and high-visibility clothing. As noted in objective 3, all rescuers should be dressed in highly visible clothing. Since many EMS, police, and fire agencies wear dark-colored uniforms, you should don a brightly colored turnout coat or vest with reflective tape. You can directly apply the tape at the scene.

9. **List and describe the design element hazards and associated protective actions associated with autos and trucks, including energy-absorbing bumpers, air bag/supplemental restraint systems, catalytic converters, and conventional and nonconventional fuel systems.** pp. 409–411

Energy-absorbing bumpers. The bumpers on many vehicles come with pistons and are designed to withstand a slow-speed collision. Sometimes these bumpers become "loaded" in the crushed position and do not immediately bounce back out. When exposed to fire or even just tapped by rescue workers, the pistons can suddenly unload their stored energy. If you discover a loaded bumper, stay away from it unless you are specially trained to deal with this hazard.

Air bag/supplemental restraint systems. Air bags also have the potential to release stored energy. If they have not been deployed during the collision, they may do so during the middle of an extrication. As a result, these devices must be deactivated prior to disentanglement. Auto manufacturers can provide information about power removal or power dissipation for their particular brand of SRS. Also, keep in mind that many new model vehicles come equipped with side impact bags.

Catalytic converters. Remember that all automobiles manufactured since the 1970s have catalytic converters. They run at a temperature of around 1,200° F—hot enough to heat fuel to the point of ignition. Be especially careful when a vehicle has gone off the road into dry grass or brush. The debris can be just as dangerous as spilled fuel, especially when brought into contact with a blazing hot catalytic converter.

Conventional fuel systems. Fuel spilled at the scene increases the changes of fire. Be very careful whenever you smell or see pools of liquid at a collision. Keep in mind that bystanders who are smoking can cause a bigger problem than the original accident if they flick lighted ashes into a fuel leak. DO NOT drive your emergency vehicle over a fuel spill—or worse yet, park on one!

Nonconventional fuel systems. Be cautious of vehicles powered by alternative fuel systems. High-pressure tanks, especially if filled with natural gas, are extremely volatile. Even vehicles powered by electricity can be dangerous. The storage cells possess the energy to spark, flash, and more.

10. **Given a diagram of a passenger auto, identify the A, B, C, and D posts, firewall, and unibody versus frame construction.** pp. 411–412

Basic vehicle constructions

Vehicles can have either a unibody or a frame construction. Most automobiles today have a unibody design, while older vehicles and lightweight trucks have a frame construction. For unibody vehicles to maintain their integrity, all the following features must remain intact: roof posts, floor, firewall, truck support, and windshield.

Both types of construction have roofs and roof supports. The support posts are lettered from front to back. The first post, which supports the roof at the windshield, is called the "A" post. The next post is the "B" post. The third post, found in sedans and station wagons, is the "C" post. Station wagons have an additional rear post, known as the "D" post.

Firewalls

The firewall separates the engine compartment from the occupant compartment. Frequently, the firewall can collapse on a patient's legs during a high-speed, head-on collision. Sometimes, a patient's feet may go through the firewall.

11. **Explain the difference between tempered and safety glass, identify its locations on a vehicle, and describe how to break it.** pp. 411–412

Safety Glass

Safety glass is made from three layers of fused materials: glass–plastic laminate–glass. It is found in windshields and designed to stay intact when shattered or broken. However, safety glass can still produce glass dust or fracture into long shards. These materials can easily get into a patient's eyes, nose, or mouth and/or create cuts. As a result, be sure to cover a patient whenever you remove this type of glass. Safety glass is usually cut out with a GlasMaster saw or a flat-head axe.

Tempered Glass

Tempered glass has high tensile strength. However, it does not stay intact when shattered or broken. It fractures into many small beads of glass, all of which can cause injuries or cuts. Tempered glass is usually broken using a spring-loaded center punch.

12. Explain typical door anatomy and methods to access through stuck doors. p. 412

The doors of most new vehicles contain a reinforcing bar to protect the occupant in side-impact collisions. They also have a case-hardened steel "Nader" pin. Named after consumer advocate Ralph Nader, these pins help keep the doors from blowing open and ejecting the occupants. If the Nader pin has been engaged, it will be difficult to pry open the door. You must first disentangle the latch or use hydraulic jaws.

Before attempting to assist a patient through a door, you should be trained in proper extrication techniques. In general, follow these steps:

- Try all four doors first—a door is the easiest means of access.
- Otherwise, gain access through the window farthest away from the patient(s).
- Alternatively, use simple hand tools to peel back the outer sheet of metal on the door, exposing the lock mechanism. Unlock the lock and pry the cams from the Nader pin. Then pry open the door.

13. Describe methods for emergency stabilization using rope, cribbing, jacks, spare tires, and come-alongs for vehicles found in various positions. pp. 413–414

Motor vehicles can land in all kinds of unstable positions. They can roll over onto their side or roof. They can stop on an incline or unstable terrain. They can be suspended over a cliff or a river. They can come to rest on a patch of ice or on an on-site spill or leak.

As a result, vehicles must be stabilized before accessing the patient. Sometimes vehicle stabilization can be as simple as making sure the vehicle is in "Park" and chocking the wheels so it will not roll. Other times, such as in the case of an overturned vehicle, you might need to use ropes, cribbing, jacks, or even a spare tire to help prevent it from rolling over. If a vehicle is hanging over an embankment, you might use a combination of cribbing and a come-along tied onto the guard rail (if one is present). However, only attempt these techniques if you have the skills to do so. Otherwise, you need to request the necessary stabilization crews and/or equipment. (For more on vehicle stabilization equipment, see Table 10-1 on page 413 of the text.)

14. Describe electrical and other hazards commonly found at highway incidents (above and below the ground). pp. 409–411

Contact with downed power lines or underground electrical feeds can be lethal. If a vehicle is in contact with electrical lines, consider it to be "charged" and call the power company immediately. In most newer communities, electric lines run underground. However, a vehicle can still run into a transformer or an electric feed box. As a result, make sure you look under the car and all around it during your scene size-up. DO NOT touch a vehicle until you have ruled out all electrical hazards. (Other hazards commonly found at highway incidents are listed/discussed in objectives 4 and 9.)

15. Define low-angle rescue, high-angle rescue, belay, rappel, scrambling, and hasty rope slide. pp. 414–416

- **Low-angle rescue**—rescues up to 40° over faces that are not excessively smooth; requires rope, harnesses, hardware, and the necessary safety systems
- **High-angle rescue**—rescues involving ropes, harnesses, and specialized equipment to ascend and descend a steep and/or smooth face; also known as "vertical" rescue

- **Belay**—procedure for safeguarding a climber's progress by controlling a rope attached to an anchor; person controlling the rope is sometimes also called the belay
- **Rappel**—to descend by sliding down a fixed double rope, using the correct anchor, harness, and gear
- **Scrambling**—climbing over rocks and/or downed trees on a steep trail without the aid of ropes
- **Hasty rope slide**—using a rope to assist in balance and footing on rough terrain; rescuers do not actually "clip into" the rope as they do in low-angle and high-angle rescues

16. Describe the procedure for Stokes litter packaging for low-angle evacuations.   pp. 416–417

A Stokes litter is the standard stretcher for rough terrain evacuation. It provides a rigid frame for patient protection and is easy to carry with an adequate number of personnel. When using a Stokes litter (also called a Stokes basket stretcher) for high-angle or low-angle evacuation, take the following steps:

- Apply a harness to the patient.
- Apply leg stirrups to the patient.
- Secure the patient to a litter to prevent movement.
- Tie the tail of one litter line to the patient's harness.
- Use a helmet or litter shield to protect the patient.
- Administer fluids (IV or orally).
- Allow accessibility for taking BP, performing suction, and assessing distal perfusion.
- Apply extra strapping or lacing as necessary (for rough terrain evacuation and/or extrication).

17. Explain anchoring, litter/rope attachment, and lowering and raising procedures as they apply to low-angle litter evacuation.   pp. 415–416, 418

Before beginning patient removal, rescuers must ensure that all anchors are secure. They must check their own safety equipment and recheck patient packaging. They must also have the necessary lowering and hauling systems in place, again doing the recommended safety checks.

Materials, especially ropes, should never be used if there is any question of their safety. If you see a frayed rope or any stressed or damaged equipment, do not hesitate to point it out to the rescuers in a polite, but professional manner. Also, because hauling sometimes requires many "helpers," you may be asked to assist. Make sure you understand all directions given by the rescuers. Evacuation is a team effort.

18. Explain techniques used in nontechnical litter carries over rough terrain.   p. 417

When removing a patient in a nontechnical litter over flat, rough terrain, make sure you have enough litter carriers to "leapfrog" ahead of each other to save time and to rotate rescuers. An adequate number of litter bearers would be two or, better yet, three teams of six. Litter bearers on each carry should be approximately the same height.

Several devices exist to ease the difficulty of a litter carry. For example, litter bearers can run webbing straps over the litter rails, across their shoulders, and into their free hands. This will help distribute the weight across the bearers' backs. Another helpful device is the litter wheel. It attaches to the bottom of a Stokes basket frame and takes most of the weight of the litter. Bearers must keep the litter balanced and control its motion. As you might suspect, the litter wheel works best across flatter terrain.

19. Explain nontechnical high-angle rescue procedures using aerial apparatus.   p. 418

When using aerial apparatus, it is necessary to provide a litter belay during movement to a bucket. Litters, of course, must then be correctly attached to the bucket. Use of aerial ladders can be difficult because upper sections are usually not wide enough to slot the litter. The litter must always be properly belayed if being slid down the ladder. Finally, ladders or other aerial apparatus should NOT be used as a crane to move a litter. They are neither designed nor rated for this work. Serious stress can cause accidents resulting in patient death.

20. **Explain assessment and care modifications (including pain medication, temperature control, and hydration) necessary for attending entrapped patients.**   pp. 419–420

Protocols for extended care, which is often the case with entrapped patients, can vary substantially from standard EMS procedures. If SOPs for such situations do not already exist, procedures adopted from wilderness medical research will prove useful. Position papers written by the Wilderness Medical Society or the National Association for Search and Rescue can serve as guidelines for protocols.

   In most situations, you should prepare for long-term hydration management. You should also look for signs and symptoms of hypothermia, which is not uncommon for these patients. You may have to apply nonpharmacological pain management (distracting questions, proper splinting, use of sensory stimuli) when doing painful procedures. Alternatively, you may need to turn to pharmacological pain management—morphine or nitrous oxide—depending upon the patient's condition, the length of entrapment, and/or advice from medical direction.

21. **List the equipment necessary for an "off-road" medical pack.**   pp. 385–420

An off-road medical pack should contain at least the following items:

- **Airway**—oral and nasal airways, manual suction, intubation equipment
- **Breathing**—thoracic decompression equipment, small oxygen tank/regulator, masks/cannulas, pocket mask/BVM
- **Circulation**—bandages/dressings, triangular bandages, occlusive dressings, IV administration equipment, blood pressure cuff, and stethoscope
- **Disability**—extrication collars
- **Expose**—scissors
- **Miscellaneous**—headlamp/flashlight, space blanket, added aluminum splint (SAM splint), PPE (leather gloves, latex gloves, eye shields), provisions for drinking water, clothing for inclement weather, snacks for a few hours, temporary shelter, butane lighter, and some redundancy in lighting in case of light source failure

22. **Explain the different types of "Stokes" or basket stretchers and the advantages and disadvantages associated with each.**   pp. 416–417

Stokes baskets come in wire and tubular as well as plastic styles. The older "military style" wire mesh Stokes basket will not accept a backboard. Newer models, however, offer several advantages. They include:

- Generally greater strength
- Less expense per unit
- Better air/water flow through the basket
- Better flotation, an important concern in water rescues

   Plastic basket stretchers are usually weaker than their wire mesh counterparts. They are often rated for only 300 to 600 pounds. However, they tend to offer better patient protection. In general, Stokes baskets with plastic bottoms and steel frames are best. These versatile units can also be slid in snow, when necessary.

23. **Given a list of rescue scenarios, provide the victim survivability profile and identify which are rescue versus body recovery situations.**   pp. 381–420

During your classroom, clinical, and field training, you will be presented with a number of rescue scenarios in which you will be called upon to provide a victim survivability profile and to distinguish between rescue and body recovery situations. Use information presented in this text, the information on rescue operations presented by your instructors, and the guidance given by your clinical and field preceptors to develop a high level of rescue awareness and the skills needed to implement the various phases of a rescue operation. Continue to refine these skills once your training ends and you begin your career as a paramedic.

24. Given a series of pictures, identify those considered "confined spaces" and potentially oxygen deficient. pp. 404–408

Confined-space rescues present any number of potentially fatal threats, but one of the most serious is an oxygen-deficient environment. At first glance, most confined spaces might appear relatively safe. As a result, you might mistakenly think rescue procedures will be easier and/or less time consuming and dangerous than they really are. Here's where rescue awareness comes in. According to NIOSH, nearly 60 percent of all fatalities associated with confined spaces are people attempting to rescue a victim.

While "confined space" can have a variety of interpretations, OSHA regulation CFR 1910 interprets the term to mean any space with limited access/egress that is not designed for human occupancy or habitation. In other words, confined spaces are not safe for people to enter for any sustained period of time. Examples of confined spaces include transport or storage tanks, grain bins and silos, wells and cisterns, manholes and pumping stations, drainage culverts, pits, hoppers, underground vaults, and the shafts of mines or caves. (Pictures of some of these confined spaces appear on pages 405 and 407 of the text.)

Before going into a confined space, special entry teams monitor the atmosphere to determine oxygen concentration, levels of hydrogen sulfide, explosive limits, flammable atmosphere, or toxic contaminants. They are also aware that increases in oxygen content for any reason—for example, a gust of wind—can give atmospheric monitoring meters a false reading. The bottom line is this: Confined spaces often mean hazardous atmospheres.

Case Study Review

Reread the case study on pages 380 and 381 in Paramedic Care: Special Considerations/Operations *and then read the following discussion.*

The case study emphasizes the importance of rescue awareness and the cooperative effort that takes place between medical and technical crews.

It was critical that the rescue team immediately called for specialized resources, in this case a high-angle team and helicopter. As indicated, it takes time for these resources to arrive on-scene and, once there, even more time to reach and package the patient. It would have helped if more EMS teams had been sent in for backup. For example, additional personnel could have helped in carrying the Stokes litter to the helicopter. Even the short distance of 200 yards can be a difficult carry for two people.

Fortunately, the patient was removed before the storm hit. However, if the storm had come in faster, the helicopter might not have been able to make the call. In such an instance, many rescuers would have been required to access the patient, now exposed to severe environmental conditions. They also would have faced evacuation during a storm. Don't be surprised if a helicopter is not always able to respond to your call for assistance. Plan for the worst-case scenario. As stressed in this chapter, "Don't undersell overkill."

Content Self-Evaluation

Multiple Choice

_____ 1. As applied to rescue operations, awareness training involves a(n):
   A. command of the technical skills to execute a rescue.
   B. ability to recognize hazards.
   C. realization of the need for additional resources.
   D. detailed knowledge of rescue specialties.
   E. both B and C.

_____ 2. Most PPE used in rescue situations has been designed for the field of EMS.
   A. True   **B.** False

_____ 3. The person(s) who makes a "go/no go" decision in a rescue operation is the:
   A. medical dispatcher.
   B. Incident Commander.
   C. specialized rescue crew.
   D. Safety Officer.
   E. first responders.

_____ 4. In what phase of a rescue operation does patient access take place?
   A. first
   B. second
   C. third
   D. fourth
   E. fifth

_____ 5. The technical phase of a rescue begins with:
   A. scene size-up.
   B. medical treatment.
   C. access.
   D. hazard control.
   E. packaging.

_____ 6. During an extended rescue, take all the following steps to calm patient fears EXCEPT to:
   A. explain all delays.
   B. tell the patient you will not abandon him.
   C. minimize the dangers of the situation.
   D. explain unfamiliar technical aspects of the operation.
   E. be sure the patient knows your name.

_____ 7. Water causes heat loss 25 times faster than the air.
   A. True
   B. False

_____ 8. Actions to delay the onset of hypothermia in water rescues include all of the following EXCEPT:
   A. use of PFDs.
   B. use of HELP.
   C. huddling together.
   D. treading water.
   E. both C and D.

_____ 9. The first action you should take in a water rescue is to:
   A. reach for the patient with a pole.
   B. swim to the patient.
   C. row to the patient.
   D. throw a flotation device to the patient.
   E. talk the patient into a self-rescue.

_____ 10. At a low head dam, one of the biggest dangers to rescue is a(n):
   A. strainer.
   B. foot pin.
   C. recirculating current.
   D. eddy.
   E. large rocks.

_____ 11. Factors that affect the survival of a patient in a near-drowning accident include:
   A. age.
   B. lung volume.
   C. water temperature.
   D. posture.
   E. all of the above.

_____ 12. You should attempt resuscitation on any hypothermic and/or pulseless, nonbreathing patient who has been submerged in cold water.
   A. True
   B. False

_____ 13. The primary reason confined spaces present a potentially fatal threat is because:
   A. a patient cannot get out and panics.
   B. of a lack of OSHA regulations.
   C. the space is oxygen deficient.
   D. of faulty retrieval devices.
   E. none of the above.

_____ 14. Although all of the following present risks, the largest single hazard associated with EMS highway operations is:
   A. sharp objects.
   B. traffic flow.
   C. rollover situations.
   D. hazardous cargoes.
   E. alternative fuel systems.

_____ 15. The post that supports the roof at the windshield is the:
   A. "A" post.
   B. "B" post.
   C. "C" post.
   D. "D" post.
   E. "E" post.

_____ 16. The easiest means of accessing a motor vehicle patient is through the:
   A. windshield.
   B. door.
   C. window closest to the patient.
   D. hatch.
   E. rear window.

_____ 17. Removal of the patient from the vehicle almost always precedes patient care.
   A. True
   B. False

_____ 18. The least important skill to a member of a high-angle rescue team is:
   A. rappelling.
   B. scrambling.
   C. belaying.
   D. anchoring.
   E. rigging a hauling system.

_____ 19. Most Stokes stretchers are not equipped with adequate restraints.
   A. True
   B. False

_____ 20. Which of the following probably would NOT be found in a downsized backcountry pack?
   A. SAM splints
   B. small oxygen tank/regulator
   C. ECG monitor
   D. intubation equipment
   E. extrication collars

MATCHING

Write the letter of the term in the space provided next to the appropriate description.

A. recirculating currents
B. mammalian diving reflex
C. extrication
D. come-along
E. eddies

F. HELP
G. safety glass
H. active rescue zone
I. short haul
J. tempered glass

_____ 21. area where special rescue teams operate

_____ 22. use of force to free a patient from entrapment

_____ 23. an in-water, head-up tuck or fetal position designed to reduce heat loss

_____ 24. movement of currents over a uniform obstruction

_____ 25. type of glass with a high tensile strength that fractures into small beads when shattered

_____ 26. helicopter extrication technique where a person is attached to a rope that is, in turn, attached to a helicopter

_____ 27. ratcheting cable device used to pull in a straight direction

_____ 28. water that flows around especially large objects and, for a time, flows upstream on the downside of the object

_____ 29. a type of glass made from three layers of fused materials that is designed to stay intact when shattered

_____ 30. the body's natural response to submersion in cold water, the end process of which increases blood flow to the heart and brain

Special Project

Specialized Mechanical Support

Check with your service chief or an EMS director to find out which special rescue units or teams you would call for backup in each of the following types of emergencies. Record the information in the spaces below.

Vehicle Rescue

Name: _____

Contact number: _____

Services provided: _____

_____

_____

_____

Swift-Water Rescue

Name: _____

Contact number: _____

Services provided: _____

_____

_____

_____

High-Angle Rescue

Name: _____

Contact number: _____

Services provided: _____

_____

_____

_____

Ice Rescue

Name: _____

Contact number: _____

Services provided: _____

_____

_____

_____

Confined-Space Rescue

Name: _____

Contact number: _____

Services provided: _____

_____

_____

_____

Trench Rescue

Name: _____

Contact number: _____

Services provided: _____

_____

_____

_____

11 Hazardous Materials Incidents

Review of Chapter Objectives

After reading this chapter, you should be able to:

1. **Explain the role of the paramedic/EMS responder at the hazardous material incident in terms of the following:**

   a. Incident size-up   **pp. 429–438**

   One of the most critical aspects of any HAZMAT response is the simple awareness that a dangerous substance may be present. Virtually every emergency site—residential, business, or highway—possesses the potential for hazardous materials. Always keep the possibility of dangerous substances in mind whenever you approach the scene of an emergency. In addition, learn the various placard systems and the resources for identifying them (see objective 1b).

   Priorities at a HAZMAT incident are the same as for any other major incident: life, safety, and property conservation. However, you should be prepared for the special circumstances surrounding most HAZMAT emergencies. In performing early HAZMAT interventions, you face the challenge of avoiding exposure to the hazardous material yourself. As a result, never compromise scene safety during the early phase of a HAZMAT operation.

   In addition, expect a number of agencies to be involved in a HAZMAT incident. As a result, you should be skilled in the use of the Incident Management System (IMS) discussed in Chapter 9. As you learned in that chapter, you will need to quickly determine whether the HAZMAT emergency is an open or a closed incident. In reaching your decision, remember that some chemicals have delayed effects. Triage must be ongoing, as patient conditions can change rapidly.

   Finally, you must take into account certain conditions when choreographing the scene. The most preferable site for deploying resources will be uphill and upwind. This will help prevent contamination from ground-based liquids, high-density vapor gases, runoff water, and vapor clouds. A backup plan for areas of operation must be determined early in the event. For example, what would you do if the wind direction suddenly shifted and a cloud of chlorine gas headed toward your staging area?

   b. Assessment of toxicologic risk   **pp. 432–438, 440–445**

   To aid in the visual recognition of hazardous materials, two simple systems have been developed. The Department of Transportation (DOT) has implemented placards to identify dangerous substances in transit, while the National Fire Protection Association (NFPA) has devised a system for fixed facilities.

   When DOT placards are used on vehicles, you can spot them easily by their diamond shape. Some placards also carry a UN number—a four-digit number specific to the actual chemical. For quick reference, keep in mind these general classifications.

Hazard Classes and Placard Colors

Hazard Class	Hazard Type	Color Code
1	explosives	orange
2	gases	red or green
3	liquids	red
4	solids	red and white
5	oxidizers and organic peroxides	yellow
6	poisonous and etiologic agents	white
7	radioactive materials	yellow and white
8	corrosives	black and white
9	miscellaneous	black and white

In addition to numbers and colors, placards also use symbols to indicate hazard types. For example, a flame symbol indicates a flammable substance, and a skull-and-crossbones symbol indicates a poisonous substance.

The NFPA 704 System identifies hazardous materials at fixed facilities. Like the DOT placards, the system uses diamond-shaped figures, which are divided into four sections and colors. The top section is red and indicates the flammability of the substance. The left section is blue and indicates the health hazards. The right segment is yellow and indicates the reactivity. The bottom segment is white and indicates special information such as water reactivity, oxidizer, or radioactivity.

Flammability, health hazard, and reactivity are measured on a scale of 0 to 4. A designation of 0 indicates no hazard, while a designation of 4 indicates extreme hazard.

See objective 2 for resources used to identify toxic substances and objective 3 for levels of toxicity.

c. Appropriate decontamination methods
pp. 445–449

There are four methods of decontamination—dilution, absorption, neutralization, and isolation. The method used depends upon the type of hazardous substance and the route of exposure. In many instances, rescuers will use two or more of these methods during the decontamination process. (For a detailed description of each of these methods, see page 436 of the textbook.)

d. Treatment of semidecontaminated patients
pp. 443–445, 449

Remember that no patient who undergoes field decontamination is truly decontaminated. Field-decontaminated patients, sometimes called semidecontaminated patients, may still need to undergo a more invasive decon procedure at a medical facility.

When treating critically ill HAZMAT patients, it is important to perform a rapid risk-to-benefit assessment. Ask yourself these questions: How much risk of exposure will I incur by intubating a patient during decon? Does the patient really need an intravenous line established right now? Few ALS procedures will truly make a difference if performed rapidly, but one mistake can make any rescuer into a patient. Take a few moments and think before you act.

At incidents where patients are noncritical, rescuers can take a more contemplative approach, especially if they can identify the substance. Decontamination and treatment can proceed simultaneously, depending upon the substance. You might also have time to give special attention to other matters, such as containing runoff water, reclothing patients, isolating or containing patients, and so on.

e. Transportation of semidecontaminated patients
p. 445

When transporting field-contaminated patients, always recall that they still have some contamination in or on them. For example, a patient may have ingested a chemical, which can be expelled if the patient coughs or vomits. As a result, use as much disposable equipment as possible. Keep in mind that any airborne hazard will not only incapacitate the crew in the back of the ambulance, but will affect the driver as well. Although it is not practical to line the ambulance in plastic, you can isolate the patient using a stretcher decon pool. The pool can help contain any potentially contaminated body fluids. Plastic can also be used to cover the pool—yet another protective barrier.

2. **Identify resources for substance identification, decontamination, and treatment information.** pp. 435–438

Many sources for information can be used to identify HAZMAT substances, methods of contamination, and treatment information. Some of the most common include:

- *Emergency Response Guidebook* (ERG)
- Shipping papers
- Material safety data sheets
- Monitors/chemical tests
- Databases (CAMEO)
- HAZMAT telephone hot lines (CHEMTREC, CHEMTEL)
- Poison control centers
- Toxicologists
- Reference books

3. **Identify primary and secondary decontamination risk.** p. 442

Whenever people or equipment come in contact with a potentially toxic substance, they are considered to be contaminated. The contamination may be either primary or secondary.

Primary contamination occurs when someone or something is directly exposed to a hazardous substance. At this point, the contamination is limited—that is, the exposure has not yet harmed others.

Secondary contamination takes place when a contaminated person or object comes in contact with an uncontaminated person or object—that is, the contamination is transferred. Touching a contaminated patient, for example, can result in a contaminated care provider. Although gas exposure rarely results in secondary contamination, liquids and particulate matter are much more likely to be transferred.

4. **Describe topical, respiratory, gastrointestinal, and parenteral routes of exposure.** p. 442

There are four ways in which a patient can be exposed to a hazardous substance. The most common method is respiratory inhalation. Gases, liquids, and particulate solids can all be inhaled through the nose or mouth. Once substances enter the bronchial tree, they can be quickly absorbed, especially in oxygen-deficient atmospheres. The substance then enters the central circulation system and is distributed throughout the body. As a result, inhaled substances often trigger a rapid onset of symptoms.

Toxic substances may also be introduced into the body through the skin, either by topical absorption or parenteral injection. Any toxic substance placed topically on intact skin and transferred into the person's circulation is considered a medical threat. In the case of injections, poisons directly enter the body via a laceration, a burn, or a puncture.

In HAZMAT situations, the least common route of exposure is through gastrointestinal ingestion. In occupations involving hazardous materials, people can be exposed to poisons by eating, drinking, or smoking around deadly substances. Foodstuffs can be exposed to a chemical and then eaten. People can forget to wash their hands and introduce the substance into their mouths.

5. **Explain acute and delayed toxicity, local versus systemic effects, dose response, and synergistic effects.** pp. 442–443

Basically, a poison's actions may be acute or delayed. Acute effects include those signs and symptoms that manifest themselves immediately or shortly after exposure. Delayed effects may not become apparent for hours, days, weeks, months, or even years.

Effects from a chemical may be local or systemic. Local effects involve areas around the immediate site and should be evaluated based upon the burn model. You can usually expect some skin irritation (topical) or perhaps acute bronchospasm (respiratory).

Systemic effects occur throughout the body. They can affect the cardiovascular, neurologic, hepatic, and/or renal systems.

Once a substance is introduced into the body, it is distributed to target organs. The organs most commonly associated with toxic substances are the liver and kidneys. The liver metabolizes most substances by chemically altering them through a process known as biotransformation. The kidneys can usually excrete the substances through the urine. However, both the liver and kidneys can be adversely affected by chemicals as are other organ systems. In such situations, the body may not be able to eliminate substances, creating a life-threatening situation.

When treating patients exposed to toxic substances, keep in mind that two substances or drugs may work together to produce an effect that neither of them can produce on its own. This effect, known as synergism, is part of the standard pharmacological approach to medicine. Before administering any medication, be sure to consult with medical direction or the poison control center on possible synergistic effects or treatments.

6. Explain how the substance and route of contamination alters triage and decontamination methods. pp. 445–447

See objective 1c.

7. Explain the employment and limitations of field decontamination procedures. pp. 447–449

The decontamination method and type of PPE depend upon the substance involved. If in doubt, assume the worst-case scenario. When dealing with unknowns, do not attempt to neutralize. Brush dry particles off the patient before the application of water to prevent possible chemical reactions. Next, wash with great quantities of water—the universal decon agent—using tincture of green soap, if possible. Isopropyl alcohol is an effective agent for some isocyanates, while vegetable oil can be used to decon water-reactive substances.

As noted in objective 1d, field decontamination is never true contamination. Depending on the type of exposure, wounds may need debridement, hair or nails may need to be trimmed or removed, and so on. However, it is always better to deliver a grossly decontaminated living patient to the hospital than a perfectly decontaminated corpse. Just make sure that field-contaminated patients are transported to facilities capable of performing more thorough decon procedures.

8. Explain the use and limitations of personal protective equipment (PPE) in hazardous material situations. pp. 449–451

EMS personnel should not become involved in any HAZMAT situation without the proper PPE. All ambulances carry some level of PPE—even if not ideal. Hard hats, for example, protect rescuers against impacts to the head.

If the situation is emergent or the chemical unknown, use as much barrier protection as possible. Full turnout gear or a Tyvek suit is better than no gear at all. HEPA filter masks and double or triple gloves offer good protection against some hazards. Keep in mind that latex gloves are not chemically resistant. Instead, use nitrile gloves, which have a high resistance to most chemicals. Also remember that leather boots will absorb chemicals permanently, so be sure to don rubber boots.

In general, there are basically four levels of HAZMAT protective equipment, ranging from Level A (the highest level) to Level D (the minimum level).

- **Level A**—provides the highest level of respiratory and splash protection. This HAZMAT suit offers a high degree of chemical breakthrough time and fully encapsulates the rescuer, even covering the SCBA. The sealed, impermeable suits are typically used by HAZMAT teams entering the hot zones with an unknown substance and a significant potential for both respiratory and dermal hazards.
- **Level B**—offers full respiratory protection when there is a lower probability of dermal hazard. The Level B suit is nonencapsulating but chemically resistant. Seams for zippers, gloves, boots, and mask interface are usually sealed with duct tape. The SCBA is worn outside the suit, allowing increased maneuverability and greater ease in changing SCBA bottles. The decon team typically wears Level B protective equipment.
- **Level C**—includes a nonpermeable suit, boots, and gear for protecting eyes and hands. Instead of SCBA, Level C protective equipment uses an air-purifying respirator (APR). The APR relies

on filters to protect against a known contaminant in a normal environment. As a result, the canisters in the APR must be specifically selected and are not usually implemented in a HAZMAT emergency response. Level C clothing is usually worn during transport of patients with the potential for secondary contamination.

- **Level D**—consists of structural firefighter, or turnout, gear. Level D gear is usually not suitable for HAZMAT incidents.

9. **List and explain the common signs, symptoms, and treatment of the following substances:**

   a. **Corrosives (acids/alkalis)**   **p. 443**

   Corrosives—acids and alkalis (bases)—can be inhaled, ingested, absorbed, or injected. Primary effects include severe skin burns and respiratory burns and/or edema. Some corrosives may also have systemic effects.

   When decontaminating a patient exposed to solid corrosives, brush off dry particles. In the case of liquid corrosives, flush the exposed area with large quantities of water. Tincture of green soap may help in decontamination. Irrigate eye injuries with water, possibly using a topic ophthalmic anesthetic such as tetracaine to reduce eye discomfort. In patients with pulmonary edema, consider the administration of furosemide (Lasix) or albuterol. If the patient has ingested a corrosive, DO NOT induce vomiting. If the patient can swallow and is not drooling, you may direct the person to drink 5cc/kg water up to 200 cc. As with other injuries, maintain and support the ABCs.

   b. **Pulmonary irritants (ammonia/chlorine)**   **p. 444**

   Many different substances can be pulmonary irritants, including the fumes from chlorine and ammonia. Primary respiratory exposure cannot be decontaminated. However, you should remove the patient's clothing to prevent any trapped gas from being contained near the body. You should also flush any exposed skin with large quantities of water. Irrigate eye injuries with water, possibly using tetracaine to reduce eye discomfort. Treat pulmonary edema with furosemide, if indicated. Again, treatment includes maintaining and supporting the ABCs.

   c. **Pesticides (carbamates/organophosphates)**   **p. 444**

   Toxic pesticides or insecticides primarily include carbamates and organophosphates. These substances can act to block acetylcholinesterase (AChE)—an enzyme that stops the action of acetylcholine, a neurotransmitter. The result is overstimulation of the muscarinic receptors and the SLUDGE syndrome: salivation, lacrimation, urination, diarrhea, gastrointestinal distress, and emesis. Stimulation of the nicotinic receptor may also trigger involuntary contraction of the muscles and pinpoint pupils.

   These chemicals will continue to be absorbed as long as they remain on the skin. As a result, decontamination with large amounts of water and tincture of green soap is essential. Remove all clothing and jewelry to prevent the chemical from being trapped against the skin. Maintain and support airway, breathing, and circulation. Secretions in the airway may need to be suctioned.

   The primary treatment for significant exposure to pesticides is atropinization. The dose should be increased until the SLUDGE symptoms start to resolve. For carbamates, Pralidoxime is NOT recommended. If an adult patient presents with seizures, administer 5 to 10 mg of diazepam. DO NOT induce vomiting if the patient has ingested the chemical. However, if the patient can swallow and has an intact gag reflex, you can administer 5 cc/kg up to 200 cc of water.

   d. **Chemical asphyxiants (cyanides/carbon monoxide)**   **pp. 444–445**

   The most common chemical asphyxiants include carbon monoxide (CO) and cyanides such as bitter almond oil, hydrocyanic acid, potassium cyanide, wild cherry syrup, prussic acid, and nitroprusside. Keep in mind that both CO and cyanides are byproducts of combustion, so patients who present with smoke inhalation may need to be assessed for these substances as well.

   These two chemicals have different actions once inhaled. Carbon monoxide has a high affinity for hemoglobin. As a result, it displaces oxygen in the red blood cells. Cyanides, on the other hand, inhibit the action of cytochrome oxidase. This enzyme complex enables oxygen to create the adenosine triphosphate (ATP) required for all muscle energy. Primary effects of CO exposure include changes in mental status and other signs of hypoxia such as chest pain, loss of consciousness, and seizures. Primary effects of cyanides include rapid onset of unconsciousness, seizures, and cardiopulmonary arrest.

Decontamination of patients exposed to CO and cyanide asphyxiants is usually unnecessary. However, they must be removed from the toxic environment without exposing rescuers to inhalation. Take off the patient's clothing to prevent entrapment of any toxic gases while maintaining airway, breathing, and circulatory support. Definitive treatment for CO inhalation is oxygenation. In some cases, it may be provided through hyperbaric therapy.

Definitive treatment for cyanide exposure can be provided by several interventions carried in a cyanide kit. Basically follow these steps:

- Administer an ampule of amyl nitrite for 15 seconds.
- Repeat at 1-minute intervals until the sodium nitrite is ready.
- Administer an infusion of sodium nitrite, 300 mg IV push over 5 minutes.
- Follow with an infusion of sodium thiosulfate, 12.5 g IV push over 5 minutes.
- Repeat at half the original doses, if necessary.

e. Hydrocarbon solvents (xylene, methylene chloride)   **p. 445**

Many different chemicals can act as solvents, including xylene and methylene chloride. Usually found in liquid form, they give off easily inhaled vapors. Primary effects include dysrhythmias, pulmonary edema, and respiratory failure. Delayed effects include damage to the central nervous system and the renal system. If the patient ingests the chemical and vomits, aspiration may lead to pulmonary edema.

Treatment varies with the route of exposure. In cases of topical contact, decontaminate the exposed area with large quantities of warm water and tincture of green soap. If the patient has ingested the solvent, DO NOT induce vomiting. If the adult patient presents with seizures, administer 5 to 10 mg diazepam. In the case of inhalation, maintain and support the ABCs.

**10. Describe the characteristics of hazardous materials and explain
their importance to the risk assessment process.**   **pp. 427–428, 446–449**

Keep in mind the definition of hazardous materials offered by the DOT. A hazardous material can be regarded as "any substance which may pose an unreasonable risk to health and safety of operating or emergency personnel, the public, and/or the environment if not properly controlled during handling, storage, manufacture, processing, packaging, use, disposal, and transportation."

Some of the characteristics that will be important to consider when doing a risk assessment of chemicals include a material's boiling point, flammable/explosive limits, flash point, ignition temperature, specific gravity, vapor density, vapor pressure, and water solubility. (For definitions of these terms, see pages 439–440 of the textbook.)

These characteristics, as well as other on-scene factors and substance-specific qualities, will help you decide the best and safest mode of operation. In general, you will engage in either "fast-break" or long-term decision making. Fast-break decision making occurs at incidents that call for immediate action to prevent rescuer contamination and/or to handle obvious life threats. Long-term decision making takes place at extended events in which HAZMAT teams retrieve patients, identify the substance(s), and determine methods of decontamination and treatment.

**11. Describe the hazards and protection strategies for alpha, beta,
and gamma radiation.**   **pp. 440–441**

The levels of radiation and strategies for protection from their particles include:

- **Alpha radiation**—neutrons and protons released by the nucleus of a radioactive substance. These are very weak particles and will only travel a few inches in the air. Alpha particles are stopped by paper, clothing, or intact skin. They are hazardous if inhaled or ingested.
- **Beta radiation**—electrons released with great energy by a radioactive substance. Beta particles have more energy than alpha particles and will travel 6 to 10 feet in the air. Beta particles will penetrate a few millimeters of skin.
- **Gamma radiation**—high-energy photons, such as X-rays. Gamma rays have the ability to penetrate most substances and to damage any cells within the body. Heavy shielding is needed for protection against gamma rays. Because gamma rays are electromagnetic (instead of particles), no decontamination is required.

(For more information on the hazards of and protection strategies for these types of radiation, see Volume 3, Chapter 10 of this series.)

12. Define the toxicologic terms and their use in the risk assessment process. **p. 440**

Here are the most important toxicological terms used in the field during the risk assessment process:

- **Threshold limit value/time-weighted average (TLV/TWA)**—maximum concentration of a substance in the air that a person can be exposed to for 8 hours each day, 40 hours per week, without suffering any adverse health effects. The lower the TLV/TWA, the more toxic the substance. The **permissible exposure limit (PEL)** is a similar measure of toxicity.
- **Threshold limit value/short-term exposure limit (TLV/STEL)**—maximum concentration of a substance that a person can be exposed to for 15 minutes (time weighted), not to be exceeded or repeated more than four times daily with 60-minute rests between each of the four exposures.
- **Threshold limit value/ceiling level (TLV/CL)**—maximum concentration of a substance that should never be exceeded, even for a moment.
- **Lethal concentration/lethal doses (LCt/LD)**—concentration (in air) or dose (if ingested, injected, or absorbed) that results in the death of 50 percent of the test subjects. Also referred to as the LCt50 or LD50.
- **Parts per million/parts per billion (ppm/ppb)**—representation of the concentration of a substance in the air or a solution, with parts of the substance expressed per million or billion parts of the air or solution.
- **Immediately dangerous to life and health (IDLH)**—level of concentration of a substance that causes an immediate threat to life. It may also cause delayed or irreversible effects or interfere with a person's ability to remove himself or herself from the contaminated area.

13. Given a specific hazardous material, research the appropriate information about its physical and chemical properties and hazards, suggest the appropriate medical response, and determine the risk of secondary contaminations. **pp. 432–438**

Once you have identified the hazardous material, it is necessary to research the appropriate information about the physical and chemical properties and hazards and then determine the appropriate medical response and any risk of secondary contamination. It is strongly suggested that a number of resources be consulted in developing the plan of action. The resources include, but are not limited to, those listed in objective 2.

14. Identify the factors that determine where and when to treat a hazardous material incident patient. **pp. 438, 446–448**

As noted in objective 10, EMS personnel generally engage in one of two modes of operation at HAZMAT incidents that generate patients: "fast-break" or long-term decision making.

Fast-Break Decision Making
At HAZMAT incidents where patients are conscious, contaminated victims will often self-rescue. They will walk themselves from the primary incident site to the EMS unit. In such cases, you must make fast-break decisions to prevent rescuer contamination. Keep in mind that it may take time for a HAZMAT team to arrive and set up operations. In the interim, the conscious, contaminated patients may try to leave the scene entirely. As a result, all EMS units must be prepared for gross decontamination. Basic personal protection equipment should be on board and all personnel should be familiar with the two-step decontamination procedures (see objective 16).

Implement this mode of decision making at all incidents with critical patients and unknown life-threatening materials. Fire apparatus often respond very quickly and carry large quantities of water that can be used for decon. Remove patient clothing, treat life-threatening problems, and

©2006 Pearson Education, Inc.
Paramedic Care: Principles & Practice, Vol. 5

wash with water. While it is preferable to use warm water to prevent hypothermia, this option is not always available. Please remember that the first rule of EMS is NOT TO BECOME A PATIENT! At no time should you and other crew members expose yourselves to contaminants—even to rescue a critically injured patient. Instead, contain and isolate the patient as best as possible until the proper support arrives.

Long-Term Decision Making

At more extended events, you will engage in long-term decision making. Traditionally, EMS personnel have not been trained or equipped to enter a contaminated area to retrieve patients. Instead, a HAZMAT team is summoned promptly, and the EMS crew awaits the team's arrival. The team will not make their entry until you or members of your crew perform the necessary medical monitoring and establish a decontamination corridor (see below). It often takes 60 minutes or more for actual team deployment.

Typically, three zones will be established at a HAZMAT incident:

- **Hot (red) zone:** This zone, also known as the exclusionary zone, is the site of contamination. Prevent anyone from entering this area unless they have the appropriate high-level PPE. Hold any patients that escape from this zone in the next zone, where contamination and/or treatment will be performed.
- **Warm (yellow) zone:** This zone, also called the contamination reduction zone, lies immediately adjacent to the hot zone. It forms a "buffer zone" in which a decontamination corridor is established for patients and decontamination personnel leaving the hot zone. The corridor has both a "hot" and a "cold" end.
- **Cold (green) zone:** The cold zone, or "safe zone," is the area where the incident operation takes place. It includes the command post, medical monitoring and rehabilitation, treatment areas, and apparatus staging. The cold zone must be free of any contamination. No people or equipment from the hot zone should enter until undergoing the necessary decontamination. You and your crew should remain inside this zone unless you have the necessary training, equipment, and support to enter other areas.

15. Determine the appropriate level of PPE for various hazardous material incidents including: **pp. 449–451**

     a. Types, application, use, and limitations
     See objective 8.

     b. Use of a chemical compatibility chart
     When chemicals can be identified, consult a permeability chart to determine the breakthrough time on a HAZMAT site. No single material is suitable to all HAZMAT situations. Some materials are resistant to certain chemicals and nonresistant to others.

16. Explain decontamination procedures including: **p. 448**

     a. Critical patient rapid two-step decontamination process
     Use the two-step decon process for gross decontamination of patients who cannot wait for a more comprehensive decon process, usually patients at a fast-break incident. Remove all clothing, including shoes, socks, and jewelry. (Remember to have some method of accounting for personal effects BEFORE HAZMAT incidents occur.) Wash and rinse the patients with soap and water, making sure that they do not stay in the runoff. Repeat the process, paying particular attention to the body areas noted in objective 18.

     b. Noncritical patient eight-step decontamination process   **p. 448**
     The eight-step process takes place in a complete decontamination corridor and is much more thorough. To leave the hot zone, the HAZMAT rescuers follow these steps:
     - **Step 1:** Rescuers enter the decon area at the hot end of the corridor and mechanically remove contamination from the victims.
     - **Step 2:** Rescuers drop equipment in a tool-drop area and remove outer gloves.

- **Step 3:** Decon personnel shower and scrub all victims and rescuers, using gross decontamination. As surface contamination is removed, the runoff is conducted into a contained area. Victims may be moved ahead to Step 6 or Step 7.
- **Step 4:** Rescuers remove and isolate their SCBA. If reentry is necessary, the team dons new SCBA from a noncontaminated side.
- **Step 5:** Rescuers remove all protective clothing. Articles are isolated, labeled for disposal, and placed on the contaminated side.
- **Step 6:** Rescuers remove all personal clothing. Victims who have not had their clothing removed have it taken off here. All items are isolated in plastic bags and labeled for later disposal or storage.
- **Step 7:** Rescuers and patients receive a full-body washing, using soft scrub brushes or sponges, water, and mild soap or detergent. Cleaning tools are bagged for later disposal.
- **Step 8:** Patients receive rapid assessment and stabilization before being transported to hospitals for further care. EMS crews medically monitor rescuers, complete exposure records, and transport rescuers to hospitals as needed.

These procedures are not set in stone. Small variations may exist from system to system. You should become familiar with the specific procedures in the jurisdiction where you work.

17. Identify the four most common solutions used for decontamination.   **p. 448**

The most common solutions used for decontamination are water, tincture of green soap, isopropyl alcohol, and vegetable oil.

18. Identify the body areas that are difficult to decontaminate.   **p. 448**

Body areas that are difficult to decontaminate include:

- Scalp and hair
- Ears
- Nostrils
- Axilla
- Fingernails
- Navel
- Genitals
- Groin
- Buttocks
- Behind the knees
- Between the toes
- Toenails

19. Explain the medical monitoring procedures for hazardous material team members.   **p. 451**

Entry Readiness
Prior to entry, you or other EMS crew members will assess rescuers and document the following information on an incident flow sheet: blood pressure, pulse, respiratory rate, temperature, body weight, ECG, and mental/neurologic status. If you observe anything abnormal, do not allow the HAZMAT team member to attempt a rescue.

After-Exit "Rehab"
After the HAZMAT team exits the hot zone and completes decontamination, they should report back to EMS for post-entry monitoring. Measure and document the same parameters on the flow sheet. Rehydrate the team with more water or diluted sports drink. You can use weight changes to estimate fluid losses. Check with medical direction or protocols to determine fluid replacement by means of PO or IV. Entry teams should not be allowed to reenter the hot zone until they are alert, nontachycardic, normotensive, and within a reasonable percentage of their normal body weight.

20. Explain the factors that influence the heat stress of hazardous material team personnel. p. 451

To evaluate heat stress, you will need to take into account many factors. Primary considerations include ambient temperature and humidity. Prehydration, duration and degree of activity, and the team member's overall physical fitness will also have a bearing on your evaluation. Keep in mind that Level A suits protect a rescuer, but prevent cooling. A rescuer essentially works inside an encapsulated sauna. The same suit that seals out hazards also prevents heat loss by evaporation, conduction, convection, and radiation. Therefore, place heat stress at the top of your list of tasks for post-exit medical monitoring.

21. Explain the documentation necessary for HAZMAT medical monitoring and rehabilitation operations. p. 451

The documentation for HAZMAT medical monitoring and rehabilitation operations should include the following: blood pressure, pulse, respiratory rate, temperature, body weight, ECG, and mental status. (See objective 19.)

22. Given a simulated hazardous substance, use reference material to determine the appropriate actions. pp. 435–438

Begin by collecting any information provided on the placards—numbers, symbols, colors, and so on. Then use several of the references identified in objective 2 to augment this information. Become familiar with the latest edition of the *Emergency Response Guidebook*, which should be aboard the EMS unit at all times.

23. Integrate the principles and practices of hazardous materials response in an effective manner to prevent and limit contamination, morbidity, and mortality. pp. 427–452

As a paramedic, you will play an important role at any HAZMAT incident. You may establish command, make the first incident decisions, and help protect all on-scene personnel, including the HAZMAT team. As a result, you should practice skills that you can expect to use in most HAZMAT incidents.

Here are some things that you should routinely do. Put on and take off Level B HAZMAT protective equipment. Set up a rapid two-step decontamination process and an eight-step decontamination process, preferably with the help of the local HAZMAT team. With a crew member, identify a simulated chemical, determine the correct PPE, and establish the proper decontamination methods. Practice preentry and post-exit medical monitoring and documentation. Prepare a patient and ambulance for transport. As these skills may be rarely used except in the busiest EMS systems, you should work closely with your local HAZMAT team to practice these skills on a regular basis.

24. Size up a hazardous material (HAZMAT) incident and determine:

a. Potential hazards to the rescuers, public, and environment pp. 429–438

Sizing up a HAZMAT incident is a very difficult task. You often receive inaccurate or incomplete information. Plus events tend to develop very quickly during each phase of the incident. Also, you can expect other agencies to be involved in the event.

As indicated in objective 1a, you must remember that almost every emergency response has the potential for hazardous materials. For example, most households keep ammonia and liquid bleach in the kitchen or laundry room. When combined, these substances can produce a toxic gas. Homes with kerosene heaters or blocked flues can be filled with carbon monoxide. Don't take any chances. Always keep the possibility of dangerous substances in mind whenever you approach the scene of an emergency.

Transportation incidents. Be especially wary of any transportation collision—automobile, truck, or railroad. Maintain a high degree of HAZMAT awareness whenever you are summoned to MVCs involving commercial vehicles, pest control vehicles, tanker trucks, tractor-trailers, or cars powered by alternative fuels. Do not rule out the presence of hazardous materials just because you do not see a warning placard. Hospitals and laboratories, for example, routinely and legally transport medical radioactive isotopes in unmarked passenger cars.

Railroad collisions merit special attention for two reasons. First, railroad cars can carry large quantities of hazardous materials. Second, there may be several tank cars hitched together on a freight train. Obviously there is a greater chance for a major incident if one or more of these tanks rupture during a collision.

Incidents at fixed facilities. HAZMAT incidents can take place in a variety of fixed facilities where hazardous substances are stored. Chemical plants and all manufacturing operations have tanks, storage vessels, and pipelines used to transport products and/or wastes. Additional fixed sites with possible hazardous materials include warehouses, hardware or agricultural stores, water treatment centers, and loading docks. If you work in a rural area, keep in mind the number of places where you can find hazardous materials on a farm or ranch—silos, barns, greenhouses, and more.

Terrorist incidents. As a last note, remember that a new type of HAZMAT incident has emerged in recent years in the form of terrorism. The terrorists may use any variety of chemical, biological, or nuclear devices to strike at government or high-profile targets.

  b. Potential risk of primary contamination to patients   **p. 442**

In sizing up a HAZMAT incident (real or simulated), remember that whenever people or equipment come in contact with potentially toxic substances they should be considered contaminated. Direct contact, as indicated in objective 3, means primary contamination.

  c. Potential risk of secondary contamination to rescuers   **p. 442**

See objectives 3 and 14. Keep in mind the high risk of secondary contaminations to rescuers in "fast-break" situations.

25. Given a contaminated patient, determine the level of decontamination necessary and:

  a. Level of rescuer PPE   **pp. 449–451**

See objective 8 for the information that you will be applying.

  b. Decontamination methods   **pp. 445–449**

See objectives 1c, 7, 9, 16, 17, and 18 for the information that you will be applying.

  c. Treatment   **pp. 443–445**

See objectives 1d, 5, 9, and 14 for the information that you will be applying.

  d. Transportation and patient isolation techniques   **p. 449**

See objective 1e for the information that you will be applying.

26. Determine the hazards present to the patient and paramedic given an incident involving a hazardous material.   **pp. 427–452**

During your classroom, clinical, and field training, you will given a chance to participate in, or observe, all of the phases of a HAZMAT incident. Use the information presented in this text chapter, the information on hazardous materials presented by your instructors, and guidance given by your clinical and field preceptors to develop good safety skills at a HAZMAT incident. Continue to refine these skills once your training ends and you begin your career as a paramedic.

Case Study Review

Reread the case study on pages 426 and 427 in Paramedic Care: Special Considerations/Operations *and then read the following discussion.*

This case study presents the decisions facing paramedics summoned to the scene of a chemical burn incident. Luckily, a plant supervisor is able to identify the hazardous material. Remember, however, this is not always the case, and you will have to try to determine the substance before approaching the scene.

Even if the paramedics know nothing about the incident, patient symptoms provide a clue to the presence of a hazardous material. Although it is not unusual to respond to a call with multiple patients, it is noteworthy when all the patients exhibit similar symptoms, in this case shortness of breath. Any time you arrive at a scene to find multiple patients with similar medical complaints, suspect that they have been exposed to a hazardous material. The most common toxic inhalant is carbon monoxide from a faulty heating system in a residence. Treat similar symptoms as a "red flag."

As with most HAZMAT incidents, the team immediately initiates the Incident Management System. Other steps that might have been taken in the initial stages of the incident would include donning appropriate PPE and, perhaps, looking up the properties and recommended treatment for anhydrous ammonia in one of the references mentioned in this chapter (or consulting with medical direction).

Important points in the case include the use of gross contamination, efforts to relocate all personnel away from the runoff (to avoid further contamination), and the way in which the EMS crew interacted with the HAZMAT team, including the appropriate pre- and post-monitoring steps.

In this case, treatment was provided. However, this should only be done after ensuring your own safety and conferring with medical direction to avoid any synergistic complications.

Content Self-Evaluation

MULTIPLE CHOICE

_____ 1. Upon arriving at the scene of a potential HAZMAT incident, the first step you should take is to:
   A. size up the scene.   **D.** refer to OSHA CFR 1910.120.
   B. don PPE.   **E.** establish command.
   C. activate the IMS.

_____ 2. Which first responders need to be trained to the HAZMAT Awareness Level?
   A. all EMS personnel   **D.** A and C
   B. police officers   **E.** A, B, and C
   C. firefighters

_____ 3. The most preferable site for deploying resources at a HAZMAT scene is:
   A. uphill and downwind.   **D.** 1 mile away.
   B. uphill and upwind.   **E.** 100 yards away.
   C. across the street from the incident.

_____ 4. The basic IMS at a HAZMAT incident will require all of the following EXCEPT a:
   A. staging area.   **D.** command post.
   B. decontamination corridor.   **E.** treatment area.
   C. transport zone.

_____ 5. One of the most critical aspects of any hazmat response is:
   A. working with unified command.
   B. establishing the time the incident began.
   C. transporting all patients who have been exposed.
   D. the awareness that a dangerous substance is present.
   E. treating critically injured patients.

_____ 6. A diamond-shaped graphic placed on vehicles to indicate hazard classification is a(n):
   A. placard.   **D.** NFPA label.
   B. MSDS.   **E.** ERG.
   C. UN number sign.

_____ 7. One of the most difficult aspects of dealing with a HAZMAT incident is:
   A. reading HAZMAT references.
   B. identifying the particular substance.
   C. working with uncooperative patients.
   D. establishing EMS command.
   E. communicating with the media.

_____ 8. Data sheets containing detailed information about all potentially hazardous substances found at a work site are called:
A. placards.
B. MSDS.
C. UN number signs.
D. NFPA labels.
E. reactivity data sheets.

_____ 9. Shipping papers that contain accurate information about a transported substance are known as:
A. transport vouchers.
B. MSDS.
C. bills of lading.
D. cargo filing.
E. special protection information.

_____ 10. HAZMAT monitoring devices should be routinely used by EMS personnel for quick identification of a substance.
A. True
B. False

_____ 11. Which safety zone is also called the contamination reduction or buffer zone?
A. hot zone
B. warm zone
C. cold zone
D. treatment zone
E. extrication zone

_____ 12. Which of the following is least likely to result in secondary contamination?
A. acids and alkalis
B. carbon monoxide
C. organophosphates
D. liquid corrosives
E. carbamates

_____ 13. In HAZMAT situations, the least common route(s) of exposure is (are) through:
A. respiratory inhalation.
B. parenteral injection.
C. topical absorption.
D. gastrointestinal ingestion.
E. both A and C.

_____ 14. In a HAZMAT situation, the most common route(s) of exposure is (are) through:
A. respiratory inhalation.
B. parenteral injection.
C. topical absorption.
D. gastrointestinal ingestion.
E. both B and D.

_____ 15. If a patient was exposed to a hazardous gas and developed acute bronchospasm, this could be called a _____ effect.
A. local
B. systemic
C. biotransformation
D. synergistic
E. secondary

_____ 16. The most common route of exposure of cyanides is through inhalation, although cyanides can also be ingested, absorbed, or injected.
A. True
B. False

_____ 17. Definitive treatment for CO inhalation is:
A. oxygenation.
B. hyperbaric therapy.
C. use of a cyanide kit.
D. infusion of sodium thiosulfate.
E. none of the above.

_____ 18. All of the following are methods of decontamination EXCEPT:
A. stabilization.
B. dilution.
C. absorption.
D. isolation.
E. neutralization.

_____ 19. Which priority should guide your decision making while performing decontamination?
A. life safety
B. incident stabilization
C. property conservation
D. triage
E. neutralization

_____ 20. All the following are common decontamination solvents EXCEPT:
   A. water.
   B. tincture of green soap.
   C. isopropyl alcohol.
   D. baking soda.
   E. vegetable oil.

_____ 21. Two methods for decontamination in the field are the:
   A. two-step and twelve-step processes.
   B. complete and incomplete methods.
   C. gross decon and neutralizing methods.
   D. two-step and eight-step processes.
   E. fast-break and long-term methods.

_____ 22. The lowest level of HAZMAT protective equipment is:
   A. Level A.
   B. Level B.
   C. Level C.
   D. Level D.
   E. Level E.

_____ 23. The highest level of HAZMAT protective equipment uses a(n):
   A. HEPA filter mask.
   B. air-purifying respirator.
   C. SCBA.
   D. SCUBA.
   E. PBI flash protector.

_____ 24. Which of the following should be consulted to determine the breakthrough time of a specific chemical on a HAZMAT suit?
   A. CAMEO Website
   B. _Emergency Response Guidebook_
   C. permeability chart
   D. OSHA publication CFR 1910.120
   E. NFPA table

_____ 25. One of the primary roles of EMS personnel at a HAZMAT incident is medical monitoring of entry personnel.
   A. True
   B. False

MATCHING

Write the letter of the term in the space provided next to the appropriate description.

A. boiling point

B. warm zone

C. CHEMTREC

D. hazardous material

E. flash point

F. ignition temperature

G. cold zone

H. placard

I. MSDS

J. hot zone

_____ 26. any substance that causes adverse health effects upon human exposure

_____ 27. diamond-shaped graphic placed on vehicles to indicate HAZMAT classification

_____ 28. easily accessible sheets of detailed information about chemicals found at fixed facilities

_____ 29. Chemical Transportation Emergency Center, which maintains a 24-hour toll-free HAZMAT information hot line

_____ 30. the location where the hazardous material and the highest levels of contamination exist

_____ 31. the location where the decontamination corridor should be set up

_____ 32. the area at a hazardous material incident where the command post and sectors are set up

_____ 33. the lowest temperature at which a liquid will give off enough vapors to ignite

_____ 34. the temperature at which a liquid becomes a gas

_____ 35. the lowest temperature at which a liquid will give off enough vapors to support combustion

Special Projects

Awareness Level Practice

To participate effectively in a HAZMAT incident, you need to be familiar with the regulations and standards that guide operations during these emergencies. You will also need to know how to identify the hazardous substances involved at the incident. To be a more valuable and informed member of a HAZMAT emergency operation, complete these activities.

Part I: Regulations and Standards

Obtain a copy of the following regulations and review them to determine how they apply to you and your agency. Record information in the spaces provided.

OSHA CFR 1910.120

Main Provisions: _____

_____

Local Application: _____

_____

_____

_____

EPA 40 CFR 311

Main Provisions: _____

_____

Local Application: _____

_____

_____

_____

NFPA 473
Main Provisions: _____
_____
Local Application: _____
_____
_____
_____

Part II: Identifying Hazardous Substances

Obtain the latest copy of the *Emergency Response Guidebook*. After reviewing the book's format, find an example of a chemical in each of the following UN classifications. Write down the name of the substance and any special precautions that should be taken when you find this substance at a HAZMAT incident.

UN Classification	Chemical Name	Special Precautions to Take
1		
2		
3		
4		
5		
6		
7		
8		
9		

12

Crime Scene Awareness

Review of Chapter Objectives

After reading this chapter, you should be able to:

1. **Explain how EMS providers are often mistaken for the police.**   **pp. 459, 464**

Depending upon your uniform colors and the use of badges, people might mistake you for the police— especially if you exit from a vehicle with flashing lights and a siren. They might expect you to intervene in a violent situation, or they might direct aggression toward you as an authority figure.

    When entering gang territory, you are especially at risk if your uniform resembles that of the police. Gangs with a history of arrest may in fact make every effort to prevent you from transporting one of their members to a hospital or any other place beyond their reach. Do not force the situation if your safety is at stake.

2. **Explain specific techniques for risk reduction when approaching the following types of routine EMS scenes:**

a. **Highway encounters**   **pp. 461–462**

To make a safe approach to a vehicle at a roadside emergency, follow these steps:
- Park the ambulance in a position that provides safety from traffic.
- Notify dispatch of the situation, location, the vehicle make and model, and the state and number of the license plate.
- Use a one-person approach. The driver should remain in the ambulance, which is elevated and provides greater visibility.
- The driver should remain prepared to radio for immediate help and to back or drive away rapidly once the other medic returns.
- At nighttime, use the ambulance lights to illuminate the vehicle. However, do not walk between the ambulance and the other vehicle. You will be backlit, forming an easy target.
- Since police approach vehicles from the driver's side, you should approach from the passenger's side, which is an unexpected route.
- Use the A, B, and C door posts for cover.
- Observe the rear seat. Do not move forward of the C post unless you are sure there are no threats in the rear seat or foot wells.
- Retreat to the ambulance (or another strategic position of cover) at the first sign of danger.
- Make sure you have mapped out your intended retreat and escape with the ambulance driver.

b. Violent street incidents   **pp. 462–464**

You can encounter many different types of violence while working on the streets. Incidents can range from random acts of violence against individual citizens to organized efforts at domestic or international terrorism. In responding to the scene of any violent crime, keep these precautions in mind:

- Dangerous weapons may have been used in the crime.
- Perpetrators may still be on-scene or could return on-scene.
- Patients may sometimes exhibit violence toward EMS personnel, particularly if they risk criminal penalties as a result of the original incident.

When on the streets, you must remain constantly aware of crowd dynamics. Crowds can quickly become large and volatile, especially in the case of a hate crime. Violence can be directed against anyone or anything in the path of an angry crowd. Your status as an EMS provider does not give you immunity against an out-of-control mob. Whenever a crowd is present, look for these warning signs of impending danger:

- Shouts or increasingly loud voices
- Pushing or shoving
- Hostilities toward anyone on-scene, including the perpetrator of a crime, the victim, police, and so on
- Rapid increase in crowd size
- Inability of law enforcement officials to control bystanders

To protect yourself, constantly monitor the crowd and retreat if necessary. If possible, take the patient with you so that you do not have to return later. Rapid transport may require limited or tactical assessment at the scene, with more in-depth assessment done inside the safety of the ambulance. Be sure to document reasons for the quick assessment and transport.

c. Residences and "dark houses"   **pp. 459–460**

Domestic violence needs to be a consideration whenever you approach a residence and detect yelling, screaming, or any other signs of fighting. Sometimes you might spot clues such as broken glass or blood on the sidewalk. If you approach a "dark house," especially one where the front door is ajar, be very cautious—it could a setup. In such cases, ask the dispatcher to call the residence and request that occupants turn on lights and meet you at the front door, if possible. When entering a residence, look around for any potential weapons that may be used against you. If you are unsure of the safety of the scene, call for police backup. If there is a fight going on as you approach the residence, retreat and request police to secure the scene.

3. Describe the warning signs of potentially violent situations.   **pp. 459–460, 461–466**

You should remain alert throughout a call, especially in areas with a history of violence. You may enter the scene and spot weapons or drugs. Additional combative people may arrive on the scene. The patient or bystanders may become agitated or threatening. Even if treatment has begun, you must place your own safety first. You may have just two tactical options: quickly package the patient and leave the scene with the patient or retreat without the patient.

4. Explain emergency evasive techniques for potentially violent situations, including:

a. Threats of physical violence   **pp. 462–471**
See objectives 2, 5, and 6.

b. Firearms encounters   **pp. 462–471**
See objectives 5b and 6c.

c. Edged weapon encounters   **pp. 462–471**
Your best tactical response to an edged weapon is observation. If you suspect violence with any kind of weapon, stay out of danger in the first place—that is, retreat. Ideally you will re-

treat to the ambulance so that you can summon help. If the attacker pursues you, follow the evasive strategies listed in Objective 6b.

5. **Explain EMS considerations for the following types of violent or potentially violent situations:**

   a. Gangs and gang violence   pp. 463–464

   Street gangs can be found in big cities, suburban towns, and, lately, in rural communities. No EMS unit is totally immune from gang activity. In fact, some gangs have purposely branched out into smaller towns in an effort to escape surveillance and expand their illicit businesses. Commonly observed gang characteristics include:
   - **Appearance:** Gang members frequently wear unique clothing specific to the group. Because the clothing is often a particular color or hue, it is referred to as the gang's "colors." Wearing a color, even a bandana, can signify gang membership. Within the gang itself, members sometimes wear different articles to signify rank.
   - **Graffiti:** Gangs have definite territories or "turfs." Members often mark their turf with graffiti broadcasting the gang's logo, warning away intruders, bragging about crimes, insulting rival gangs, or taunting police.
   - **Tattoos:** Many gang members wear tattoos or other body markings to identify their gang affiliation. Some gangs even require these tattoos. The tattoos will be in the gang's colors and often contain the gang's motto or logo.
   - **Hand signals/language:** Gangs commonly create their own methods of communication. They give gang-related meanings to everyday words or create codes. Hand signals provide quick identification among gang members, warn of approaching law enforcement, or show disrespect to other gangs. Gang members often perform signals so quickly that an uninformed outsider may not spot them, much less understand them.

   Always remember that gang members are usually armed and expect your respect. Do not cut their "colors" or clothing without permission, or you will be displaying a public show of disrespect. Finally, keep in mind the attitudes toward authority mentioned in objective 1.

   b. Hostages/sniper situations   pp. 469–471

   The provision of care in hostage/sniper situations often necessitates risks far beyond those found on most EMS calls. Medical personnel assigned to such incidents require special training and authorization. Like HAZMAT teams, they must don special equipment, function with compact gear, and, in most cases, work as medical adjuncts to the police or military.

   If you find yourself in one of these situations, be sure to stage your ambulance outside the "kill zone," or the range of a typical rifle. If you are unsure of the distance, ask the police. Do not approach the scene, as you may end up being taken as a hostage also.

   A good precaution for any dangerous situation is the use of prearranged verbal and nonverbal clues. Be sure to alert dispatch to the meaning of spoken clues. Choose signals that indicate a variety of circumstances while sounding harmless to an attacker. This can be a lifesaving technique in situations where you find yourself, the crew, and/or the patient held hostage. Your so-called "routine" radio reports can spell out the nature of the trouble and summon help from a special weapons and tactics (SWAT) team.

   c. Clandestine drug labs   pp. 465–466

   Drug raids on clandestine ("clan") labs have a way of turning into HAZMAT operations. All too often, the labs contain toxic fumes and volatile chemicals. The people on-scene complicate matters by fighting or shooting at the rescuers who come to extricate them from the toxic environment. As they retreat, drug dealers may also trigger booby traps or wait for police or EMS personnel to trigger them. If you ever come upon a clan lab, take these actions:
   - Leave the area immediately.
   - Do not touch anything.
   - Never stop any chemical reactions already in progress.
   - Do not smoke or bring any source of flame near the lab.
   - Notify the police.

©2006 Pearson Education, Inc.
Paramedic Care: Principles & Practice, Vol. 5

- Initiate ICS and HAZMAT procedures.
- Consider evacuation of the area.

Remember that laboratories can be found anywhere—on farms, in trailers, in city apartments, and more. They may be mobile, roaming from place to place in a camper or a truck. Or they may be disassembled and stored in almost any variety of locations. The job of raiding clan labs belongs to specialized personnel—not EMS.

d. Domestic violence   p. 466
Domestic violence involves people who live together in an intimate relationship. The violence may be physical, emotional, sexual, verbal, or economic. It may be directed against a spouse or partner, or it may involve children and/or older relatives who live at the residence.

When called to the scene of domestic violence, the abuser may turn on you or other members of the crew. You have two main concerns: your own personal safety and protection of the patient from further harm. For more on the indications of domestic violence and the appropriate actions of EMS crews, see Chapter 4, "Abuse and Assault."

e. Emotionally disturbed people   p. 466
The prudent strategy is to retreat whenever you spot indicators of violence or physical confrontations with an emotionally disturbed person. Conduct the retreat in a calm but decisive manner. Be aware that the danger is now at your back and integrate cover into your retreat. For information on emotionally disturbed patients, see Volume 3, Chapter 12, "Psychiatric and Behavioral Emergencies."

6. Explain the following techniques:

a. Field "contact and cover" procedures during assessment and care   pp. 468–469
The concept of "contact and cover" comes from a police procedure developed in San Diego, California. When adapted to EMS practice, the procedure assigns the roles shown in the following table.

Contact Provider	*Cover Provider*
Initiates and provides direct patient care.	Observes the scene for danger while the "contact" cares for the patient.
Performs patient assessment.	Generally avoids patient care duties that would prevent observation of the scene.
Handles most interpersonal scene contact.	In small crews, may perform limited functions such as handling equipment.

As with any tactic adopted from another discipline, contact and cover has obvious correlations and drawbacks. The tactic is ideal for street encounters with intoxicated persons or subjects acting in a suspicious manner. An obvious drawback is that two medics working on a cardiac arrest will not be able to designate one person to act solely as a "cover" medic.

Perhaps the best application of this police procedure to EMS is its emphasis on the importance of observation and teamwork. A crew that works well together will assign roles—formally or informally—to guarantee safety and patient care. In its most basic form, contact and cover means that you will watch your partner's back while he or she watches yours.

b. Evasive tactics   p. 468
Some specific techniques to avoid violence include:
- Throwing equipment to trip, slow, or distract an aggressor
- Wedging a stretcher in a doorway to block an attacker
- Using an unconventional path while retreating
- Anticipating the moves of the aggressor and taking countermoves
- Overturning objects in the path of the attacker
- Using preplanned tactics with your partner to confuse or "throw off" an aggressor

The key to the success of these safety tactics is your own physical well-being. Regular exercise and good health ensure that you will have the strength to outrun or, if necessary, defend yourself against an attacker. Some units provide basic training in self-defense or have protocols on its use. Make sure you take advantage of this training and/or know the protocols related to the application of force.

c. Concealment techniques pp. 467–468

When faced with danger, two of your most immediate and practical strategies are cover and concealment. Concealment hides your body, as when you crouch behind bushes, wallboards, or vehicle doors. However, most common objects do not stop bullets. During armed encounters, seek cover by hiding your body behind solid and impenetrable objects such as brick walls, rocks, large trees, telephone poles, and the engine block of vehicles.

For cover and concealment to work, they must be used properly. In applying these safety tactics, keep in mind the following general rules.

- As you approach any scene, remain aware of the surroundings and any potential sources of protection in case you must retreat or are "pinned down."
- Choose your cover carefully. You may have only one chance to pick your protection. Select the item that hides your body adequately while shielding you against bullets.
- Once you have made your choice of cover, conceal as much of your body as possible. Be conscious of any reflective clothing that you may be wearing. Armed assailants can use it as a target, especially at night.
- Constantly look to improve your protection and location.

7. Describe police evidence considerations and techniques to assist in evidence preservation. pp. 471–475

When on the scene of a call where a crime has been committed, the paramedic should never jeopardize patient care for the sake of evidence. However, do not perform patient care with disregard to the criminal investigation that will follow. Remember that EMS and the police are on the same side—so work together. If you are the first person on the scene of a crime, be aware that anything you touch, walk on, pick up, cut, wipe off, or move could be evidence. Developing an awareness of evidence will even affect the way you treat patients. You will need to observe the patient carefully and to disturb as little direct evidence as possible. Also, when examining a patient, remember that you may be at risk. The patient may have a concealed weapon, such as a knife or gun.

Types of Evidence

Gathering evidence is a specialized and time-consuming job. While it is unrealistic to train EMS personnel in the details of police work, it is not unrealistic to ask them to develop an awareness of the general types of evidence that they may expect to encounter at a crime scene. Some of the main categories of evidence include prints, blood and body fluids, and particulate evidence. See pages 473–474 of the textbook for steps that you can take to help preserve each of these types of evidence.

On-Scene Observations

Everything that you and other members of the EMS crew see and hear can serve as evidence. Your observations on the scene will become part of the police record—and ultimately part of the court record. Be sure to look for and record the following information:

- Conditions at the scene—absence or presence of lights, locked or unlocked doors, open or closed curtains, and so on
- Position of the patient/victim
- Injuries suffered by the patient/victim
- Statements of persons on the scene
- Statements by the patient/victim
- Dying declarations
- Suspicious persons at, or fleeing from, the scene
- Presence and/or location of any weapons

Documenting Evidence

Record only the facts at the scene of a crime and record them accurately. Otherwise, they might be thrown out of court as inadmissible evidence. Use quotation marks to indicate the words of bystanders and any remarks made by the patient. Avoid opinions not relevant to patient care. If the patient has died, do not offer any judgments that might contradict later findings by the medical examiner.

Finally, follow local policies and regulations regarding confidentiality surrounding any crime case. Any offhand remarks that you make might later become testimony in a courtroom, along with other documents that you prepare at the scene.

8. **Given several crime scene scenarios, identify potential hazards and determine if the scene is safe to enter, then provide care preserving the crime scene as appropriate.**   **pp. 458–475**

During your classroom, clinical, and field training, you will have a chance to practice your approach to violent or potentially violent crime scenes. Use the information presented in this text chapter, the information on crime scene awareness presented by your instructors, and the guidance given by your clinical and field preceptors to develop the skills to protect yourself and your partner, as well as to preserve on-scene evidence. Continue to refine these skills once your training ends and you begin your career as a paramedic.

Case Study Review

Reread the case study on pages 457 and 458 in Paramedic Care: Special Considerations/Operations *and then read the following discussion.*

This case underscores the cautious approach that should be used with any scene that holds the potential for violence. Although this turned out to be a routine call, the paramedics had no way of knowing that during the initial phases of the incident.

A quiet call can be just as dangerous as a call that involves shouting, yelling, and other obvious signs of potential violence. You should not drop your guard just because the call is in a "well-kept" neighborhood or the patient is "too old" or "too young" to be capable of violence. In this case, the paramedics park the ambulance a safe distance from the house and observe through the windshield before exiting the vehicle. They approach with only the necessary equipment, taking separate and unpredictable paths. After looking in the window, the paramedics deem the scene safe and approach the patient.

Even on routine runs, think about safety, contact and cover, escape routes, and other strategies that can help you make better decisions when you are faced with actual danger. Borrowing a phrase from professional sports: "You will play the game the way you practice." If you have rehearsed the responses to danger before you actually need them, you will be more likely to use them successfully.

Content Self-Evaluation

MULTIPLE CHOICE

_____ 1. According to the Division of Violence Prevention at the National Center for Injury Prevention, arrest rates for homicide, rape, robbery, and aggravated assault are consistently higher for people ages:
   A. 10 to 14.
   B. 15 to 34.
   C. 35 to 50.
   D. 51 to 65.
   E. over age 65.

2. A computer-aided dispatch (CAD) program can assist in preventing an attack on EMS personnel by:
   A. predicting when crimes are most likely to occur.
   B. noting addresses with a history of violence.
   C. maintaining a list of known criminals.
   D. linking an EMS unit to a special forces team.
   E. all of the above.

3. The EMS unit should follow the police units to the scene.
   A. True   B. False

4. One of the main purposes of the scene size-up at a crime scene is to search for:
   A. possible evidence.   D. law enforcement officials.
   B. alleged assailants.   E. a way to rescue the victim.
   C. hazards.

5. Even if a scene has been declared secure by the police, violence may still occur.
   A. True   B. False

6. When approaching a residence that may be hazardous, you should:
   A. be careful not to backlight yourself.
   B. hold your flashlight to the side.
   C. take an unconventional approach to the door.
   D. keep your partner in sight.
   E. all of the above.

7. Before knocking on the door, you should do all of the following EXCEPT:
   A. stand on the hinge side of the door.
   B. listen for loud noises.
   C. listen for items breaking.
   D. listen for the lack of any sounds at all.
   E. look in the windows for the presence of weapons.

8. If you must defend yourself, use the maximum amount of force possible.
   A. True   B. False

9. To make a safe approach to a suspicious roadside emergency, you should take all of the following safety steps EXCEPT:
   A. use a one-person approach.
   B. use the ambulance lights to illuminate the vehicle.
   C. approach the vehicle from the driver's side.
   D. use the A, B, and C posts for cover.
   E. observe the rear seat.

10. According to the U.S. Department of Justice, the most common location for violent crimes is on the streets.
    A. True   B. False

11. Crimes committed against a person solely on the basis of the individual's actual or perceived race, color, national origin, ethnicity, gender, disability, or sexual orientation are known as:
    A. bias crimes.   D. selective crimes.
    B. hate crimes.   E. none of the above.
    C. nondiscriminatory crimes.

_____ 12. When responding to the scene of any violent crime, you should remember that:
   A. dangerous weapons may have been used in the crime.
   B. perpetrators may still be on-scene.
   C. patients may sometimes exhibit violence toward EMS personnel.
   D. perpetrators may return to the scene.
   E. all of the above.

_____ 13. Warning signs of impending danger from a crowd include all of the following EXCEPT:
   A. a rapid increase in the crowd size.
   B. hostility toward anyone on the scene.
   C. pushing or shoving.
   D. inability of police to control bystanders.
   E. a decreasing level of noise.

_____ 14. A gang's "colors" refers to their:
   A. clothing.   D. graffiti.
   B. flag.   E. logo.
   C. language.

_____ 15. Gang activities are confined to urban areas and are of minimal concern to EMS units outside cities.
   A. True   B. False

_____ 16. One of the most common substances manufactured in clandestine drug labs is:
   A. cocaine.   D. methadone.
   B. methamphetamine.   E. morphine.
   C. heroin.

_____ 17. If you ever come upon a clan lab, all of the following are appropriate actions EXCEPT to:
   A. leave the area immediately.
   B. stop any chemical reactions in progress.
   C. notify the police.
   D. initiate ICS and HAZMAT procedures.
   E. evacuate the area.

_____ 18. Clan labs generally have the following requirements:
   A. privacy.   D. heating mantles or burners.
   B. utilities.   E. all of the above.
   C. glassware.

_____ 19. All of the following strategies can be employed as safety tactics in a potentially violent situation EXCEPT:
   A. retreat.   D. distraction and evasion.
   B. cover and concealment.   E. contact and cover.
   C. confrontation and interrogation.

_____ 20. Concealment is hiding your body behind solid and impenetrable objects such as brick walls.
   A. True   B. False

_____ 21. Most body armor is able to stop all bullets and all but a few knives.
   A. True
   B. False

_____ 22. Which of the following describes how tactical EMS differs from normal or non-tactical EMS?
   A. A major priority is patient extraction.
   B. Trauma is more frequent than medical emergencies.
   C. Treatment interventions must be coordinated with the IC.
   D. Complete assessment occurs after patient movement.
   E. All of the above.

_____ 23. Which of the following is NOT appropriate when providing care at the possible crime scene?
   A. Cut through bullet or knife holes in clothing.
   B. Place clothing in paper bags.
   C. Place patient care before crime scene preservation.
   D. Wear gloves and otherwise limit any finger prints you might leave behind.
   E. All of the above are appropriate actions at a crime scene.

_____ 24. Gloves worn by EMS providers generally limit the fingerprints left behind at the scene but will not prevent other prints from being smudged.
   A. True
   B. False

_____ 25. Which of the following is proper for documenting a crime scene response?
   A. Record only the facts at the crime scene.
   B. Use quotation marks to indicate exact words from bystanders or the patient.
   C. Do not offer opinions as to the victim's cause of death.
   D. Describe the nature and shape of a wound, not the suspected cause.
   E. All of the above.

MATCHING

Write the letter of the term in the space provided next to the appropriate description.

A. TEMS   F. EMT-Ts

B. particulate evidence   G. blood splatter evidence

C. concealment   H. cover

D. SWAT   I. CONTOMS

E. body armor   J. graffiti

_____ 26. painting on walls to mark a gang's territory, membership, or threats

_____ 27. trained police unit equipped to handle hostage takers and other difficult law enforcement situations

_____ 28. hiding the body behind objects that shield a person from view but offer little or no protection against bullets or other ballistics

_____ 29. vest made of tightly woven, strong fibers that offers protection against handgun bullets, most knives, and blunt trauma

_____ 30. counternarcotics tactical operations program that manages training and certification of EMT-Ts and SWAT-medics

_____ 31. hairs or fibers that cannot be readily seen with the human eye

_____ 32. a specially trained unit that provides on-site medical support to law enforcement

_____ 33. hiding the body behind solid and impenetrable objects that protect a person from bullets

_____ 34. pattern that blood forms when it is dropped at the scene of a crime

_____ 35. EMS personnel trained to serve with a law enforcement agency

SHORT ANSWER

Part A

List seven things that you or any member of an EMS team can do to preserve blood evidence at the scene of a crime.

36. _____

_____

37. _____

_____

38. _____

_____

39. _____

_____

40. _____

_____

41. _____

_____

42. _____

_____

Part B

In addition to blood and body fluids, list three other categories of evidence that EMS personnel should be aware of at a crime scene.

43. _____

44. _____

45. _____

Special Project

Crime Hazard Awareness

Take a walk around each room in your residence and inventory all the items that could easily be used as weapons against a responding paramedic. You should note things like ashtrays, scissors, letter openers, statues, and bottles—then there are all those knives in the woodblock on the kitchen counter!

List the items you found:

Living Room: _____

_____

_____

_____

Kitchen: _____

_____

_____

_____

Dining Room: _____

_____

_____

_____

Bedroom: _____

_____

_____

_____

Bathroom: _____

_____

_____

_____

13 Rural EMS

Review of Chapter Objectives

Note: The objectives for this chapter are not included in the DOT paramedic curriculum.

After reading this chapter, you should be able to:

*1. Identify situations and conditions unique to rural EMS.   **pp. 480–483, 486–487**

The U.S. government defines rural areas in terms of their sparse populations and distances from cities, towns, or villages. In relation to health care, rural areas can also be characterized by their higher percentage of elderly people and their lower physician-to-patient ratios. While one in five people in the United States live in a rural setting, only about one in ten doctors chooses to practice in these locations.

It has been found that rural residents experience a disproportionate number of serious injuries and chronic health conditions. Because of the greater distance to health care facilities, rural residents suffer a higher level of mortality associated with trauma and medical emergencies. In many cases, an EMS unit may provide the definitive care.

*2. Discuss various challenges facing rural EMS providers.   **pp. 480–483, 486–487**

Some of the most critical challenges facing rural EMS providers include:

Distance and Time
Rural EMS often relies on volunteer services. In responding to calls, volunteers must first travel varying distances to a squad building. Once aboard the ambulance, they then travel the distance to the patient and later the distance to the hospital. As a result, every decision that a paramedic makes in a rural setting needs to be made with the thought of distance in mind. (For more on this all-important topic, see objective 4.)

Communication Difficulties
In some rural areas, poor or old communications equipment may hamper public access to EMS. An area may lack a universal access number such as 911, leading people to dial the operator, police stations, and other such "emergency" numbers. They may even use antiquated "fire phones" or "crash bars" to notify EMS of an emergency.

While traveling aboard the ambulance, rural EMS crews may experience dead spots where they cannot transmit or receive radio or cellular communications. Frequencies can be overloaded with static from highway departments and school buses.

Enrollment Shortages

Because many EMS providers work on a volunteer basis, units or squads can experience enrollment shortages. Volunteers must respond to calls from their jobs or homes. The greater distances and time involved in many rural EMS calls can take volunteers from their work or families for lengthy periods. This situation can impact upon their ability to earn a living or raise their children. As a result, they often serve for only short stretches or resign entirely.

Training and Practice

Access to training and continuing education is not readily available in many rural areas. In addition, the cost and amount of time required for certification as a paramedic have increased. For the volunteer, this means increased personal expense and time away from home. The net effect can be EMS providers with a less advanced level of training than their paid urban counterparts.

This situation can be further complicated by the low volume of EMS calls in some rural areas. EMS providers simply do not have the opportunity to practice their skills on a consistent basis. Members of rescue squads may experience what has become known as "rust-out," or an inability to keep abreast of new technologies and standards. The networking opportunities or volume of calls simply do not exist.

Inadequate Medical Supplies

Rural areas sometimes have inadequate medical direction. Local physicians may lack the training in EMS operations or feel EMS operations should not be part of their jobs.

In addition, rural areas may not have the budget to buy new equipment and ambulances. Moreover, air medical transport may not always be readily available due to many factors, such as distance, lack of landing areas, cost, or too few helicopters for a large area.

Finally, hospitals and rural EMS agencies may not always implement protocols or standards for prehospital providers. A rural paramedic may be faced with two different sets of protocols for prehospital care. That means that volunteers must seek out and familiarize themselves with these protocols, often on their own.

*3. Describe some of the possible solutions to problems commonly faced by rural EMS units. pp. 483–485

Some of the possible solutions to problems commonly faced by rural EMS units are as follows.

Improved Communication

Ideas for improved communication include the following:

- Apply for grants to modernize or supplement communications equipment.
- Join rural counties together to share in the cost of implementing 911 systems.
- With access to 911, train dispatchers in Medical Priority Dispatch or Medical-Assist Dispatch (to provide lifesaving instructions while an EMS crew is en route).
- Eliminate or reduce radio dead spots and crowded frequencies by requesting additional frequencies and/or upgrading radio equipment (e.g., more powerful base station radios and towers).
- Form a 911 user advisory board or consortium of agencies to help improve communications.
- Use cell phones.

Recruitment and Certification

Strategies for increasing access to education and, by extension, the pool of trained ALS personnel include:

- Provide for flexible training sessions and ongoing education.
- Organize interagency educational pools.
- Utilize "explorer" and "ride-along" programs, when appropriate, to increase interest in volunteer EMS service.
- Use the computer for instruction and training (via CD-ROMs and appropriate software).
- Access valid sources of information over the Internet.
- Network over the Internet to promote creative problem solving and to share new ideas.

©2006 Pearson Education, Inc.
Paramedic Care: Principles & Practice, Vol. 5

Improved Medical Support

- Approach physicians and determine their willingness to serve as Emergency Medical Directors.
- Inform interested physicians of the educational opportunities available through the National Association of EMS Physicians.
- Encourage EMS personnel to spend time at hospitals that serve their district and, when possible, request to sit in on relevant in-service training sessions provided for hospital staff.

Ingenuity and Increased Responsibilities

Rural EMS requires ingenuity. For most rural agencies, it is a constant struggle to retain members, supplement budgets, update equipment, provide quality education programs, and network with other health care facilities. Rural paramedics can also expect to be faced with new responsibilities, possibly working in hospital outreach programs such as prompt care facilities or becoming involved in the public health system. Whatever the future may hold, rural paramedics will be challenged to raise the standard of prehospital care offered to the rural residents who make up nearly one quarter of the nation's population.

*4. Differentiate between rural and urban EMS when considering treatment and response time. pp. 481, 486–487

Distance is one of the key differences between rural and urban EMS response time and treatment. The axiom of the Golden Hour may be impossible to meet. As a result, you may spend far more time with the patient on-board the ambulance than at the scene itself. With this in mind, actions taken by a rural paramedic during transport can have a definitive impact upon the patient's outcome. For this reason, you must keep detailed documentation during any lengthy transport.

Another factor to consider is the availability of emergency staff at the local hospital. In most urban areas, hospitals stay active all night. They have full-time emergency departments with around-the-clock staffing able to handle complicated procedures 24 hours a day, 7 days a week. Some rural hospitals, however, may only have a part-time emergency department with one or two doctors on staff. In such cases, you may have to call the hospital from the patient's home to arrange for the necessary personnel to be in the building when you arrive. You may also have to make a judgment call on whether or not to transport a critically ill patient to a more distant full-time trauma center. In the case of cardiac problems, the availability of thrombolytic therapy might be the deciding factor.

Since paramedics live in a world of ACLS and PHTLS, you may have access to advanced equipment that is unavailable at your local hospital. A rural hospital under budget constraints, for example, may be unable to purchase equipment such as the Life Pack 12. In such instances, you might decide, with approval from medical direction, to use your equipment at the local hospital or to transport the patient to a definitive treatment center at a more distant location.

In treating seriously ill or injured patients, keep in mind that you may see all phases of a patient's death before reaching a distant medical facility. You face such situations knowing that there is little or nothing you can do to change the patient's outcome due to transport time.

*5. Identify important issues when faced with agricultural emergencies. pp. 489–496

Agriculture provides one of the major sources of income in the rural setting. Emergencies related to farming or ranching can range from equipment-related injuries to pesticide poisoning to any number of medical problems exacerbated by agricultural labor. When faced with an agricultural emergency, keep in mind the following considerations:

- **Safety issues:** Potential dangers include livestock, chemicals, fuel tanks, fumes in storage bins and silos, and heavy and outdated equipment.
- **Potential for trauma:** Farmers and ranchers often work 7 days a week, from sunrise to sunset, in extreme weather conditions, often in remote locations, using heavy equipment with the potential for almost every conceivable type of injury, including entrapment.
- **Mechanisms of injury:** Common mechanisms of injury in accidents involving agriculture equipment are wrap points, pinch points, shear points, and crush points.

In general, provide the same emergency medical care to patients involved in agricultural emergencies as you would to any other patient with similar injuries. However, at all times, keep in mind the effect of time and distance on the potential for shock. A farmer involved in a minor accident may lay injured for hours in harsh weather conditions before someone suspects any trouble. In cases involving long response and/or transport times, any serious bleeding injury can result in inadequate tissue perfusion if not treated promptly and effectively. In addition, because of unsanitary work conditions, sepsis and poisoning are very real possibilities.

*6. Review typical rural EMS scenarios, and identify what decisions a rural EMS provider needs to consider.   **pp. 488, 493, 496, 497–498**

In a typical rural EMS scenario, some of the considerations that the paramedic would need to consider include:

- Impact of lengthy response times and lengthy travel times to the hospital
- Possibility that the location of the patient may be difficult to find and not on a street map
- Possibility that the patient may be pinned or entangled in a complex piece of agricultural machinery
- Existence of hazardous materials on most farms and ranches
- Delays in the time it took to call EMS and/or locate the patient
- Radio dead spots that delay communications or make it necessary to obtain medical direction orders by the telephone prior to leaving the patient's residence
- Possibility that the patient's condition may change considerably during lengthy transport times
- Difficulty in meeting the guideline of the Golden Hour
- Need for an early decision on aeromedical evacuation or special extrication equipment
- Unavailability of specialized physicians or around-the-clock services normally found at urban hospitals
- Higher-than-average potential for shock (due to time-related factors)
- Availability of adequately trained EMS personnel, especially in volunteer agencies serving a wide geographic area

Case Study Review

Reread the case study on pages 479 and 480 in Paramedic Care: Special Considerations/Operations *and then read the following discussion.*

This case study shows how, due to the "distance factor," rural ALS teams often spend more time with patients than they would in an urban setting. In the sample scenario, the team performs lifesaving interventions that compensate for the lengthy transport to a hospital.

As in any situation, safety was the top priority for the paramedics who responded to this call. Prior to actually assessing the patient, the crew sized up the scene to rule out hazardous materials or "silo gas"—very real possibilities in an agricultural setting. Once they appraised scene safety, they approached the patient to begin assessment.

Throughout the case, the issue of time is dealt with: "5 minutes to assemble and get a volunteer squad en route to the farm," "1 minute to get a full-time paid agency off the floor," "the downtime is now 40 minutes," "total time of treatment prior to transport is 11 minutes," and the implied time in stating that the patient "is taken to a local hospital 33 miles away." As you can see, distance made it difficult for the crew to adhere to the guideline of the Golden Hour. Also, they probably spent more time with the patient en route to the hospital than they did on-scene.

Anticipating the possibility of dead spots—and changing patient conditions during a lengthy transport—the paramedics request additional orders from medical direction according to ALS protocols. The actions taken by this ALS crew, working with the volunteer BLS team, made the difference between life and death.

Content Self-Evaluation

MULTIPLE CHOICE

_____ 1. According to recent census data, the number of people who live in rural parts of the United States is about:
  A. one in two.
  B. one in three.
  C. one in four.
  D. one in five.
  E. one in ten.

_____ 2. It has been found that rural residents experience a disproportionate number of:
  A. chronic health conditions.
  B. serious injuries.
  C. trauma-related mortalities.
  D. medical-related mortalities.
  E. all of the above.

_____ 3. In the case of natural disasters, rural EMS personnel may be the only available medical support.
  A. True
  B. False

_____ 4. All of the following complicate rural EMS EXCEPT:
  A. radio dead spots.
  B. use of cell phones.
  C. the distance factor.
  D. crowded frequencies.
  E. enrollment shortages.

_____ 5. One of the most important ways to improve rural EMS systems is the effort to increase the number of:
  A. dispatchers.
  B. fire phones.
  C. paramedics.
  D. air medical helicopters.
  E. prompt care facilities.

_____ 6. Rural paramedics must be highly skilled and highly practiced to compensate for the extended run times and more complicated logistics found in many rural settings.
  A. True
  B. False

_____ 7. All of the following conditions or situations are reasons for considering the use of a helicopter EXCEPT:
  A. a lengthy extrication.
  B. the need for a hyperbaric chamber.
  C. high altitude pulmonary edema.
  D. a post-trauma cardiac arrest.
  E. multisystem trauma.

_____ 8. The risk of serious agricultural accidents and injuries is increased by:
  A. the long distances to hospitals.
  B. equipment and machines routinely used by farmers.
  C. radio communications problems.
  D. lack of cooperation by rural patients.
  E. high percentage of people over 65.

_____ 9. MOIs associated with agricultural equipment include:
  A. wrap points.
  B. shear points.
  C. crush points.
  D. pinch points.
  E. all of the above.

_____ 10. In some instances, ground transport may be more efficient than air medical transport, even if it means carrying a patient out in a basket stretcher.
  A. True
  B. False

MATCHING

Write the letter of the term in the space provided next to the appropriate description.

A. air bags

B. lock-out/tag-out

C. compartmentalization syndrome

D. silo gas

E. rust out

F. wrap points

G. prompt care facilities

H. distance factor

I. cribbing

J. PTO

_____ 11. an inability to keep abreast of new technologies and standards

_____ 12. hospital agencies that provide limited care and nonemergent medical treatment

_____ 13. locking off of a machinery switch and then placing a tag on the switch stating why it is shut off

_____ 14. fumes produced in a grain storage bin

_____ 15. inflatable high-pressure pillows that, when inflated, can lift up to 20 tons, depending on the brand

_____ 16. wooden slats used to shore up heavy equipment

_____ 17. condition that occurs when circulation to a portion of the body is cut off

_____ 18. mechanisms of injury in which an appendage gets caught and significantly twisted

_____ 19. power takeoff

_____ 20. a consideration for the extended times to respond to, arrive at, and transport to a hospital facility

SHORT ANSWER

List five challenges faced in practicing EMS in rural areas.

21. _____

22. _____

23. _____

24. _____

25. _____

Special Project

Going On-Line

The Internet is an excellent resource that brings rural EMS agencies closer to urban and suburban services. Not only can every paramedic assess vital information from national EMS agencies but he or she can also participate in continuing medical education through use of Brady's Companion Websites. A Companion Website is a site on the Internet that has been developed to enrich an EMS educational course. If you have not yet utilized the Companion Website for your paramedic training, now is a good time to check it out! Simply go to the Website **www.prenhall.com/bledsoe,** *and follow the prompts to* *the Paramedic Care: Principles & Practice Companion Website. Summarize the information that can be found at that site. Then click on the suggested Web links for Chapter 13, "Rural EMS." Record resources found at each site.*

1. Information available at the Companion Website for *Paramedic Care: Principles & Practice*:

   _____

   _____

   _____

   _____

   _____

   _____

2. Web Links

   Name of Website:_____

   URL: _____

   Resources: _____

   Name of Website: _____

   URL: _____

   Resources: _____

   Name of Website: _____

   URL: _____

   Resources: _____

   Name of Website: _____

   URL: _____

   Resources: _____

   Name of Website: _____

   URL: _____

   Resources: _____

Responding to Terrorist Acts

Review of Chapter Objectives

After reading this chapter, you should be able to:

1. Identify the typical weapons of mass destruction likely to be used by terrorists. **pp. 505–517**

The most likely weapon of mass destruction used by the terrorist, either foreign or domestic, is the conventional explosive. As terrorists gain greater funding and sophistication, however, the risk of terrorists using nuclear, biological, and chemical weapons is increasing. Terrorists may also use agents and mechanisms not yet mentioned as they search for new ways to terrify the public and bring attention to their causes. An example of this was crashing commercial airliners, laden with fuel, into large buildings.

2. Explain the mechanisms of injury associated with conventional and nuclear weapons of mass destruction. **pp. 505–508**

Chemical reactions in the conventional explosion release tremendous amounts of heat energy in milliseconds. This energy instantaneously creates super-heated gases and results in extreme pressure at the detonation site. This pressure moves outward rapidly, first creating a pressure wave traveling at sonic speeds and then becoming a forceful blast wind. The pressure wave (called overpressure) rapidly compresses and then decompresses all with which it comes in contact. Serious injury may result to any hollow and air-filled spaces, such as those in the middle ear, the bowel, and the lungs. The blast wind can propel the explosive container parts or other debris, such as glass or wood splinters, causing injury to those it strikes. The blast wind may also throw victims, resulting in blunt trauma as they strike objects or the ground. The pressure wave and blast wind may also cause structural collapse, resulting in crushing injury and/or entrapment. Finally, the blast heat may cause serious burn injury directly or burns from combustion of material it ignites.

The nuclear weapon releases energy as atoms are broken apart and reassembled. The energy released from a relatively small bomb is thousands of times greater than a conventional explosive of equal size. The nuclear detonation injures through the same mechanisms as the conventional explosion. The resulting injuries, however, are more extensive and serious. Additionally, the nuclear detonation releases exceptional amounts of heat energy that kills most individuals in the detonation area and causes serious burns at some distance from the blast epicenter. Lastly, the detonation emits great amounts of nuclear radiation causing direct radiation exposure and energizes dust and debris causing radioactive fallout. The fallout may travel with upper air currents and fall to earth many miles from the detonation site.

3. **Identify and describe the major subclassifications of chemical and biological weapons of mass destruction.** pp. 508–517

Chemical Weapons

—*Nerve agents.* Nerve agents attack the central nervous system by causing an impulse transmission overload. This results in muscle spasms, convulsions, unconsciousness, and respiratory failure.

—*Vesicants.* Vesicants are chemical agents that damage exposed skin and cause blistering. They may also damage the eyes, respiratory tract, and lung tissue and may induce general illness as well.

—*Pulmonary agents.* Pulmonary agents attack the airway and lungs, producing inflammation and pulmonary edema. Their use frequently results in nasal and throat irritation, wheezing, cough, dyspnea, and hypoxia.

—*Biotoxins.* Biotoxins are chemicals produced by living organisms and behave more like chemical agents. Botulinum is the most toxic, 15,000 times more potent than the worst of the nerve agents (VX).

Biological Weapons

—*Pulmonary or pneumonia-like agents.* Pulmonary agents are the most likely biological agents to be used by terrorists. These agents are transmitted via the respiratory system and induce cough, dyspnea, fever, and malaise.

—*Encephalitis-like agents.* Encephalitis-like agents affect the central nervous system and present with flulike signs and symptoms. However, these biological agents usually carry a much higher mortality rate than the flu or similar diseases.

Other Biological Agents

Cholera and *viral hemorrhagic fever* are other biological agents terrorists may use. Cholera causes profuse diarrhea, and viral hemorrhagic fever attacks the blood's ability to coagulate.

4. **List the scene evidence that might alert the EMS provider to a terrorist attack that involves a weapon of mass destruction.** p. 518

Terrorists are likely to target public places where the effects of their actions are the greatest on structures that symbolize an institution they oppose. The results of a conventional or nuclear explosion make them easy to recognize but chemical and biological releases may be insidious. Whenever a large number of people appear to be complaining of similar signs and symptoms, suspect the deployment of chemical or biological weapons. In a chemical release, the effects are likely to occur immediately or shortly after exposure. Confined spaces, such as within a building or in a subway terminal, are likely targets although terrorists may release an agent upwind of a large public gathering. A biological release is even more difficult to detect. You, or more likely, Emergency Department personnel, may recognize many patients with similar generalized signs and symptoms. Only after extensive diagnostic tests and investigation may someone confirm that a weapon of mass destruction was deployed.

5. **Describe the special safety precautions and safety equipment appropriate for an incident involving nuclear, biological, or chemical weapons.** pp. 517, 518

The first step in responding to a possible weapon of mass destruction incident is to maintain the proper index of suspicion and to assure that you, fellow rescuers, and the public are not exposed to danger. Approach the scene from upwind and when in doubt about scene safety, request that a properly trained response team assess and enter the scene before you. Only after the response team determines the scene is safe should you enter (if at all).

Affected patients must be properly decontaminated before you can offer care, both for your protection and theirs. This occurs whether they are brought to you or you enter the scene to treat them.

When responding to a nuclear incident, act at the direction of persons trained in radiation detection. Wear a dosimeter when appropriate and have your exposure level checked periodically. When off duty, properly decontaminate and move a good distance from the scene to limit cumulative exposure.

For biological agents, employ appropriate body substance isolation precautions. In this case, BSI usually means a properly fitted HEPA-filter mask and gloves. While it is unlikely that you will recognize the release of an agent, you may be called on to treat victims days after the initial exposure.

Chemical agent releases may present with a recognizable and immediate danger. Remain at a distance and upwind from the scene and call for the victims to self-evacuate. Only properly trained personnel wearing the appropriate protective gear (a properly trained and equipped HAZMAT team) should enter the scene. Patients must be properly decontaminated before it is safe for you to care for them.

6. Identify the assessment and management concerns for victims of conventional, nuclear, biological, and chemical weapons.   pp. 505, 507–508, 510–513, 516–51

Conventional. Victims of a conventional weapon detonation suffer compression injuries from the blast wave. The most serious injury is to the lungs. Any sign of compression injury such as middle ear or bowel injury signs or any dyspnea should suggest lung injury. Blast victims may also suffer penetrating and blunt injuries due to debris propelled by the blast wind or from being thrown by the wind. Finally, the victim may be injured during structural collapse.

Focus management of the blast victim on care for the respiratory injury. Administer high-flow, high-concentration oxygen. Provide intermittent positive-pressure ventilation as needed, but conservatively, as the blast may have injured the alveolar walls. Care for other blunt and penetrating injuries as indicated.

Nuclear. Victims of a nuclear blast are most likely to receive burns as their most serious injuries. Radiation exposure may come from the initial blast or from radioactive fallout at or downwind from the explosion. There will be limited signs and symptoms unless the radiation exposure was very high. With high radiation exposure, the patient will display nausea, vomiting, and malaise. The greater the radiation exposure, the faster these signs will appear following exposure.

Patient care includes decontamination and then care for thermal burns. Protection from fallout is an additional concern and best addressed by moving the victims away from the expected fallout path. Care for the patient exposed to radioactivity is mostly supportive.

If there is a recognized release of radiation through a conventional explosion or other mechanism, direct your first efforts to reduce futher exposure. Then assure that the patients are properly decontaminated. Only then, concentrate your efforts on specific injury care.

Biological. It is unlikely that anyone will immediately detect the release of a biological agent. It is more likely that you or other health care workers will notice a group of people complaining of similar symptoms. These symptoms will most likely be fever, nausea, body aches, and malaise (symptoms similar to the flu).

Care for the victims of a biological agent release is first directed at reducing transmission. At the first sign of a possible biological agent (or any potentially contagious disease), don a mask and gloves and isolate the patient (or patients). Provide supportive care as for any other serious contagious disease.

Chemical. A chemical release is likely to affect its victims very quickly. They will complain of respiratory symptoms such as chest tightness or burning or possibly skin irritation. If you receive reports of several or many individuals complaining of similar symptoms, suspect a chemical release and approach the scene with great caution. Alert the fire department or the designated hazardous materials team and position your vehicle upwind from the scene. Assure the evacuation of persons downwind and decontamination of those victims brought to you for care.

Care for the victims of a chemical release includes high-flow, high-concentration oxygen, respiratory support as needed (including bag-valve masking and intubation), and antidote administration as indicated.

7. Given a narrative description of a conventional, nuclear, biological, or chemical terrorist attack, identify the elements of scene size-up that suggest terrorism, and identify the likely injuries and any special patient management considerations necessary. pp. 504–519

During your classroom training and practical skills session you will learn and practice the skills associated with recognizing, taking the proper protective precautions for you and the public, and caring for patients subject to illness or injury from weapons of mass destruction. Use this training and practice to perfect your skills of WMD care.

Case Study Review

Reread the case study on pages 503 and 504 in Paramedic Care: Special Considerations/Operations *and then read the following discussion.*

This case study illustrates how the events of September 11, 2001, have affected EMS profession-als and their responsibilities. It highlights the need to include the possibility of terrorist acts in all as-pects of emergency care decision making.

Adam and Sean have a heightened index of suspicion for a weapon of mass destruction incident that comes following the events of September 11, 2001. When presented with several patients with similar symptoms, they suspect a chemical agent release and request activation of the country's WMD plan. They also approach the scene with care, arriving upwind of the building and directing dispatch to re-quest evacuation (thereby evacuating the building without risk to rescuers). Sean and Adam also re-quest the fire department (their local HAZMAT team) to respond as well. Finally, by using a cell phone rather than using the EMS radio, they assure their suspicion of a WMD incident is not made public.

Adam and Sean direct the potential patients to their care station using the public address system, again reducing any risk to the rescuers. They establish incident management and effectively communi-cate pertinent information regarding the numbers and types of patients they are encountering. This helps the emergency department prepare for arrival of numerous patients with the same complaints. Before stepping from their rig, Sean and Adam don HEPA-filter masks and gloves to further protect themselves from any biological threat.

Adam relinquishes incident management responsibilities as soon as someone from the fire depart-ment arrives. He communicates his knowledge of the scene and then joins Sean in administering to the patients. Since the number of patients outnumbers the resources available, Sean and Adam provide oxygen only to the most seriously affected patients. Thankfully, the symptoms are only minor and other ambulances arrive quickly. As more information is gathered about the scene, the initial information suggests a simple furnace or chimney malfunction. However, further investigation suggests that this was truly a WMD incident involving the intentional production of carbon monoxide. The scene then becomes a crime scene and is investigated thoroughly by the police department.

Content Self-Evaluation

MULTIPLE CHOICE

_____ 1. Which of the following is the most likely weapon of choice for terrorist groups?
   A. conventional explosives
   B. nuclear weapons
   C. biological agents
   D. chemical agents
   E. incendiary devices

_____ 2. Terrorists are likely to target which of the following?
   A. an embassy
   B. a symbol of government
   C. their employer
   D. corporations
   E. all of the above

_____ 3. The blast pressure wave is likely to injure all of the following EXCEPT:
A. the lungs.
B. the ears.
C. the bowel.
D. the heart.
E. the sinuses.

_____ 4. Incendiary agents differ from conventional explosives in that they:
A. have greater explosive energy.
B. cause more burn injuries.
C. consume more oxygen.
D. are dropped from a high altitude.
E. combine both explosive and nuclear damage.

_____ 5. Which of the following is the mechanism of injury associated with most deaths from a nuclear blast?
A. radiation burns
B. radiation illness
C. cancer
D. thermal burns
E. pressure injuries

_____ 6. The best way to detect radiation in the absence of a Geiger counter is:
A. by a strange taste in your mouth.
B. a warm sensation in your muscles.
C. immediate nausea.
D. a tingling sensation from the exposed surface.
E. none of the above.

_____ 7. Fallout associated with nuclear detonation is not likely to be a factor until how long after the detonation?
A. 10 minutes
B. 30 minutes
C. 1 hour
D. 4 hours
E. 2 days

_____ 8. Once a victim is exposed to nuclear radiation and debris has been properly decontaminated, he poses no danger to himself or others.
A. True
B. False

_____ 9. Which of the following is a symptom associated with radiation exposure?
A. nausea
B. fatigue
C. malaise
D. hypertension
E. all of the above except D

_____ 10. Which of the following influence the delivery of a chemical weapon?
A. wind strength
B. the agent's specific gravity
C. the agent's volatility
D. precipitation
E. all of the above

_____ 11. Which of the following is NOT a common sign or symptom of a nerve agent?
A. dry mouth
B. tearing eyes
C. urination
D. defecation
E. vomiting

_____ 12. Blistering agents are also known as:
A. organophosphates.
B. vesicants.
C. carbamates.
D. chambering agents.
E. none of the above.

_____ 13. Which of the following is NOT a blistering agent?
A. lewisite
B. phosgene oxime
C. botulinum
D. sulfur mustard
E. nitrogen mustard

©2006 Pearson Education, Inc.
Paramedic Care: Principles & Practice, Vol. 5

_____ **14.** One of the most toxic agents known to man is:
- **A.** sulfur mustard.
- **B.** ricin.
- **C.** VX gas.
- **D.** botulinum.
- **E.** none of the above.

_____ **15.** Which of the following suggests a chemical agent release?
- **A.** a strange smell
- **B.** numerous patients complaining of the same symptoms
- **C.** a cloud of dust or gas
- **D.** incapacitated or dead birds and insects
- **E.** all of the above

_____ **16.** Which of the following is NOT a biological agent capable of spreading from person to person?
- **A.** Ebola
- **B.** smallpox
- **C.** plague
- **D.** anthrax
- **E.** cholera

_____ **17.** A biological release can be recognized by which of the following?
- **A.** a distinctive cloud
- **B.** a distinctive color
- **C.** immediate signs and symptoms
- **D.** very distinct signs and symptoms
- **E.** none of the above

_____ **18.** The most likely biological agents to be used by terrorists are:
- **A.** pulmonary agents.
- **B.** flulike agents.
- **C.** encephalitis-like agents.
- **D.** Ebola.
- **E.** all of the above.

_____ **19.** Almost all biological weapons are transmitted via the respiratory route; therefore, the HEPA respirator is very effective at reducing transmission.
- **A.** True
- **B.** False

_____ **20.** Dangers of a conventional explosion used by terrorists include all of the following EXCEPT:
- **A.** the danger of a secondary explosion.
- **B.** inability to recognize the incident.
- **C.** radioactive contamination.
- **D.** structural collapse.
- **E.** all of the above.

SPECIAL CONSIDERATIONS/OPERATIONS
Content Review

Content Self-Evaluation

Chapter 1: Neonatology

_____ 1. Complication(s) that may result from hypoxia during the birth process include:
  A. persistent fetal circulation.
  B. spinal cord defects.
  C. hypothermia.
  D. hypovolemia.
  E. both A and C.

_____ 2. Persistent fetal circulation is best described as which of the following?
  A. cardiovascular flow causing the pink extremities and blue trunk.
  B. a bradycardia, post delivery.
  C. bypass of the respiratory system.
  D. ongoing asphyxia, also called secondary hypoxia.
  E. umbilical circulation continuing after delivery.

_____ 3. The congenital condition where the tongue is large, the jaw is small, and the patient has a cleft palate is:
  A. Pierre Robin syndrome
  B. choanal atreia
  C. menigomyelocele
  D. enhanced cleft palate
  E. none of the above.

_____ 4. Heat loss from the newborn occurs through which of the following routes:
  A. evaporation
  B. convection
  C. conduction
  D. radiation
  E. all of the above

_____ 5. The 2nd tier of the pediatric resuscitation pyramid includes which of the following?
  A. drying
  B. warming
  C. suctioning
  D. oxygen
  E. tactile stimulation

_____ 6. The most common cause of cardiac arrest in a newborn is:
  A. congenital abnormalities.
  B. meconium aspiration.
  C. hypovolemia.
  D. hypoxia.
  E. diaphragmatic hernia.

_____ 7. A newborn infant presents with peripheral cyanosis and signs of respiratory distress. Your exam reveals a small, flat abdomen with bowel sounds present in the chest. Heart sounds are displaced to the right. You suspect:
  A. ductus arteriosus.
  B. Pierre Robin syndrome.
  C. diaphragmatic hernia.
  D. omphalocele.
  E. congenital defect.

_____ 8. Reasons for hypothermia in preterm newborns include all of the following EXCEPT:
   A. underdeveloped lungs and respiratory structures.
   B. smaller subcutaneous reserves of insulating fat.
   C. underdeveloped thermoregulatory mechanisms.
   D. large body surface area in relation to small weight.
   E. inability to shiver and maintain body temperature.

_____ 9. Seizures in neonatal patients are often the result of:
   A. developmental abnormalities.   D. metabolic disturbances.
   B. drug withdrawal.   E. all of the above.
   C. fever.

_____ 10. Vomiting in the neonate is most frequently an isolated incident, unrelated to other pathology.
   A. True   B. False

Chapter 2: Pediatrics

_____ 11. Care of the pediatric patient includes care for the child's parents or caregivers.
   A. True   B. False

_____ 12. The child's most common response to illness or injury is fear. Common fears of children include all of the following EXCEPT fear of:
   A. separation.   D. being hurt.
   B. disfigurement.   E. automobiles.
   C. the unknown.

_____ 13. In assessing a pediatric patient for shock, which of the following statements is NOT true?
   A. A smaller absolute volume of loss is needed to cause shock.
   B. A child in shock will always have decreased blood pressure.
   C. Hypotension is an ominous sign of imminent cardiac arrest.
   D. Assessment is based upon clinical signs of tissue perfusion.
   E. A larger relative volume of loss is needed to cause shock.

_____ 14. It is a good idea to let a parent remain with the small child during care and transport.
   A. True   B. False

_____ 15. What percentage of birth weight is lost by the newborn in the first few days of life?
   A. none   D. 20%
   B. 5%   E. 35%
   C. 10%

_____ 16. All of the following signs indicate acute distress in the pediatric patient EXCEPT a:
   A. heart rate of 160 in a 7-year-old child.
   B. respiratory rate greater than 60.
   C. heart rate above 180 in a 5-year-old child.
   D. heart rate of 65 in a 4-year-old child.
   E. 5-year-old child with an altered mental state.

_____ 17. What size cuff would you use when taking a pediatric blood pressure?
   A. its width, equal to the width of the arm
   B. its width, equal to two thirds the width of the arm
   C. simply assure an adult cuff is tight
   D. use an adult cuff but reduce the reading value by 30%
   E. pediatric blood pressures are unreliable

_____ 18. Mild hypotension is a common and relatively insignificant sign in the pediatric patient.
   A. True   B. False

©2006 Pearson Education, Inc.
Paramedic Care: Principles & Practice, Vol. 5

_____ 19. The best size approximation of a nasopharyngeal airway is:
A. use an airway number equal to the patient age in years.
B. use a #10 French for neonates and a 12 for toddlers.
C. measure length against the patient's jaw.
D. size to the external diameter of the child's little finger.
E. none of the above.

_____ 20. Nasogastric tube insertion should be considered in the pediatric patient because it relieves gastric distention and improves the adequacy of ventilations.
A. True   B. False

_____ 21. Rapid sequence intubation is an advanced airway procedure that may be indicated in all of these pediatric patients EXCEPT a(n):
A. combative 6-year-old child with head trauma.
B. 9-year-old child experiencing generalized tonic-clonic seizures.
C. 8-year-old patient without a gag reflex.
D. 14-year-old patient attempting suicide by overdose.
E. vomiting 3-year-old with head trauma from a fall.

_____ 22. The appropriate second defibrillation charge for a 15-kilogram pediatric patient is:
A. 7.5 joules.   D. 60 joules.
B. 15 joules.   E. 85 joules.
C. 45 joules.

_____ 23. Being able to recognize the stages of respiratory compromise quickly is paramount for the paramedic. Normal mental status, tachypnea, nasal flaring (in infants), and grunting are all signs and symptoms of:
A. respiratory distress.   D. respiratory arrest.
B. respiratory shunting.   E. all of the above.
C. respiratory failure.

_____ 24. Signs of decompensated shock in a pediatric patient include all of the following EXCEPT:
A. tachycardia.   D. cyanosis.
B. bradycardia.   E. hypotension.
C. hypertension.

_____ 25. If intravenous diazepam cannot be administered to a pediatric patient because intravenous access has not been made, oral diazepam should be administered.
A. True   B. False

_____ 26. Which of the following is a likely cause of vomiting in the pediatric patient?
A. fever   D. respiratory infections
B. ear infections   E. all of the above
C. gastroenteritis

_____ 27. In treating older pediatric diabetic patients, remember that they have been taught about their condition and can participate in their care.
A. True   B. False

_____ 28. Pediatric patients account for the majority of poisonings treated by EMS.
A. True   B. False

_____ 29. What percentage of pediatric near-drowning patients suffer neurologic deficits?
A. less than 5%   D. 30 to 35%
B. 10 to 20%   E. more than 40%
C. 20 to 25%

_____ 30. Which of the following is NOT true regarding pediatric airway care?
A. The sniffing position best maintains the airway.
B. Airway pressures are relatively high.
C. Needle cricothyrotomy is rarely indicated.
D. Gastric tubes are frequently placed to decompress the stomach.
E. It may be necessary to disable the pop-off value on the BVM.

_____ 31. Which of the following is NOT a sign of increasing intracranial pressure?
A. elevated blood pressure
B. bradycardia
C. rapid deep respirations, progressing to slow deep respirations
D. constricted pupils
E. buldging fontanelles

_____ 32. What percentage of pediatric spinal fractures occur at the C1-C2 level?
A. 15 to 20%   D. 50 to 60%
B. 20 to 25%   E. 60 to 70%
C. 40 to 50%

_____ 33. What percentage of the body's surface does the head receive in the pediatric rule of nines?
A. 9%   D. 13.5%
B. 18%   E. 6.25%
C. 14.5%

_____ 34. Which of the following is least likely to indicate possible child abuse?
A. a fracture in a child under 2 years
B. a greenstick fracture in an 8-year old
C. multiple injuries in various stages of healing
D. intra-abdominal trauma in the young child
E. injury that does not fit the described mechanism of injury

_____ 35. A common complication associated with tracheostomy tubes for pediatric patients is:
A. obstruction by a mucus plug.   D. infection.
B. an air leak.   E. all of the above.
C. a dislodged tube.

Chapter 3: Geriatric Emergencies

_____ 36. It is predicted that by 2040, the elderly population will reach 20% of the total population.
A. True   B. False

_____ 37. Which of the following is a federal program that is most responsible for paying for medical care for the elderly patient?
A. Social Security   D. Veteran's Administration
B. Medicare   E. none of the above
C. Medicaid

_____ 38. In the elderly, signs and symptoms are more likely directly related to the disease process causing them.
A. True   B. False

_____ 39. A contributing factor to decreased medication compliance by the elderly is:
A. polypharmacy.   D. prolonged therapy.
B. income limitations.   E. all of the above.
C. sensory impairment.

_____ 40. Effective continence requires:
  A. an anatomically correct GI/GU tract.   D. A, B, and C.
  B. a competent sphincter mechanism.   E. A and C only.
  C. adequate cognition and mobility.

_____ 41. All of the following are byproducts of malnutrition EXCEPT:
  A. vitamin deficiencies.   D. hyperlipidemia.
  B. dehydration.   E. both A and B.
  C. hyperglycemia.

_____ 42. Factors that complicate the assessment of geriatric patients include:
  A. diminished pain perception.   D. dementia.
  B. presence of multiple diseases.   E. all of the above.
  C. failure to report symptoms.

_____ 43. Common symptoms of senility and organic brain syndrome include all of the following EXCEPT:
  A. delirium.   D. restlessness.
  B. serenity.   E. hostility.
  C. confusion.

_____ 44. It is often difficult for the paramedic to differentiate acute from chronic physical findings in the elderly patient.
  A. True   B. False

_____ 45. Which of the following statements about the aging process is NOT true?
  A. Chest wall compliance decreases.   D. The left ventricular wall thickens.
  B. The lungs lose their elasticity.   E. The skin becomes thicker.
  C. The brain shrinks.

_____ 46. Syncope occurring as a result of the body's inability to compensate for movement from the supine position to the seated position or from the seated position to the standing position is known as:
  A. cardiac syncope.   D. nocturnal syncope.
  B. vasovagal syncope.   E. vasodepressor syncope.
  C. orthostatic syncope.

_____ 47. Risk factors for strokes include all of the following EXCEPT:
  A. atherosclerosis.   D. dementia.
  B. hypertension.   E. immobility.
  C. atrial fibrillation.

_____ 48. Strokes are a common cause of blindness in the elderly patient.
  A. True   B. False

_____ 49. Which of the following is NOT a common cause of seizures in the elderly patient?
  A. stroke   D. alcohol withdrawal
  B. mass lesion (tumor or bleed)   E. hypoglycemia
  C. hyperventilation

_____ 50. Which of the following is NOT true regarding dementia?
  A. more than 50% of nursing home residents have some form of dementia
  B. delerium is a form of dementia
  C. it is a global cognitive impairment
  D. it is often irreversible
  E. Alzheimer's disease is a form of dementia

_____ 51. The primary cause of Parkinson's disease is a neuromuscular disease triggered by a small stroke and related to diet.
  A. True   B. False

_____ 52. Which of the following is NOT a cause of lower GI bleeding?
A. esophageal varicies
B. diverticulosis
C. tumors
D. ischemic colitis
E. arterio-venous malformations

_____ 53. A significant contributing factor to osteoarthritis in the elderly is:
A. obesity
B. inflammatory arthritis
C. trauma
D. congenital abnormalities
E. all of the above

_____ 54. Which of the following predisposes the elderly to hypothermia?
A. previous CNS disorders like stroke
B. chronic illness
C. malnutrition
D. drugs that interfere with heat generation mechanisms
E. all of the above

_____ 55. Aging results in reduced size and weight of the brain. Which of the following statements about traumatic head injuries in the elderly patient is TRUE?
A. Signs and symptoms of brain injury appear faster.
B. Signs and symptoms of brain injury occur slower.
C. Brain injury is less common in elderly patients.
D. Elderly patients recover faster from brain injury.
E. Brain injuries are less severe in elderly patients.

Chapter 4: Abuse and Assault

_____ 56. A paramedic could potentially identify an abusive family situation by recognizing which of the following generic risk factors?
A. The children are all in school.
B. Both parents are employed.
C. The residence is untidy.
D. The family is below the poverty level.
E. All of the children are sick.

_____ 57. Two signs of domestic elder abuse are:
A. head injury and loss of speech.
B. untreated decubitus ulcers and bruising.
C. dementia and loss of freedom.
D. poor hygiene and loss of appetite.
E. good hygiene and bruising.

_____ 58. Abuse as a child is typically isolated and forgotten once the abused child becomes an adult.
A. True
B. False

_____ 59. Shaken baby syndrome can cause permanent brain damage and may also result in:
A. hair loss.
B. malnutrition.
C. chest trauma.
D. blindness.
E. cerebral palsy.

_____ 60. Hostility, drug abuse, promiscuity, and nightmares are indicative of:
A. mental abuse.
B. physical abuse.
C. sexual abuse.
D. neglect.
E. none of the above.

_____ 61. Paramedics can help the victim of a suspected rape by:
A. assisting the patient with bathing and dressing.
B. provide private and safe environment for assessment and care.
C. treating the patient at the residence without transporting.
D. avoiding talk about the attack as it may upset the patient more.
E. completing a thorough patient assessment, including genitalia.

©2006 Pearson Education, Inc.
Paramedic Care: Principles & Practice, Vol. 5

Chapter 5: The Challenged Patient

_____ 62. A paramedic can improve communication with a hearing-impaired patient by:
   A. addressing the patient face-to-face.
   B. speaking clearly using exaggerated gestures.
   C. making up hand signals the patient recognizes.
   D. talking loudly without using exaggerated gestures.
   E. all of the above.

_____ 63. Paramedics should always ask permission before touching a service animal, its harness, or leash.
   A. True
   B. False

_____ 64. A speech disorder characterized by an inability to understand the spoken word is called:
   A. dysphasia.
   B. sensory aphasia.
   C. motor aphasia.
   D. global aphasia.
   E. anuria.

_____ 65. A traumatic spinal cord injury in the area of C3 to C5 is especially important because it affects the ability to:
   A. move the legs.
   B. move the arms.
   C. move the head.
   D. breathe.
   E. move the fingers.

_____ 66. Fetal alcohol syndrome patients are often born with small eyes with short slits, a small jaw, and a small head.
   A. True
   B. False

_____ 67. Cancer is a blanket term for many different diseases, each with its own characteristics but having in common the abnormal growth of cells in normal tissue.
   A. True
   B. False

_____ 68. Which of the following is NOT a common cause of cerebral palsy?
   A. maternal drug overdose
   B. encephalitis
   C. meningitis
   D. head injury
   E. premature birth

_____ 69. Which of the following is true regarding mucoviscidosis?
   A. it is also called multiple sclerosis
   B. it is an acquired disorder
   C. it primarily affects the muscular system
   D. it causes a decrease in pancreatic enzymes
   E. all of the above

_____ 70. Which of the following is a disease of the autoimmune system characterized by chronic weakness in the voluntary muscles.
   A. multiple sclerosis
   B. myasthenia gravis
   C. cycstic fibrosis
   D. poliomyelitis
   E. muscular dystrophy

Chapter 6: Acute Interventions for the Chronic-Care Patient

_____ 71. According to the National Center for Health Statistics, almost 75 percent of home care patients are members of what age group?
   A. under 18 years old
   B. under 45 years old
   C. 45 to 55 years old
   D. 55 to 65 years old
   E. 65 years or older

72. Upon arriving at the home of a chronic home care patient, the paramedic should:
    A. not treat the patient if a home care provider is on the way.
    B. assume the home care provider has less training than you.
    C. respectfully get a report from home care provider on the scene.
    D. ask any home care provider to leave the scene.
    E. none of the above.

73. An infection at the cellular level is called cellulitis and is a life-threatening condition requiring acute emergency care.
    A. True   B. False

74. An acute viral infection that damages the myelin sheath covering peripheral nerves, causing rapid loss of motor function is:
    A. multiple sclerosis.   D. Guillain-Barré syndrome.
    B. cerebral palsy.   E. cystic fibrosis.
    C. myasthenia gravis.

75. You are called to the residence of a home care patient with a history of myasthenia gravis. What type of respiratory assistance device might you expect to find?
    A. ventilator   D. colostomy bag
    B. heart/lung machine   E. urinary bag
    C. IV pump

76. The airway ventilator option that adds a small pressure at the end of expiration is:
    A. CPAP.   D. PEEP.
    B. BiPAP.   E. all of the above except C.
    C. ADRS.

77. The patient with a vascular access device (VAD) such as a PICC line will be on anticoagulant therapy and predisposed to bleeding disorders such as stroke and GI bleeding.
    A. True   B. False

78. Signs and symptoms associated with VADs and air embolism include all of the following except:
    A. headache.   D. dyspnea without crackles.
    B. elevated pulse oximetry readings.   E. altered mental status.
    C. chest pain.

79. Care for the postpartum mother with serious hemorrhage should include which of the following:
    A. fundal massage   D. rapid transport
    B. fluid administration   E. all of the above
    C. possible pitocin administration

80. In the newborn, discharged from the hospital, and displaying cyanosis, bradycardia (<100 beat per minute), respiratory crackles, and respiratory distress you should suspect which of the following?
    A. respiratory insufficiency   D. severe infection
    B. cardiac insufficiency   E. both A and B
    C. hypovolemia

Chapter 7: Assessment-Based Management

81. The list of possible causes for the patient's complaint is referred to as the:
    A. field diagnosis.   D. narrowing process.
    B. index of suspicion.   E. nature of the illness.
    C. differential diagnosis.

_____ 82. Your decision making is based largely on:
- A. the patient's medical history.
- B. your physical exam findings.
- C. pattern recognitions and intuition.
- D. BLS/ALS protocols.
- E. all of the above.

_____ 83. All EMS systems have protocols devised by the medical director that can never be deviated from by the EMT-Basic or paramedic.
- A. True
- B. False

_____ 84. When treating a patient for substance abuse, one of the most positive things a paramedic can do for the patient is to:
- A. refer the patient to detox.
- B. don full BSI precautions.
- C. remain nonjudgmental.
- D. transport to the nearest hospital.
- E. contact law enforcement.

_____ 85. All of the following are roles of the patient care provider EXCEPT:
- A. providing scene cover.
- B. acting as triage group leader.
- C. directing the team in patient care.
- D. talking to relatives to gather information.
- E. performing interventions.

_____ 86. An effective oral presentation of the patient's condition meets all of the following guidelines EXCEPT:
- A. last less than one minute
- B. use well defined medical jargon
- C. are concise and clear
- D. include pertinent negatives
- E. conclude with a request associated with the care plan

_____ 87. The best way to develop good assessment skills is to practice:
- A. in the lab setting.
- B. on co-workers.
- C. on patients.
- D. on friends.
- E. all of the above.

Chapter 8: Ambulance Operations

_____ 88. Reasons for routine inspection of the ambulance and equipment include all of the following EXCEPT:
- A. ensuring that equipment is ready and available.
- B. ensuring that the work environment is safe.
- C. reminding personnel where all supplies are.
- D. ensuring the cleanliness of the ambulance.
- E. evaluating the performance of other paramedics.

_____ 89. Responsibility for reporting ambulance or equipment problems lies with:
- A. inspectors for the local, regional, or state EMS offices.
- B. the paramedic who identifies the problem.
- C. the paramedic or responder on the next shift.
- D. the supervisor responsible for vehicles or supplies.
- E. none of the above.

_____ 90. Maneuvering ambulances and crews in an effort to reduce response times is a strategy known as:
- A. deployment.
- B. reserve capacity.
- C. system status management.
- D. peak load response.
- E. tiered response.

_____ 91. The term for the ability of an EMS agency to respond to calls beyond those handled by the on-duty crews is called:
   A. deployment.
   B. reserve capacity.
   C. system status management.
   D. peak load response.
   E. tiered response.

_____ 92. According to recent studies, motorists do not hear sirens or see emergency lights until the ambulance is within:
   A. 50 feet or less.
   B. 50 to 100 feet.
   C. 100 to 150 feet.
   D. 50 to 100 yards.
   E. 100 to 150 yards.

Chapter 9: Medical Incident Management

_____ 93. The incident management system today used by the emergency response system originated from:
   A. Southern California fire service.
   B. Federal Department of Transportation.
   C. OSHA.
   D. National Incident Management System.
   E. Homeland Security Administration.

_____ 94. What event served as the precipitating impetus for development of a national incident management program?
   A. California wildfires
   B. Terrorist attacks in 2001
   C. the anthrax letters
   D. re-organization of the National Fire Service
   E. all of the above

_____ 95. The C-FLOP mnemonic identifies the five elements of the incident management system. The "P" stands for which of the following?
   A. patient assessment
   B. political coordination
   C. planning
   D. pre-emptive action
   E. past experience

_____ 96. Managers from different jurisdictions for law enforcement, fire, and EMS coordinate their activities and share responsibility for command through a process known as:
   A. unified command.
   B. ultimate authority.
   C. singular command.
   D. span of control.
   E. none of the above.

_____ 97. Generally, the IMS would be implemented in which of these situations?
   A. when an ambulance is deployed to an MVC
   B. at the scene of a technical rescue operation
   C. at the scene of a traumatic cardiac arrest
   D. when two or more units respond to an incident
   E. all of the above

_____ 98. The officers who perform supervisory roles in the IMS rather than those who actually perform a task are called:
   A. section chiefs.
   B. management staff.
   C. staff function officers.
   D. demobilizing officers.
   E. medical officers.

_____ 99. Monitoring the emotional status of all on-scene personnel and providing support as needed is the job of the:
A. management staff.
B. agency chaplain.
C. command staff.
D. mental health support.
E. Incident Commander.

_____ 100. Which of the following units are usually under EMS branch authority at a typical multi-casualty incident?
A. triage
B. treatment
C. transport
D. decontamination
E. staging

_____ 101. At the disaster, which patients are collected at the morgue?
A. emergent
B. delayed
C. expectant
D. minimal
E. both B and C

_____ 102. The IMS unit responsible for monitoring and supporting on-scene responders is the:
A. extrication unit.
B. scene safety officer.
C. triage sector.
D. rehabilitation unit.
E. staging unit.

Chapter 10: Rescue Awareness and Operations

_____ 103. Which of the following is not considered a special rescue operation?
A. low-head dam
B. high-angle rescue
C. confined space rescue
D. cardiac arrest
E. vehicle rescue

_____ 104. Every rescue operation should have a Safety Officer who has the knowledge and authority to intervene in unsafe situations.
A. True
B. False

_____ 105. When approaching a rescue scene, your scene size-up should provide you with information about:
A. the nature of the situation.
B. scene safety and hazards.
C. the total number of victims.
D. the need for special rescue teams.
E. all of the above.

_____ 106. Initial responding units often overestimate their capability to handle a rescue situation or are hesitant to request reserves or specialty teams.
A. True
B. False

_____ 107. Which of the following situations does NOT require extrication of the patient prior to treatment?
A. a trapped radio tower worker
B. a patient entrapped in an industrial machine
C. a person stranded in swirling, running, or rising water
D. a patient overcome by life-threatening atmosphere
E. a patient trapped by a partially collapsed trench wall

_____ 108. Care for an entrapped patient during a lengthy rescue differs from normal patient care because it involves:
A. greater patient stabilization skills.
B. more psychological support for the patient.
C. protection from a more hostile environment.
D. protection from extended rescue operations.
E. all of the above.

_____109. Water immersion causes body heat to be lost how many times faster than air?
- A. 2
- B. 10
- C. 15
- D. 25
- E. 40

_____110. Factors that contribute to drowning associated with cool or cold water immersion include which of the following?
- A. inability to self rescue
- B. laryngospasm
- C. inability to grasp a line
- D. inability to follow simple directions
- E. all of the above

_____111. The proper order for the water rescue method is which of the following?
- A. row-throw-go-reach
- B. reach-throw-row-go
- C. throw-go-reach-row
- D. go-throw-reach-row
- E. row-throw-reach-go

_____112. Which of the following is the most likely location for a drowning?
- A. salt water
- B. private swimming pool
- C. bathtub
- D. fish ponds
- E. inland lakes or rivers

_____113. The longest cold water submersion that resulted in successful resuscitation was for what length of time?
- A. 10 minutes
- B. 45 minutes
- C. just over an hour
- D. 2½ hours
- E. 4 hours

_____114. Who is the most likely victim of a hazardous atmosphere?
- A. a farmer
- B. an industrial worker
- C. an excavator
- D. petroleum or chemical plant worker
- E. rescuer

_____115. The greatest hazard associated with the motor vehicle collision is which of the following?
- A. traffic flow
- B. spilled fuel
- C. spilled toxic chemicals (battery acid)
- D. glass
- E. jagged metal

_____116. The term that describes descending by sliding down a fixed double rope is:
- A. belaying.
- B. dynamic anchoring.
- C. rappelling.
- D. controlled descent.
- E. high angle scrambling.

_____117. Extended care issues that need specific protocols include which of the following?
- A. long-term hydration management
- B. removal of impaled objects
- C. wound cleansing
- D. hyperthemia management
- E. all of the above

Chapter 11: Hazardous Materials Incidents

_____118. Priorities for a HAZMAT incident are the same as for any other major incident: life safety, incident stabilization, and property conservation.
- A. True
- B. False

_____119. Paramedics should suspect hazardous material involvement at a(n):
- A. overturned tractor-trailer.
- B. fire alarm at a hospital.
- C. accident at a railroad crossing.
- D. explosion at a government office.
- E. all of the above.

_____120. Chemical, biological, or nuclear devices used by terrorists to strike at government or high-profile targets are called:
  A. clandestine weapons of terror.
  B. international weapons of ruin.
  C. weapons of mass destruction.
  D. domestic implements of war.
  E. weapons of motivational destruction.

_____121. A four-digit identification number specific to a given chemical is a(n):
  A. NFPA code.
  B. UN number.
  C. U.S. number.
  D. IDLH.
  E. bill of lading.

_____122. An example of a computer-aided database used for HAZMAT references and operations is the:
  A. CAMEO.
  B. UN computer system.
  C. MSDS database.
  D. Canadian material sort system.
  E. *Emergency Response Guidebook.*

_____123. Which of the following zones is associated with and contains the primary contamination, at the hazardous materials incident?
  A. red zone
  B. yellow zone
  C. green zone
  D. blue zone
  E. none of the above

_____124. The lowest temperature that a chemical will give off enough vapor to ignite is the:
  A. boiling point.
  B. flash point.
  C. flammable limit.
  D. ignition temperature.
  E. vapor pressure.

_____125. The radiation capable of traveling only a few inches through air is:
  A. alpha.
  B. beta.
  C. gamma.
  D. neutron.
  E. X-ray.

_____126. The only poisoning where the administration of epecac is appropriate to induce vomiting is for severe corrosive ingestion.
  A. True
  B. False

_____127. The level of HAZMAT protection worn by firefighters and not suitable for HAZMAT situations is:
  A. level A.
  B. level B.
  C. level C.
  D. level D.
  E. level E.

Chapter 12: Crime Scene Awareness

_____128. The age group with the highest arrest rates for violent crimes is which of the following?
  A. 0 to 10 years of age
  B. 10 to 14 years of age
  C. 15 to 34 years of age
  D. 35 to 50 years of age
  E. 50 years and older

_____129. In most cases, you can legally leave a patient behind when there is a documented danger.
  A. True
  B. False

_____130. A crime that is committed against a person solely on the basis of the individual's religion is an example of:
  A. assault and battery.
  B. a federal crime.
  C. a crime of passion.
  D. a hate crime.
  E. a racist act.

_____131. One of the most common substances manufactured in drug laboratories is:
    A. marijuana.
    B. methamphetamine.
    C. date rape drugs.
    D. opiate narcotics.
    E. methadone.

_____132. All of the following are safety tactics the paramedic could use in a dangerous situation EXCEPT:
    A. retreat.
    B. cover and concealment.
    C. distraction and evasion.
    D. camouflage and cover.
    E. contact and cover.

_____133. EMS personnel trained to serve with a Technical Emergency Medical Service or a law enforcement agency are called:
    A. EMT-Swats.
    B. SWATEMs.
    C. EMT-TEMs.
    D. EMT-Tacticals.
    E. CONTOMs.

_____134. Clothing samples should be placed in a clear plastic bag when taken from the crime scene as this prevents contamination from chemicals in the air.
    A. True
    B. False

_____135. When required to cut clothing off the patient for essential assessment or care, which of the following is not appropriate?
    A. Try carefully to cut through rather than around any holes.
    B. Place the clothing remnant in a brown paper bag.
    C. Leave clothing on even if assessment would otherwise require its removal.
    D. Place all soiled clothing in a bio-hazard bag.
    E. Both A and D.

_____136. Exam gloves prevent you from leaving print evidence at the scene and reduce the chances of you smudging prints left by others.
    A. True
    B. False

_____137. Blood splatter evidence is important because it helps identify:
    A. the type of weapon used.
    B. the position of the attacker in relation to the victim.
    C. the direction of the attack.
    D. the force of the attack.
    E. all of the above.

Chapter 13: Rural EMS

_____138. Rural residents suffer a higher level of mortality associated with medical emergencies because:
    A. there are greater distances to health care.
    B. of a lack of experienced EMS providers.
    C. helicopter transport is overutilized.
    D. rural residents are sicker to begin with.
    E. of a lack of adequately equipped ambulances.

_____139. Communication difficulties are a major problem in rural areas simply because of a lack of cell phone coverage.
    A. True
    B. False

_____140. A term for an inability to keep abreast of new technologies and standards is:
    A. lost opportunity.
    B. block out.
    C. rust out.
    D. poor management.
    E. deficient networking.

©2006 Pearson Education, Inc.
Paramedic Care: Principles & Practice, Vol. 5

_____141. Facilities that provide limited care and nonemergent medical treatment are:
A. fast tracks.
B. "Docs in a box."
C. rural hostels.
D. prompt care facilities.
E. health care outreaches.

_____142. Which of the following would you expect to be thinly distributed in the rural or wilderness setting?
A. full service hospitals
B. fire service
C. EMS units
D. physicians
E. all of the above

_____143. Rural emergency care is likely to cause which of the following changes to the normal EMS response?
A. less dependable detection
B. longer response times to the scene
C. longer transport times
D. less dependable physician availability at rural hospitals
E. all of the above

_____144. Hazards associated with agricultural activities include which of the following:
A. machinery entrapment
B. hazardous materials
C. entombment under grain or silage
D. confined space/toxic environment
E. all of the above

_____145. The procedure that calls for turning equipment off and marking it so it is not turned on is called:
A. positive lock out.
B. definitive shut down.
C. keyed/disabled.
D. lock-out/tag-out.
E. none of the above.

_____146. Which of the following is an advantage to using an EMS helicopter in a rural or wilderness area.
A. transport is less expensive
B. they are available in all types of weather
C. it is rare that a helicopter will not be available
D. they can travel quickly over rough terrain
E. none of the above

_____147. A potential complication for patients suffering from agricultural injuries is:
A. extended response and transport times.
B. extended time to detection of the accident.
C. possible contamination with manure.
D. possible contamination by farm chemicals.
E. all of the above.

Chapter 14: Responding to Terrorist Acts

_____148. The most likely weapon used by terrorists is which of the following?
A. nuclear agent
B. chemical agent
C. biological agent
D. dirty bomb
E. conventional explosive

_____149. The aspect of a nuclear blast that will affect persons the greatest distance from the epicenter is:
A. initial radiation.
B. fallout.
C. burns.
D. structural collapse.
E. electromagnetic pulse.

_____150. The first medication administered to a victim of nerve agent release is:
   A. nitroglycerine.
   B. amyl nitrate.
   C. atropine.
   D. coumadin.
   E. none of the above.

_____151. In general, after a terrorist attack, the scene is safe to enter as the damage of contamination and disease transmission passes very quickly.
   A. True
   B. False

_____152. The materials most commonly used by terrorists in the United States has been:
   A. sarin gas.
   B. fertilizer and diesel fuel.
   C. ricin.
   D. automatic weapons.
   E. anthrax spores.

_____153. Which of the following is a likely injury induced by an explosion?
   A. compression injury
   B. burn injury
   C. blunt trauma
   D. penetrating trauma
   E. all of the above

_____154. Which type of injuries associated with a nuclear ignition is the most lethal?
   A. penetrating trauma
   B. blunt trauma
   C. compressional injuries
   D. burn injuries
   E. all of the above

_____155. After a nuclear detonation, the immediate area is likely to be radiation free for:
   A. the first 2 minutes.
   B. 2 miles or more.
   C. 4 miles.
   D. the first hour.
   E. none of the above

_____156. The radiation injury patient who has been properly decontaminated presents no danger to care providers.
   A. True
   B. False

_____157. Generally, the patients who present with the earliest and most severe signs of radiation exposure are the least severely affected.
   A. True
   B. False

_____158. Which of the following locations is a likely place for a chemical weapon attack?
   A. subway
   B. large building
   C. shopping mall
   D. convention center
   E. all of the above

_____159. Which of the following chemical agents is classified as a nerve agent?
   A. lewisite
   B. ricin
   C. VX
   D. mustard
   E. all of the above

_____160. The smell of newly mown grass is often associated with which chemical agent?
   A. mace
   B. hydrogen sulfide
   C. botulinum
   D. phosgene
   E. none of the above

_____161. EMS and emergency department workers are at special risk for biological agents–induced disease when an attack occurs.
   A. True
   B. False

_____162. A biological agent release is likely to be recognized early as a cloud of gas or particles or the presentation of immediate signs and symptoms.
   A. True
   B. False

_____ **163.** The most effective action against biological agents is the use of personal protective equipment (BSI).
  A. True   **B.** False

_____ **164.** The first sign that a biological weapon attack has taken place may be numerous patients displaying flulike symptoms out of season.
  A. True   **B.** False

_____ **165.** Which of the following is a reason to be concerned about safety at the scene of a potential terrorist attack?
  A. Chemical agents may linger.
  B. Radiation danger may remain.
  C. Terrorists may set secondary explosions.
  D. Biological agents risk disease transmission.
  E. All of the above.

_____ **166.** Your first role in responding to a possible act of terrorism is to ensure your own safety and that of your patient, other rescuers, and the public.
  A. True   **B.** False

WORKBOOK ANSWER KEY

Note: Throughout the Answer Key, textbook page references are shown in italic.

Chapter 1: Neonatology

CONTENT SELF-EVALUATION

MULTIPLE CHOICE

1.	B	*p. 5*	19.	B	*p. 14*
2.	A	*p. 5*	20.	D	*p. 17*
3.	C	*p. 6*	21.	B	*p. 18*
4.	E	*p. 6*	22.	A	*p. 17*
5.	B	*p. 6*	23.	A	*p. 17*
6.	A	*p. 6*	24.	C	*p. 18*
7.	A	*p. 6*	25.	A	*p. 20*
8.	B	*p. 8*	26.	E	*p. 21*
9.	E	*p. 8*	27.	D	*p. 22*
10.	D	*p. 8*	28.	A	*p. 23*
11.	B	*p. 9*	29.	A	*p. 26*
12.	C	*p. 9*	30.	B	*p. 27*
13.	B	*p. 10*	31.	D	*p. 28*
14.	E	*p. 11*	32.	E	*p. 28*
15.	B	*p. 11*	33.	A	*p. 30*
16.	E	*p. 12*	34.	A	*p. 31*
17.	A	*p. 13*	35.	B	*p. 32*
18.	B	*p. 14*			

SPECIAL PROJECT: The APGAR Scale

Part I: TOTAL SCORE = 4

Part II: From top to bottom, items should read—oxygen, bag-mask ventilation, chest compressions, intubation, medications.

Part III: TOTAL SCORE = 9

Chapter 2: Pediatrics

CONTENT SELF-EVALUATION

MULTIPLE CHOICE

1.	C	*p. 41*	20.	A	*p. 65*
2.	D	*p. 41*	21.	C	*p. 65*
3.	A	*p. 42*	22.	D	*p. 69*
4.	B	*p. 44*	23.	E	*p. 71*
5.	E	*p. 44*	24.	C	*p. 75*
6.	C	*p. 45*	25.	E	*p. 76*
7.	C	*p. 45*	26.	C	*p. 77*
8.	B	*p. 46*	27.	D	*p. 80*
9.	C	*p. 51*	28.	A	*p. 83*
10.	E	*p. 50*	29.	C	*p. 83*
11.	A	*p. 51*	30.	B	*p. 85*
12.	B	*p. 52*	31.	C	*p. 94*
13.	B	*p. 53*	32.	E	*p. 95*
14.	B	*p. 53*	33.	C	*p. 96*
15.	B	*p. 56*	34.	A	*p. 97*
16.	E	*p. 56*	35.	D	*p. 100*
17.	E	*p. 60*	36.	B	*p. 101*
18.	A	*p. 64*	37.	A	*p. 104*
19.	D	*p. 65*	38.	B	*p. 110*

39.	C	*p. 111*	43.	E	*p. 127*
40.	A	*p. 117*	44.	D	*p. 129*
41.	C	*p. 120*	45.	C	*p. 132*
42.	C	*p. 125*			

MATCHING

46.	G	*p. 130*	56.	O	*p. 108*
47.	M	*p. 131*	57.	N	*p. 102*
48.	Q	*p. 64*	58.	H	*p. 103*
49.	P	*p. 123*	59.	C	*p. 98*
50.	K	*p. 123*	60.	I	*p. 95*
51.	A	*p. 123*	61.	E	*p. 94*
52.	D	*p. 112*	62.	T	*p. 52*
53.	J	*p. 92*	63.	R	*p. 42*
54.	B	*p. 111*	64.	L	*p. 45*
55.	F	*p. 108*	65.	S	*p. 103*

SPECIAL PROJECT: Burn Injuries

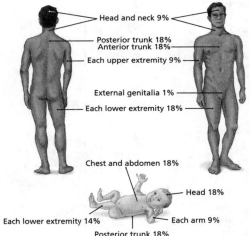

1. 45 percent

2. 40 1/2 percent

3. Sample Answer: The modified rule of nines for the pediatric patient gives less body surface area to the legs and more to the head of an infant.

4. "rule of palms"

Chapter 3: Geriatric Emergencies

CONTENT SELF-EVALUATION

MULTIPLE CHOICE

1.	B	*p. 142*	6.	B	*p. 145*
2.	C	*p. 143*	7.	D	*p. 147*
3.	E	*p. 144*	8.	C	*p. 147*
4.	C	*p. 144*	9.	E	*p. 148*
5.	D	*p. 145*	10.	A	*p. 148*

11. C	p. 151	46. A	p. 164
12. A	p. 151	47. E	p. 165
13. B	p. 151	48. A	p. 166
14. C	p. 151	49. B	p. 169
15. D	p. 151	50. A	p. 169
16. E	p. 152	51. E	p. 170
17. A	p. 152	52. A	p. 170
18. B	p. 152	53. B	p. 171
19. B	p. 153	54. C	p. 170
20. C	p. 153	55. C	p. 172
21. D	p. 153	56. B	p. 172
22. A	p. 155	57. B	p. 173
23. E	p. 155	58. B	p. 173
24. C	p. 154	59. A	p. 174
25. A	p. 155	60. B	p. 175
26. E	p. 155	61. D	p. 176
27. C	p. 156	62. C	p. 177
28. E	p. 156	63. D	p. 177
29. A	p. 157	64. A	p. 179
30. D	p. 157	65. B	p. 182
31. A	p. 157	66. B	p. 182
32. A	p. 159	67. B	p. 182
33. E	p. 159	68. A	p. 182
34. B	p. 159	69. E	p. 183
35. E	p. 159	70. B	p. 184
36. D	p. 160	71. A	p. 185
37. E	p. 161	72. A	p. 185
38. A	p. 162	73. C	p. 187
39. A	p. 163	74. B	p. 188
40. C	p. 163	75. D	p. 190
41. A	p. 163	76. B	p. 190
42. B	p. 163	77. E	p. 193
43. C	p. 163	78. B	p. 193
44. C	p. 164	79. E	p. 195
45. B	p. 164	80. D	p. 197

MATCHING

81. J	p. 177	89. C	p. 175
82. G	p. 186	90. L	p. 177
83. A	p. 175	91. K	p. 178
84. H	p. 173	92. N	p. 200
85. M	p. 181	93. D	p. 175
86. O	p. 195	94. F	p. 176
87. I	p. 177	95. E	p. 155
88. B	p. 175		

SPECIAL PROJECT: Common Age-Related Systemic Changes (See page 197)

Chapter 4: Abuse and Assault

CONTENT SELF-EVALUATION

MULTIPLE CHOICE

1. B	p. 206	11. E	p. 212
2. A	p. 206	12. E	p. 214
3. E	p. 206	13. B	p. 214
4. C	p. 206	14. B	p. 215
5. A	p. 208	15. A	p. 217
6. B	p. 209	16. B	p. 217
7. B	p. 209	17. A	p. 219
8. C	p. 209	18. C	p. 219
9. C	p. 211	19. B	p. 220
10. D	p. 212	20. A	p. 220

MATCHING

21. I	p. 206	26. D	p. 210
22. E	p. 220	27. H	p. 220
23. F	p. 209	28. G	p. 219
24. C	p. 217	29. A	p. 206
25. J	p. 211	30. B	p. 217

SPECIAL PROJECT

The answers will vary with the state, region, or locale where you live. If the information is not readily available in special sections in the telephone book, contact the appropriate agencies, including hospital crisis units, social service agencies, and departments of health.

Chapter 5: The Challenged Patient

CONTENT SELF-EVALUATION

MULTIPLE CHOICE

1. B	p. 227	16. A	p. 237
2. B	p. 227	17. B	p. 238
3. A	p. 228	18. B	p. 238
4. B	p. 228	19. C	p. 240
5. B	p. 229	20. E	p. 241
6. B	p. 229	21. D	p. 240
7. B	p. 230	22. C	p. 242
8. A	p. 231	23. B	p. 237
9. D	p. 231	24. D	p. 242
10. B	p. 232	25. E	p. 242
11. E	p. 234	26. A	p. 242
12. B	p. 234	27. E	p. 243
13. A	p. 235	28. D	p. 243
14. E	p. 236	29. B	p. 244
15. A	p. 237	30. A	p. 244

MATCHING

31. D	p. 226	39. B	p. 227
32. N	p. 227	40. E	p. 229
33. H	p. 227	41. G	p. 231
34. O	p. 229	42. A	p. 227
35. K	p. 227	43. J	p. 229
36. C	p. 231	44. F	p. 227
37. L	p. 234	45. M	p. 240
38. I	p. 238		

SPECIAL PROJECT

1. American Cancer Society—www.cancer.org
2. American Foundation for the Blind—www.afb.org
3. American Obesity Association—www.obesity.org
4. American Speech-Language-Hearing Association—www.asha.org
5. Arthritis Foundation—www.arthritis.org
6. Down Syndrome Society—www.ndss.org
7. Cystic Fibrosis Foundation—www.cff.org
8. Multiple Sclerosis Association of America—www.msaa.com
9. Muscular Dystrophy Association—www.mdausa.org
10. Myasthenia Gravis Foundation of America—www.myasthenia.org
11. National Health Care for the Homeless Council—www.nhchc.org

Special Project: Common Age-Related Systemic Changes

Body System	Changes with Age	Clinical Importance
Respiratory	Loss of strength and coordination in respiratory muscles Cough and gas reflex reduced	Increased likelihood of respiratory failure
Cardiovascular	Loss of elasticity and hardening of arteries Changes in heart rate, rhythm, efficiency	Hypertension common Greater likelihood of strokes, heart attacks Great likelihood of bleeding from minor trauma
Neurological	Brain tissue shrinks Loss of memory Clinical depression common Altered mental status common Impaired balance	Delay in appearance of symptoms with head injury Difficulty in patient assessment Increased likelihood of falls
Endocrine	Lowered estrogen production (women) Decline in insulin sensitivity Increase in insulin resistance	Increased likelihood of fractures (bone loss) and heart disease Diabetes mellitus common with greater possibility of hyperglycemia
Gastrointestinal	Diminished digestive functions	Constipation common Greater likelihood of malnutrition
Thermoregulatory	Reduced sweating Decreased shivering	Environmental emergencies more common
Integumentary (Skin)	Thins and becomes more fragile	More subject to tears and sores Bruising more common Heals more slowly
Musculoskeletal	Loss of bone strength (osteoporosis) Loss of joint flexibility and strength (osteoarthritis)	Greater likelihood of fractures Slower healing Increased likelihood of falls
Renal	Loss of kidney size and function	Increased problems with drug toxicity
Genitourinary	Loss of bladder function	Increased urination/incontinence Increased urinary tract infection
Immune	Diminished immune response	More susceptible to infections Impaired immune response to vaccines
Hematological	Decrease in blood volume and/or RBCs	Slower recuperation from illness/injury Greater risk of trauma-related complications

12. National Organization on Fetal Alcohol Syndrome—**www.nofas.org**
13. Polio Experience Network—**www.polionet.org**
14. Spina Bifida Association of America—**www.sbaa.org**
15. United Cerebral Palsy Association—**www.ucpa.org**

Chapter 6: Acute Interventions for the Chronic-Care Patient

CONTENT SELF-EVALUATION

MULTIPLE CHOICE

1.	C	*p. 251*		16.	B	*p. 263*
2.	A	*p. 252*		17.	B	*p. 265*
3.	E	*p. 252*		18.	B	*p. 267*
4.	B	*p. 253*		19.	D	*p. 268*
5.	A	*p. 254*		20.	E	*p. 270*
6.	B	*p. 255*		21.	D	*p. 271*
7.	A	*p. 255*		22.	B	*p. 272*
8.	B	*p. 255*		23.	D	*p. 275*
9.	A	*p. 255*		24.	A	*p. 278*
10.	C	*p. 257*		25.	E	*p. 278*
11.	E	*p. 257*		26.	C	*p. 279*
12.	D	*p. 257*		27.	E	*p. 280*
13.	C	*p. 260*		28.	C	*p. 281*
14.	A	*p. 261*		29.	B	*p. 285*
15.	E	*p. 262*		30.	E	*p. 288*

MATCHING

31.	D	*p. 269*		36.	J	*p. 256*
32.	G	*p. 255*		37.	F	*p. 256*
33.	C	*p. 268*		38.	B	*p. 268*
34.	A	*p. 255*		39.	E	*p. 262*
35.	H	*p. 257*		40.	I	*p. 268*

SHORT ANSWER

41. positive end-expiratory pressure
42. continuous positive airway pressure
43. bilevel positive airway pressure
44. chronic obstructive pulmonary disease
45. acute respiratory distress syndrome
46. positive-pressure ventilation
47. vascular access device
48. peripherally inserted central catheter
49. do not attempt resuscitation orders
50. congestive heart failure

SPECIAL PROJECT

Answers will vary depending upon the agencies and hospices located in your area. You might want to discuss available services with the hospitals and health departments where you work. The information will not only familiarize you with home health care but will provide a source of referral for patients who are unaware of these services.

Chapter 7: Assessment-Based Management

CONTENT SELF-EVALUATION

MULTIPLE CHOICE

1.	B	*p. 295*		9.	E	*p. 300*
2.	C	*p. 296*		10.	B	*p. 300*
3.	B	*p. 296*		11.	C	*p. 301*
4.	E	*p. 298*		12.	C	*p. 303*
5.	C	*p. 297*		13.	C	*p. 303*
6.	E	*p. 298*		14.	B	*p. 305*
7.	A	*p. 298*		15.	B	*p. 306*
8.	D	*p. 300*				

SPECIAL PROJECT

Part I: Completion
   A. Patient identification, *age*, *sex*, and *degree of distress*
   B. Chief complaint
   C. Present illness/injury
      1. *Pertinent details about the present problem*
      2. *Pertinent negatives*
   D. *Past medical history*
      1. Allergies
      2. Medications
      3. Pertinent medical history
   E. Physical signs
      1. *Vital signs*
      2. Pertinent positive findings
      3. *Pertinent negative findings*
   F. Assessment
      1. Paramedic impression
   G. Plan
      1. *What has been done*
      2. *Orders requested*

Part II: Sample Presentation
The presentation will depend upon the preprinted form but should reflect the guidelines on pages 309–317 of the text.

Chapter 8: Ambulance Operations

CONTENT SELF-EVALUATION

MULTIPLE CHOICE

1.	A	*p. 322*		14.	B	*p. 330*
2.	A	*p. 322*		15.	A	*p. 330*
3.	C	*p. 322*		16.	C	*p. 331*
4.	E	*p. 322*		17.	E	*p. 332*
5.	C	*p. 322*		18.	B	*p. 332*
6.	B	*p. 324*		19.	B	*p. 334*
7.	C	*p. 324*		20.	B	*p. 335*
8.	D	*p. 326*		21.	E	*p. 336*
9.	C	*p. 326*		22.	A	*p. 336*
10.	B	*p. 327*		23.	A	*p. 338*
11.	B	*p. 327*		24.	C	*p. 338*
12.	B	*p. 328*		25.	A	*p. 339*
13.	D	*p. 330*				

MATCHING

26.	D	*p. 322*		31.	B	*p. 326*
27.	F	*p. 322*		32.	C	*p. 327*
28.	I	*p. 322*		33.	J	*p. 327*
29.	A	*p. 326*		34.	H	*p. 328*
30.	E	*p. 326*		35.	G	*p. 328*

SPECIAL PROJECT

Answers will depend upon state motor vehicle laws and the SOPs in the area where you will be serving as a paramedic.

Chapter 9: Medical Incident Management

CONTENT SELF-EVALUATION

MULTIPLE CHOICE

1.	C	p. 349	14.	A	p. 358
2.	A	p. 349	15.	D	p. 360
3.	C	p. 352	16.	D	p. 361
4.	A	p. 354	17.	B	p. 361
5.	A	p. 354	18.	A	p. 363
6.	A	p. 354	19.	D	p. 363
7.	A	p. 353	20.	A	p. 364
8.	A	p. 353	21.	E	p. 365
9.	E	p. 355	22.	A	p. 366
10.	D	p. 356	23.	B	p. 369
11.	A	p. 356	24.	A	p. 371
12.	A	p. 357	25.	A	p. 373
13.	E	p. 358			

MATCHING

26.	D	p. 351	31.	B	p. 353
27.	J	p. 358	32.	G	p. 357
28.	I	p. 359	33.	C	p. 361
29.	H	p. 352	34.	F	p. 351
30.	A	p. 359	35.	E	p. 354

SHORT ANSWER

36. multiple casualty incident
37. Command, Finance, Logistics, Operations, Planning
38. Emergency Operation Center
39. Incident Management System
40. Simple Triage and Rapid Transport

SPECIAL PROJECT

Your plan should reflect local SOPs and any other guidelines that affect your state or region. Ask a classmate or member of the EMS unit where you work to review your plan to ensure that you have thought of all contingencies. Then go one step further—test your plan in a tabletop drill, working out any wrinkles.

Chapter 10: Rescue Awareness and Operations

CONTENT SELF-EVALUATION

MULTIPLE CHOICE

1.	E	p. 381	11.	E	p. 401
2.	B	p. 383	12.	A	p. 402
3.	D	p. 386	13.	C	p. 404
4.	C	p. 390	14.	B	p. 408
5.	C	p. 390	15.	A	p. 411
6.	C	p. 393	16.	B	p. 412
7.	A	p. 397	17.	B	p. 413
8.	D	p. 397	18.	B	p. 415
9.	E	p. 397	19.	A	p. 417
10.	C	p. 398	20.	C	p. 420

MATCHING

21.	H	p. 393	26.	I	p. 418
22.	C	p. 392	27.	D	p. 413
23.	F	p. 397	28.	E	p. 400
24.	A	p. 398	29.	G	p. 411
25.	J	p. 412	30.	B	p. 402

SPECIAL PROJECT

The answers will depend upon the resources in your area or region. As suggested in this chapter, you might try to participate in preplanning exercises in which some of these specialized agencies are involved.

Chapter 11: Hazardous Materials Incidents

CONTENT SELF-EVALUATION

MULTIPLE CHOICE

1.	A	p. 428	14.	A	p. 442
2.	E	p. 429	15.	A	p. 443
3.	B	p. 430	16.	A	p. 444
4.	C	p. 430	17.	B	p. 445
5.	D	p. 430	18.	A	p. 446
6.	A	p. 432	19.	A	p. 446
7.	B	p. 433	20.	D	p. 448
8.	B	p. 436	21.	D	p. 448
9.	C	p. 436	22.	D	p. 449
10.	B	p. 436	23.	C	p. 449
11.	B	p. 438	24.	C	p. 449
12.	B	p. 442	25.	A	p. 451
13.	D	p. 442			

MATCHING

26.	D	p. 427	31.	B	p. 438
27.	H	p. 431	32.	G	p. 438
28.	I	p. 436	33.	E	p. 439
29.	C	p. 436	34.	A	p. 439
30.	J	p. 438	35.	F	p. 439

SPECIAL PROJECTS

Part I should accurately summarize the regulations and standards as they apply to you or your agency. Part II will depend upon the chemicals selected.

Chapter 12: Crime Scene Awareness

CONTENT SELF-EVALUATION

MULTIPLE CHOICE

1.	B	p. 458	14.	A	p. 464
2.	B	p. 459	15.	B	p. 465
3.	B	p. 459	16.	B	p. 465
4.	C	p. 459	17.	B	p. 465
5.	A	p. 459	18.	E	p. 465
6.	E	p. 460	19.	C	p. 466
7.	A	p. 460	20.	B	p. 467
8.	B	p. 461	21.	B	p. 468
9.	C	p. 462	22.	E	p. 471
10.	A	p. 462	23.	A	p. 472
11.	B	p. 463	24.	A	p. 473
12.	E	p. 463	25.	E	p. 475
13.	E	p. 463			

MATCHING

26. J	p. 464	31. B	p. 474	
27. D	p. 469	32. A	p. 471	
28. C	p. 467	33. H	p. 467	
29. E	p. 464	34. G	p. 474	
30. I	p. 471	35. F	p. 471	

SHORT ANSWER

Part A

36. Avoid mixing samples of blood whenever possible.
37. Avoid tracking blood on your shoes.
38. If you must cut bloody clothing from a victim, place each piece in a separate brown paper bag. If the garment is wet, gently roll it in the paper bag to layer it. Place the entire contents in a second paper bag and then in a plastic bag for body fluid protection.
39. Do not throw clothes stained with blood or other body fluids in a single pile or in a puddle of blood.
40. Do not clean up or smudge blood splatters left at a scene.
41. If you leave behind blood from a venipuncture, notify the police.
42. Because blood can be a biohazard, ask police whether the scene should be secured for evidence collection.

Part B

43. prints (fingerprints, footprints, tire prints)
44. particulate evidence
45. on-scene observations

SPECIAL PROJECT

Items in the list will vary with the objects in your residence. Compare your list with the "weapons" identified by your classmates.

Chapter 13: Rural EMS

CONTENT SELF-EVALUATION

MULTIPLE CHOICE

1. D	p. 481	6. A	p. 486
2. E	p. 481	7. D	p. 487
3. A	p. 481	8. B	p. 489
4. B	p. 482	9. E	p. 493
5. C	p. 483	10. A	p. 497

MATCHING

11. E	p. 483	16. I	p. 493
12. G	p. 485	17. C	p. 493
13. B	p. 489	18. F	p. 493
14. D	p. 489	19. J	p. 493
15. A	p. 493	20. H	p. 487

SHORT ANSWER

21. distance and time
22. communication difficulties
23. enrollment shortages
24. inadequate opportunities for training and practice
25. inadequate medical support

SPECIAL PROJECT

1. The Companion Website offers chapter objectives, quizzes, and EMS Web links as well as material for the instructor.
2. The addresses for Web links can change, so list the most current addresses that you find for the following sites listed on the Companion Website for *Paramedic Care: Principles & Practices*.
   - Name of site: Rural and Frontier Medical Services Toward the Year 2000 (paper on the future of rural EMS)
   - Name of site: Rural Emergency Medical Services Initiative (one state's program to assist with rural EMS)
   - Name of site: Pediatric Emergency Medicine in the Rural EMS System (paper on rural EMS)
   - Name of site: Rural Medics (a homepage for rural EMS providers)

Chapter 14: Responding to Terrorist Acts

CONTENT SELF-EVALUATION

MULTIPLE CHOICE

1. A	p. 504	11. A	p. 509
2. E	p. 504	12. B	p. 510
3. C	p. 505	13. C	p. 510
4. B	p. 506	14. D	p. 511
5. D	p. 506	15. E	p. 512
6. E	p. 506	16. D	p. 513
7. C	p. 506	17. E	p. 514
8. A	p. 508	18. A	p. 515
9. E	p. 508	19. A	p. 516
10. E	p. 509	20. B	p. 518

Special Considerations/Operations: Content Review

CONTENT SELF-EVALUATION

CHAPTER 1: NEONATOLOGY

1. A	p. 6	4. A	p. 29
2. D	p. 21	5. E	p. 31
3. C	p. 27		

CHAPTER 2: PEDIATRICS

6. A	p. 44	11. C	p. 81
7. E	p. 44	12. D	p. 85
8. B	p. 53	13. A	p. 91
9. A	p. 61	14. C	p. 100
10. A	p. 80	15. B	p. 109

CHAPTER 3: GERIATRIC EMERGENCIES

16. D	p. 154	21. E	p. 162
17. E	p. 156	22. C	p. 175
18. E	p. 156	23. D	p. 176
19. B	p. 159	24. A	p. 157
20. A	p. 156	25. B	p. 200

CHAPTER 4: ABUSE AND ASSAULT

26.	D	*p. 207*	29.	D	*p. 215*
27.	B	*p. 210*	30.	C	*p. 217*
28.	B	*p. 211*	31.	B	*p. 219*

CHAPTER 5: THE CHALLENGED PATIENT

32.	A	*p. 228*	35.	D	*p. 234*
33.	A	*p. 230*	36.	B	*p. 237*
34.	B	*p. 231*			

CHAPTER 6: ACUTE INTERVENTIONS FOR THE CHRONIC-CARE PATIENT

37.	E	*p. 252*	40.	D	*p. 269*
38.	C	*p. 253*	41.	A	*p. 274*
39.	B	*p. 256*			

CHAPTER 7: ASSESSMENT-BASED MANAGEMENT

42.	E	*p. 296*	45.	C	*p. 300*
43.	B	*p. 297*	46.	E	*p. 308*
44.	C	*p. 298*			

CHAPTER 8: AMBULANCE OPERATIONS

47.	E	*p. 324*	50.	B	*p. 327*
48.	B	*p. 325*	51.	B	*p. 331*
49.	A	*p. 326*			

CHAPTER 9: MEDICAL INCIDENT COMMAND

52.	A	*p. 354*	54.	C	*p. 358*
53.	D	*p. 352*	55.	D	*p. 359*

CHAPTER 10: RESCUE AWARENESS AND OPERATIONS

56.	D	*p. 382*	59.	A	*p. 388*
57.	A	*p. 386*	60.	B	*p. 392*
58.	E	*p. 388*	61.	B	*p. 392*

CHAPTER 11: HAZARDOUS MATERIALS INCIDENTS

62.	A	*p. 429*	65.	B	*p. 432*
63.	E	*p. 430*	66.	A	*p. 436*
64.	C	*p. 432*			

CHAPTER 12: CRIME SCENE AWARENESS

67.	A	*p. 460*	70.	D	*p. 468*
68.	D	*p. 463*	71.	D	*p. 471*
69.	B	*p. 465*			

CHAPTER 13: RURAL EMS

72.	A	*p. 481*	75.	D	*p. 485*
73.	B	*p. 482*	76.	C	*p. 493*
74.	C	*p. 483*			

CHAPTER 14: RESPONDING TO TERRORIST ACTS

77.	E	*p. 504*	87.	E	*p. 509*
78.	B	*p. 506*	88.	C	*p. 509*
79.	C	*p. 510*	89.	D	*p. 512*
80.	B	*p. 517*	90.	A	*p. 513*
81.	B	*p. 504*	91.	B	*p. 513*
82.	E	*p. 505*	92.	A	*p. 516*
83.	D	*p. 506*	93.	A	*p. 514*
84.	D	*p. 506*	94.	E	*p. 517*
85.	A	*p. 508*	95.	A	*p. 518*
86.	B	*p. 508*			

National Registry of Emergency Medical Technicians

Practical Evaluation Forms

The forms on the next pages are provided to help you identify common criteria by which you will be evaluated. It may be valuable to review your practical skills by using these sheets during your class practice sessions and as you review those skills before class, state, and any national testing. Evaluation forms will vary; however, many of the important elements of paramedic practice are common to all forms.

EMT-PARAMEDIC FORMS

The following skill instruments for the EMT-Paramedic level were developed by the National Registry of EMTs and have been approved for use in advanced level National Registry Examinations.

- Bleeding Control/Shock Management
- Dual Lumen Airway Device
- Dynamic Cardiology
- Intravenous Therapy
- Oral Station
- Patient Assessment—Medical
- Patient Assessment—Trauma
- Pediatric Intraosseous Infusion
- Pediatric (less than 2 years) Ventilatory Management
- Spinal Immobilization (Seated Patient)
- Spinal Immobilization (Supine Patient)
- Static Cardiology
- Ventilatory Management—Adult

EMT-Paramedic Form

National Registry of Emergency Medical Technicians
Advanced Level Practical Examination

BLEEDING CONTROL/SHOCK MANAGEMENT

Candidate: _____ Examiner: _____

Date: _____ Signature: _____

Time Start:_____	Possible Points	Points Awarded
Takes or verbalizes body substance isolation precautions	1	
Applies direct pressure to the wound	1	
Elevates the extremity	1	
NOTE: The examiner must now inform the candidate that the wound continues to bleed.		
Applies an additional dressing to the wound	1	
NOTE: The examiner must now inform the candidate that the wound still continues to bleed. The second dressing does not control the bleeding.		
Locates and applies pressure to appropriate arterial pressure point	1	
NOTE: The examiner must now inform the candidate that the bleeding is controlled.		
Bandages the wound	1	
NOTE: The examiner must now inform the candidate that the patient is exhibiting signs and symptoms of hypoperfusion.		
Properly positions the patient	1	
Administers high concentration oxygen	1	
Initiates steps to prevent heat loss from the patient	1	
Indicates the need for immediate transportation	1	
Time End: _____ **TOTAL**	10	

CRITICAL CRITERIA

_____ Did not take or verbalize body substance isolation precautions
_____ Did not apply high concentration of oxygen
_____ Applied a tourniquet before attempting other methods of bleeding control
_____ Did not control hemorrhage in a timely manner
_____ Did not indicate the need for immediate transportation

You must factually document your rationale for checking any of the above critical items on the reverse side of this form.

EMT-Paramedic Form

National Registry of Emergency Medical Technicians
Advanced Level Practical Examination

DUAL LUMEN AIRWAY DEVICE (COMBITUBE® OR PTL®)

Candidate: _____ Examiner: _____

Date: _____ Signature: _____

NOTE: If candidate elects to initially ventilate with BVM attached to reservoir and oxygen, full credit must be awarded for steps denoted by "**" so long as first ventilation is delivered within 30 seconds.

	Possible Points	Points Awarded
Takes or verbalizes body substance isolation precautions	1	
Opens the airway manually	1	
Elevates tongue, inserts simple adjunct [oropharyngeal or nasopharyngeal airway]	1	
NOTE: Examiner now informs candidate no gag reflex is present and patient accepts adjunct		
**Ventilates patient immediately with bag-valve-mask device unattached to oxygen	1	
**Hyperventilates patient with room air	1	
NOTE: Examiner now informs candidate that ventilation is being performed without difficulty		
Attaches oxygen reservoir to bag-valve-mask device and connects to high flow oxygen regulator [12-15 L/minute]	1	
Ventilates patient at a rate of 10-20/minute with appropriate volumes	1	
NOTE: After 30 seconds, examiner auscultates and reports breath sounds are present and equal bilaterally and medical control has ordered insertion of a dual lumen airway. The examiner must now take over ventilation.		
Directs assistant to pre-oxygenate patient	1	
Checks/prepares airway device	1	
Lubricates distal tip of the device [may be verbalized]	1	
NOTE: Examiner to remove OPA and move out of the way when candidate is prepared to insert device		
Positions head properly	1	
Performs a tongue-jaw lift	1	

☐ USES COMBITUBE®	☐ USES PTL®		
Inserts device in mid-line and to depth so printed ring is at level of teeth	Inserts device in mid-line until bite block flange is at level of teeth	1	
Inflates pharyngeal cuff with proper volume and removes syringe	Secures strap	1	
Inflates distal cuff with proper volume and removes syringe	Blows into tube #1 to adequately inflate both cuffs	1	
Attaches/directs attachment of BVM to the first [esophageal placement] lumen and ventilates		1	
Confirms placement and ventilation through correct lumen by observing chest rise, auscultation over the epigastrium, and bilaterally over each lung		1	
NOTE: The examiner states, "You do not see rise and fall of the chest and you only hear sounds over the epigastrium."			
Attaches/directs attachment of BVM to the second [endotracheal placement] lumen and ventilates		1	
Confirms placement and ventilation through correct lumen by observing chest rise, auscultation over the epigastrium, and bilaterally over each lung		1	
NOTE: The examiner confirms adequate chest rise, absent sounds over the epigastrium, and equal bilateral breath sounds.			
Secures device or confirms that the device remains properly secured		1	
TOTAL		**20**	

CRITICAL CRITERIA

_____ Failure to initiate ventilations within 30 seconds after taking body substance isolation precautions or interrupts ventilations for greater than 30 seconds at any time

_____ Failure to take or verbalize body substance isolation precautions

_____ Failure to voice and ultimately provide high oxygen concentrations [at least 85%]

_____ Failure to ventilate patient at a rate of at least 10/minute

_____ Failure to provide adequate volumes per breath [maximum 2 errors/minute permissible]

_____ Failure to pre-oxygenate patient prior to insertion of the dual lumen airway device

_____ Failure to insert the dual lumen airway device at a proper depth or at either proper place within 3 attempts

_____ Failure to inflate both cuffs properly

_____ **Combitube** - failure to remove the syringe immediately after inflation of each cuff
PTL - failure to secure the strap prior to cuff inflation

_____ Failure to confirm that the proper lumen of the device is being ventilated by observing chest rise, auscultation over the epigastrium, and bilaterally over each lung

_____ Inserts any adjunct in a manner dangerous to patient

You must factually document your rationale for checking any of the above critical items on the reverse side of this form.

EMT-Paramedic Form

National Registry of Emergency Medical Technicians
Advanced Level Practical Examination

DYNAMIC CARDIOLOGY

Candidate: _____ Examiner: _____

Date: _____ Signature: _____

SET #_____

Level of Testing: ☐ NREMT-Intermediate/99   ☐ NREMT-Paramedic

Time Start:_____

	Possible Points	Points Awarded
Takes or verbalizes infection control precautions	1	
Checks level of responsiveness	1	
Checks ABCs	1	
Initiates CPR if appropriate [verbally]	1	
Attaches ECG monitor in a timely fashion or applies paddles for "Quick Look"	1	
Correctly interprets initial rhythm	1	
Appropriately manages initial rhythm	2	
Notes change in rhythm	1	
Checks patient condition to include pulse and, if appropriate, BP	1	
Correctly interprets second rhythm	1	
Appropriately manages second rhythm	2	
Notes change in rhythm	1	
Checks patient condition to include pulse and, if appropriate, BP	1	
Correctly interprets third rhythm	1	
Appropriately manages third rhythm	2	
Notes change in rhythm	1	
Checks patient condition to include pulse and, if appropriate, BP	1	
Correctly interprets fourth rhythm	1	
Appropriately manages fourth rhythm	2	
Orders high percentages of supplemental oxygen at proper times	1	

Time End: _____   **TOTAL**   24

CRITICAL CRITERIA

_____ Failure to deliver first shock in a timely manner due to operator delay in machine use or providing treatments other than CPR with simple adjuncts

_____ Failure to deliver second or third shocks without delay other than the time required to reassess rhythm and recharge paddles

_____ Failure to verify rhythm before delivering each shock

_____ Failure to ensure the safety of self and others [verbalizes "All clear" and observes]

_____ Inability to deliver DC shock [does not use machine properly]

_____ Failure to demonstrate acceptable shock sequence

_____ Failure to order initiation or resumption of CPR when appropriate

_____ Failure to order correct management of airway [ET when appropriate]

_____ Failure to order administration of appropriate oxygen at proper time

_____ Failure to diagnose or treat 2 or more rhythms correctly

_____ Orders administration of an inappropriate drug or lethal dosage

_____ Failure to correctly diagnose or adequately treat v-fib, v-tach, or asystole

You must factually document your rationale for checking any of the above critical items on the reverse side of this form.

EMT-Paramedic Form

National Registry of Emergency Medical Technicians
Advanced Level Practical Examination

INTRAVENOUS THERAPY

Candidate: _____ Examiner: _____

Date: _____ Signature: _____

Level of Testing: ❏ NREMT-Intermediate/85   ❏ NREMT-Intermediate/99   ❏ NREMT-Paramedic

Time Start: _____

	Possible Points	Points Awarded

Checks selected IV fluid for:
  -Proper fluid (1 point)
  -Clarity (1 point)
	2	

Selects appropriate catheter	1	
Selects proper administration set	1	
Connects IV tubing to the IV bag	1	
Prepares administration set [fills drip chamber and flushes tubing]	1	
Cuts or tears tape [at any time before venipuncture]	1	
Takes/verbalizes body substance isolation precautions [prior to venipuncture]	1	
Applies tourniquet	1	
Palpates suitable vein	1	
Cleanses site appropriately	1	

Performs venipuncture
  -Inserts stylette (1 point)
  -Notes or verbalizes flashback (1 point)
  -Occludes vein proximal to catheter (1 point)
  -Removes stylette (1 point)
  -Connects IV tubing to catheter (1 point)
	5	

Disposes/verbalizes disposal of needle in proper container	1	
Releases tourniquet	1	
Runs IV for a brief period to assure patent line	1	
Secures catheter [tapes securely or verbalizes]	1	
Adjusts flow rate as appropriate	1	

Time End: _____   **TOTAL**   21

CRITICAL CRITERIA

____ Failure to establish a patent and properly adjusted IV within 6 minute time limit
____ Failure to take or verbalize body substance isolation precautions prior to performing venipuncture
____ Contaminates equipment or site without appropriately correcting situation
____ Performs any improper technique resulting in the potential for uncontrolled hemorrhage, catheter shear, or air embolism
____ Failure to successfully establish IV within 3 attempts during 6 minute time limit
____ Failure to dispose/verbalize disposal of needle in proper container

NOTE: Check here (_____) if candidate did not establish a patent IV and do not evaluate IV Bolus Medications.

INTRAVENOUS BOLUS MEDICATIONS

Time Start: _____

Asks patient for known allergies	1	
Selects correct medication	1	
Assures correct concentration of drug	1	
Assembles prefilled syringe correctly and dispels air	1	
Continues body substance isolation precautions	1	
Cleanses injection site [Y-port or hub]	1	
Reaffirms medication	1	
Stops IV flow [pinches tubing or shuts off]	1	
Administers correct dose at proper push rate	1	
Disposes/verbalizes proper disposal of syringe and needle in proper container	1	
Flushes tubing [runs wide open for a brief period]	1	
Adjusts drip rate to TKO/KVO	1	
Verbalizes need to observe patient for desired effect/adverse side effects	1	

Time End: _____   **TOTAL**   13

CRITICAL CRITERIA

____ Failure to begin administration of medication within 3 minute time limit
____ Contaminates equipment or site without appropriately correcting situation
____ Failure to adequately dispel air resulting in potential for air embolism
____ Injects improper drug or dosage [wrong drug, incorrect amount, or pushes at inappropriate rate]
____ Failure to flush IV tubing after injecting medication
____ Recaps needle or failure to dispose/verbalize disposal of syringe and needle in proper container

You must factually document your rationale for checking any of the above critical items on the reverse side of this form.

EMT-Paramedic Form

National Registry of Emergency Medical Technicians
Advanced Level Practical Examination
ORAL STATION

Candidate: _____ Examiner: _____

Date: _____ Signature: _____

Scenario: _____

Time Start: _____

	Possible Points	Points Awarded
Scene Management		
Thoroughly assessed and took deliberate actions to control the scene	3	
Assessed the scene, identified potential hazards, did not put anyone in danger	2	
Incompletely assessed or managed the scene	1	
Did not assess or manage the scene	0	
Patient Assessment		
Completed an organized assessment and integrated findings to expand further assessment	3	
Completed initial, focused, and ongoing assessments	2	
Performed an incomplete or disorganized assessment	1	
Did not complete an initial assessment	0	
Patient Management		
Managed all aspects of the patient's condition and anticipated further needs	3	
Appropriately managed the patient's presenting condition	2	
Performed an incomplete or disorganized management	1	
Did not manage life-threatening conditions	0	
Interpersonal relations		
Established rapport and interacted in an organized, therapeutic manner	3	
Interacted and responded appropriately with patient, crew, and bystanders	2	
Used inappropriate communication techniques	1	
Demonstrated intolerance for patient, bystanders, and crew	0	
Integration (verbal report, field impression, and transport decision)		
Stated correct field impression and pathophysiological basis, provided succinct and accurate verbal report including social/psychological concerns, and considered alternate transport destinations	3	
Stated correct field impression, provided succinct and accurate verbal report, and appropriately stated transport decision	2	
Stated correct field impression, provided inappropriate verbal report or transport decision	1	
Stated incorrect field impression or did not provide verbal report	0	

Time End: _____   **TOTAL**   **15**

Critical Criteria

_____ Failure to appropriately address any of the scenario's "Mandatory Actions"

_____ Performs or orders any harmful or dangerous action or intervention

You must factually document your rationale for checking any of the above critical items on the reverse side of this form.

p308/8-003k

EMT-Paramedic Form

National Registry of Emergency Medical Technicians
Advanced Level Practical Examination

PATIENT ASSESSMENT - MEDICAL

Candidate: _____ Examiner: _____

Date: _____ Signature: _____

Scenario: _____

Time Start: _____

	Possible Points	Points Awarded
Takes or verbalizes body substance isolation precautions	1	
SCENE SIZE-UP		
Determines the scene/situation is safe	1	
Determines the mechanism of injury/nature of illness	1	
Determines the number of patients	1	
Requests additional help if necessary	1	
Considers stabilization of spine	1	
INITIAL ASSESSMENT		
Verbalizes general impression of the patient	1	
Determines responsiveness/level of consciousness	1	
Determines chief complaint/apparent life-threats	1	
Assesses airway and breathing 　　-Assessment (1 point) 　　-Assures adequate ventilation (1 point) 　　-Initiates appropriate oxygen therapy (1 point)	3	
Assesses circulation 　　-Assesses/controls major bleeding (1 point)　-Assesses skin [either skin color, temperature, or condition] (1 point) 　　-Assesses pulse (1 point)	3	
Identifies priority patients/makes transport decision	1	
FOCUSED HISTORY AND PHYSICAL EXAMINATION/RAPID ASSESSMENT		
History of present illness 　　-Onset (1 point)　　　-Severity (1 point) 　　-Provocation (1 point)　-Time (1 point) 　　-Quality (1 point)　　-Clarifying questions of associated signs and symptoms as related to OPQRST (2 points) 　　-Radiation (1 point)	8	
Past medical history 　　-Allergies (1 point)　　-Past pertinent history (1 point)　　-Events leading to present illness (1 point) 　　-Medications (1 point)　-Last oral intake (1 point)	5	
Performs focused physical examination [assess affected body part/system or, if indicated, completes rapid assessment] 　　-Cardiovascular　　-Neurological　　　-Integumentary　　-Reproductive 　　-Pulmonary　　　-Musculoskeletal　　-GI/GU　　　-Psychological/Social	5	
Vital signs 　　-Pulse (1 point)　　　　-Respiratory rate and quality (1 point each) 　　-Blood pressure (1 point)　　-AVPU (1 point)	5	
Diagnostics [must include application of ECG monitor for dyspnea and chest pain]	2	
States field impression of patient	1	
Verbalizes treatment plan for patient and calls for appropriate intervention(s)	1	
Transport decision re-evaluated	1	
ON-GOING ASSESSMENT		
Repeats initial assessment	1	
Repeats vital signs	1	
Evaluates response to treatments	1	
Repeats focused assessment regarding patient complaint or injuries	1	

Time End: _____

CRITICAL CRITERIA　　　　　　　　　　　　　　　　　　　　　　　　TOTAL　　48

_____ Failure to initiate or call for transport of the patient within 15 minute time limit
_____ Failure to take or verbalize body substance isolation precautions
_____ Failure to determine scene safety before approaching patient
_____ Failure to voice and ultimately provide appropriate oxygen therapy
_____ Failure to assess/provide adequate ventilation
_____ Failure to find or appropriately manage problems associated with airway, breathing, hemorrhage or shock [hypoperfusion]
_____ Failure to differentiate patient's need for immediate transportation versus continued assessment and treatment at the scene
_____ Does other detailed or focused history or physical examination before assessing and treating threats to airway, breathing, and circulation
_____ Failure to determine the patient's primary problem
_____ Orders a dangerous or inappropriate intervention
_____ Failure to provide for spinal protection when indicated

You must factually document your rationale for checking any of the above critical items on the reverse side of this form.

EMT-Paramedic Form

National Registry of Emergency Medical Technicians
Advanced Level Practical Examination

PATIENT ASSESSMENT - TRAUMA

Candidate: _____ Examiner: _____

Date: _____ Signature: _____

Scenario # _____

Time Start: _____   NOTE: Areas denoted by "**" may be integrated within sequence of Initial Assessment

	Possible Points	Points Awarded
Takes or verbalizes body substance isolation precautions	1	
SCENE SIZE-UP		
Determines the scene/situation is safe	1	
Determines the mechanism of injury/nature of illness	1	
Determines the number of patients	1	
Requests additional help if necessary	1	
Considers stabilization of spine	1	
INITIAL ASSESSMENT/RESUSCITATION		
Verbalizes general impression of the patient	1	
Determines responsiveness/level of consciousness	1	
Determines chief complaint/apparent life-threats	1	
Airway -Opens and assesses airway (1 point) -Inserts adjunct as indicated (1 point)	2	
Breathing -Assess breathing (1 point) -Assures adequate ventilation (1 point) -Initiates appropriate oxygen therapy (1 point) -Manages any injury which may compromise breathing/ventilation (1 point)	4	
Circulation -Checks pulse (1point) -Assess skin [either skin color, temperature, or condition] (1 point) -Assesses for and controls major bleeding if present (1 point) -Initiates shock management (1 point)	4	
Identifies priority patients/makes transport decision	1	
FOCUSED HISTORY AND PHYSICAL EXAMINATION/RAPID TRAUMA ASSESSMENT		
Selects appropriate assessment	1	
Obtains, or directs assistant to obtain, baseline vital signs	1	
Obtains SAMPLE history	1	
DETAILED PHYSICAL EXAMINATION		
Head -Inspects mouth**, nose**, and assesses facial area (1 point) -Inspects and palpates scalp and ears (1 point) -Assesses eyes for PERRL** (1 point)	3	
Neck** -Checks position of trachea (1 point) -Checks jugular veins (1 point) -Palpates cervical spine (1 point)	3	
Chest** -Inspects chest (1 point) -Palpates chest (1 point) -Auscultates chest (1 point)	3	
Abdomen/pelvis** -Inspects and palpates abdomen (1 point) -Assesses pelvis (1 point) -Verbalizes assessment of genitalia/perineum as needed (1 point)	3	
Lower extremities** -Inspects, palpates, and assesses motor, sensory, and distal circulatory functions (1 point/leg)	2	
Upper extremities -Inspects, palpates, and assesses motor, sensory, and distal circulatory functions (1 point/arm)	2	
Posterior thorax, lumbar, and buttocks** -Inspects and palpates posterior thorax (1 point) -Inspects and palpates lumbar and buttocks area (1 point)	2	
Manages secondary injuries and wounds appropriately	1	
Performs ongoing assessment	1	

Time End: _____   **TOTAL**   43

CRITICAL CRITERIA

_____ Failure to initiate or call for transport of the patient within 10 minute time limit
_____ Failure to take or verbalize body substance isolation precautions
_____ Failure to determine scene safety
_____ Failure to assess for and provide spinal protection when indicated
_____ Failure to voice and ultimately provide high concentration of oxygen
_____ Failure to assess/provide adequate ventilation
_____ Failure to find or appropriately manage problems associated with airway, breathing, hemorrhage or shock [hypoperfusion]
_____ Failure to differentiate patient's need for immediate transportation versus continued assessment/treatment at the scene
_____ Does other detailed/focused history or physical exam before assessing/treating threats to airway, breathing, and circulation
_____ Orders a dangerous or inappropriate intervention

You must factually document your rationale for checking any of the above critical items on the reverse side of this form.

p301/8-003k

EMT-Paramedic Form

National Registry of Emergency Medical Technicians
Advanced Level Practical Examination

PEDIATRIC INTRAOSSEOUS INFUSION

Candidate: _____ Examiner: _____

Date: _____ Signature: _____

Time Start:_____	Possible Points	Points Awarded

Checks selected IV fluid for:
    -Proper fluid (1 point)
    -Clarity (1 point)
	2	

Selects appropriate equipment to include:
    -IO needle (1 point)
    -Syringe (1 point)
    -Saline (1 point)
    -Extension set (1 point)
	4	

Selects proper administration set	1	
Connects administration set to bag	1	
Prepares administration set [fills drip chamber and flushes tubing]	1	
Prepares syringe and extension tubing	1	
Cuts or tears tape [at any time before IO puncture]	1	
Takes or verbalizes body substance isolation precautions [prior to IO puncture]	1	
Identifies proper anatomical site for IO puncture	1	
Cleanses site appropriately	1	

Performs IO puncture:
    -Stabilizes tibia (1 point)
    -Inserts needle at proper angle (1 point)
    -Advances needle with twisting motion until "pop" is felt (1 point)
    -Unscrews cap and removes stylette from needle (1 point)
	4	

Disposes of needle in proper container	1	
Attaches syringe and extension set to IO needle and aspirates	1	
Slowly injects saline to assure proper placement of needle	1	
Connects administration set and adjusts flow rate as appropriate	1	
Secures needle with tape and supports with bulky dressing	1	

Time End: _____   **TOTAL**   23

CRITICAL CRITERIA
_____ Failure to establish a patent and properly adjusted IO line within the 6 minute time limit
_____ Failure to take or verbalize body substance isolation precautions prior to performing IO puncture
_____ Contaminates equipment or site without appropriately correcting situation
_____ Performs any improper technique resulting in the potential for air embolism
_____ Failure to assure correct needle placement before attaching administration set
_____ Failure to successfully establish IO infusion within 2 attempts during 6 minute time limit
_____ Performing IO puncture in an unacceptable manner [improper site, incorrect needle angle, etc.]
_____ Failure to dispose of needle in proper container
_____ Orders or performs any dangerous or potentially harmful procedure

You must factually document your rationale for checking any of the above critical items on the reverse side of this form.

EMT-Paramedic Form

National Registry of Emergency Medical Technicians
Advanced Level Practical Examination

PEDIATRIC (<2 yrs.) VENTILATORY MANAGEMENT

Candidate: _____ Examiner _____

Date: _____ Signature: _____

NOTE: If candidate elects to ventilate initially with BVM attached to reservoir and oxygen, full credit must be awarded for steps denoted by "**" so long as first ventilation is delivered within 30 seconds.

	Possible Points	Points Awarded
Takes or verbalizes body substance isolation precautions	1	
Opens the airway manually	1	
Elevates tongue, inserts simple adjunct [oropharyngeal or nasopharyngeal airway]	1	
NOTE: Examiner now informs candidate no gag reflex is present and patient accepts adjunct		
**Ventilates patient immediately with bag-valve-mask device unattached to oxygen	1	
**Hyperventilates patient with room air	1	
NOTE: Examiner now informs candidate that ventilation is being performed without difficulty and that pulse oximetry indicates the patient's blood oxygen saturation is 85%		
Attaches oxygen reservoir to bag-valve-mask device and connects to high flow oxygen regulator [12-15 L/minute]	1	
Ventilates patient at a rate of 20-30/minute and assures adequate chest expansion	1	
NOTE: After 30 seconds, examiner auscultates and reports breath sounds are present, equal bilaterally and medical direction has ordered intubation. The examiner must now take over ventilation.		
Directs assistant to pre-oxygenate patient	1	
Identifies/selects proper equipment for intubation	1	
Checks laryngoscope to assure operational with bulb tight	1	
NOTE: Examiner to remove OPA and move out of the way when candidate is prepared to intubate		
Places patient in neutral or sniffing position	1	
Inserts blade while displacing tongue	1	
Elevates mandible with laryngoscope	1	
Introduces ET tube and advances to proper depth	1	
Directs ventilation of patient	1	
Confirms proper placement by auscultation bilaterally over each lung and over epigastrium	1	
NOTE: Examiner to ask, "If you had proper placement, what should you expect to hear?"		
Secures ET tube [may be verbalized]	1	
TOTAL	**17**	

CRITICAL CRITERIA

_____ Failure to initiate ventilations within 30 seconds after applying gloves or interrupts ventilations for greater than 30 seconds at any time
_____ Failure to take or verbalize body substance isolation precautions
_____ Failure to pad under the torso to allow neutral head position or sniffing position
_____ Failure to voice and ultimately provide high oxygen concentrations [at least 85%]
_____ Failure to ventilate patient at a rate of at least 20/minute
_____ Failure to provide adequate volumes per breath [maximum 2 errors/minute permissible]
_____ Failure to pre-oxygenate patient prior to intubation
_____ Failure to successfully intubate within 3 attempts
_____ Uses gums as a fulcrum
_____ Failure to assure proper tube placement by auscultation bilaterally **and** over the epigastrium
_____ Inserts any adjunct in a manner dangerous to the patient
_____ Attempts to use any equipment not appropriate for the pediatric patient

You must factually document your rationale for checking any of the above critical items on the reverse side of this form.

p305/8-003k

EMT-Paramedic Form

National Registry of Emergency Medical Technicians
Advanced Level Practical Examination

SPINAL IMMOBILIZATION (SEATED PATIENT)

Candidate:_____ Examiner:_____

Date: _____ Signature:_____

Time Start: _____	Possible Points	Points Awarded
Takes or verbalizes body substance isolation precautions	1	
Directs assistant to place/maintain head in the neutral, in-line position	1	
Directs assistant to maintain manual immobilization of the head	1	
Reassesses motor, sensory, and circulatory function in each extremity	1	
Applies appropriately sized extrication collar	1	
Positions the immobilization device behind the patient	1	
Secures the device to the patient's torso	1	
Evaluates torso fixation and adjusts as necessary	1	
Evaluates and pads behind the patient's head as necessary	1	
Secures the patient's head to the device	1	
Verbalizes moving the patient to a long backboard	1	
Reassesses motor, sensory, and circulatory function in each extremity	1	

Time End: _____   **TOTAL** 12

CRITICAL CRITERIA

_____ Did not immediately direct or take manual immobilization of the head
_____ Did not properly apply appropriately sized cervical collar before ordering release of manual immobilization
_____ Released or ordered release of manual immobilization before it was maintained mechanically
_____ Manipulated or moved patient excessively causing potential spinal compromise
_____ Head immobilized to the device **before** device sufficiently secured to torso
_____ Device moves excessively up, down, left, or right on the patient's torso
_____ Head immobilization allows for excessive movement
_____ Torso fixation inhibits chest rise, resulting in respiratory compromise
_____ Upon completion of immobilization, head is not in a neutral, in-line position
_____ Did not reassess motor, sensory, and circulatory functions in each extremity after voicing immobilization to the long backboard

You must factually document your rationale for checking any of the above critical items on the reverse side of this form.

EMT-Paramedic Form

National Registry of Emergency Medical Technicians
Advanced Level Practical Examination

SPINAL IMMOBILIZATION (SUPINE PATIENT)

Candidate:_____Examiner:_____

Date: _____Signature:_____

Time Start: _____

	Possible Points	Points Awarded
Takes or verbalizes body substance isolation precautions	1	
Directs assistant to place/maintain head in the neutral, in-line position	1	
Directs assistant to maintain manual immobilization of the head	1	
Reassesses motor, sensory, and circulatory function in each extremity	1	
Applies appropriately sized extrication collar	1	
Positions the immobilization device appropriately	1	
Directs movement of the patient onto the device without compromising the integrity of the spine	1	
Applies padding to voids between the torso and the device as necessary	1	
Immobilizes the patient's torso to the device	1	
Evaluates and pads behind the patient's head as necessary	1	
Immobilizes the patient's head to the device	1	
Secures the patient's legs to the device	1	
Secures the patient's arms to the device	1	
Reassesses motor, sensory, and circulatory function in each extremity	1	

Time End: _____   **TOTAL**   14

CRITICAL CRITERIA

_____ Did not immediately direct or take manual immobilization of the head
_____ Did not properly apply appropriately sized cervical collar before ordering release of manual immobilization
_____ Released or ordered release of manual immobilization before it was maintained mechanically
_____ Manipulated or moved patient excessively causing potential spinal compromise
_____ Head immobilized to the device **before** device sufficiently secured to torso
_____ Patient moves excessively up, down, left, or right on the device
_____ Head immobilization allows for excessive movement
_____ Upon completion of immobilization, head is not in a neutral, in-line position
_____ Did not reassess motor, sensory, and circulatory functions in each extremity after voicing immobilization to the device

You must factually document your rationale for checking any of the above critical items on the reverse side of this form.

EMT-Paramedic Form

National Registry of Emergency Medical Technicians
Advanced Level Practical Examination

STATIC CARDIOLOGY

Candidate: _____ Examiner: _____

Date: _____ Signature: _____

SET #_____

Level of Testing: ☐ NREMT-Intermediate/99   ☐ NREMT-Paramedic

Note: No points for treatment may be awarded if the diagnosis is incorrect.
     Only document incorrect responses in spaces provided.

Time Start:_____

	Possible Points	Points Awarded
STRIP #1		
Diagnosis:	1	
Treatment:	2	
STRIP #2		
Diagnosis:	1	
Treatment:	2	
STRIP #3		
Diagnosis:	1	
Treatment:	2	
STRIP #4		
Diagnosis:	1	
Treatment:	2	

Time End: _____   **TOTAL   12**

EMT-Paramedic Form

National Registry of Emergency Medical Technicians
Advanced Level Practical Examination

VENTILATORY MANAGEMENT - ADULT

Candidate:_____ Examiner:_____

Date: _____ Signature: _____

NOTE: If candidate elects to ventilate initially with BVM attached to reservoir and oxygen, full credit must be awarded for
steps denoted by "**" so long as first ventilation is delivered within 30 seconds.

	Possible Points	Points Awarded
Takes or verbalizes body substance isolation precautions	1	
Opens the airway manually	1	
Elevates tongue, inserts simple adjunct [oropharyngeal or nasopharyngeal airway]	1	
NOTE: Examiner now informs candidate no gag reflex is present and patient accepts adjunct		
**Ventilates patient immediately with bag-valve-mask device unattached to oxygen	1	
**Hyperventilates patient with room air	1	
NOTE: Examiner now informs candidate that ventilation is being performed without difficulty and that pulse oximetry indicates the patient's blood oxygen saturation is 85%		
Attaches oxygen reservoir to bag-valve-mask device and connects to high flow oxygen regulator [12-15 L/minute]	1	
Ventilates patient at a rate of 10-20/minute with appropriate volumes	1	
NOTE: After 30 seconds, examiner auscultates and reports breath sounds are present, equal bilaterally and medical direction has ordered intubation. The examiner must now take over ventilation.		
Directs assistant to pre-oxygenate patient	1	
Identifies/selects proper equipment for intubation	1	
Checks equipment for: -Cuff leaks (1 point) -Laryngoscope operational with bulb tight (1 point)	2	
NOTE: Examiner to remove OPA and move out of the way when candidate is prepared to intubate		
Positions head properly	1	
Inserts blade while displacing tongue	1	
Elevates mandible with laryngoscope	1	
Introduces ET tube and advances to proper depth	1	
Inflates cuff to proper pressure and disconnects syringe	1	
Directs ventilation of patient	1	
Confirms proper placement by auscultation bilaterally over each lung and over epigastrium	1	
NOTE: Examiner to ask, "If you had proper placement, what should you expect to hear?"		
Secures ET tube [may be verbalized]	1	
NOTE: Examiner now asks candidate, "Please demonstrate one additional method of verifying proper tube placement in this patient."		
Identifies/selects proper equipment	1	
Verbalizes findings and interpretations [compares indicator color to the colorimetric scale and states reading to examiner]	1	
NOTE: Examiner now states, "You see secretions in the tube and hear gurgling sounds with the patient's exhalation."		
Identifies/selects a flexible suction catheter	1	
Pre-oxygenates patient	1	
Marks maximum insertion length with thumb and forefinger	1	
Inserts catheter into the ET tube leaving catheter port open	1	
At proper insertion depth, covers catheter port and applies suction while withdrawing catheter	1	
Ventilates/directs ventilation of patient as catheter is flushed with sterile water	1	
TOTAL	**27**	

CRITICAL CRITERIA

_____ Failure to initiate ventilations within 30 seconds after applying gloves or interrupts ventilations for greater than 30 seconds at any time
_____ Failure to take or verbalize body substance isolation precautions
_____ Failure to voice and ultimately provide high oxygen concentrations [at least 85%]
_____ Failure to ventilate patient at a rate of at least 10/minute
_____ Failure to provide adequate volumes per breath [maximum 2 errors/minute permissible]
_____ Failure to pre-oxygenate patient prior to intubation and suctioning
_____ Failure to successfully intubate within 3 attempts
_____ Failure to disconnect syringe **immediately** after inflating cuff of ET tube
_____ Uses teeth as a fulcrum
_____ Failure to assure proper tube placement by auscultation bilaterally **and** over the epigastrium
_____ If used, stylette extends beyond end of ET tube
_____ Inserts any adjunct in a manner dangerous to the patient
_____ Suctions the patient for more than 15 seconds
_____ Does not suction the patient

You must factually document your rationale for checking any of the above critical items on the reverse side of this form.

p303/8-003k

PATIENT SCENARIO FLASH CARDS

In order to help you learn the process of investigating the chief complaint and obtaining the past medical history, we have included a series of flash cards. Each one contains the dispatch and scene size-up information and then asks you to question either the patient's chief complaint or the past medical history.

Using the flash cards is a two-person exercise. Work with another member of your class, a paramedic or EMT from your service, or with someone else knowledgeable in emergency medical care. Cut the cards and shuffle them. Have your partner choose a card at random and read the dispatch and scene size-up information aloud to you. He should read the patient information to him and prepare to play the role of the patient. You should then try to determine the patient history by questioning him using the elements of the SAMPLE mnemonic. Your partner should then choose other cards and the two of you repeat the exercise until you feel comfortable in gathering the patient history.

Then have your partner repeat the exercise, reading the dispatch and scene size-up information and role playing the part of the patient with symptoms associated with the chief complaint. You should then question him about the chief complaint using the OPQRST-ASPN mnemonic. When you feel comfortable with the process of questioning for the chief complaint, repeat the exercise with your partner using information on both sides of the card. When you have gathered all the information you can, create a patient report like the one you would provide when arriving at the emergency department with your patient. Also attempt to determine the field diagnosis for the patient (listed at the bottom of the chief complaint card). Repeat the exercise until you are comfortable with the entire process.

PATIENT HISTORY

The patient history examines critical elements of the patient's past medical history, including the elements of the SAMPLE history mnemonic. (The S, for signs and symptoms, is investigated during the questioning about the chief complaint.)

A— allergies	Ask about any allergies or adverse reactions to drugs, foods, etc.
M— medications	Ask about any prescribed medications, then over-the-counter ones.
P— past medical history	Ask about recent surgeries, hospitalizations, and physician care.
L— last oral intake	Ask about the most recent meal and any fluids ingested.
E— events before the incident	Ask about activities and symptoms preceding the incident.

CHIEF COMPLAINT

During the investigation of the chief complaint, question the patient about the major symptoms of the problem to help form a field diagnosis. Investigate your patient's complaints by using the OPQRST-ASPN mnemonic.

O— onset	Ask about how the symptoms developed and what the patient was doing at the time.
P— palliation/provocation	Ask about what makes the symptoms better or worse.
Q— quality	Ask the patient to describe the nature of the pain or discomfort.
R— region/radiation	Ask where the symptom and related symptoms are found.
S— severity	Ask the patient to rate the pain on a scale from 1 to 10 (worst pain).
T— time	Ask about when the symptoms first appeared and how they progressed.
AS— associated symptoms	Ask about other or associated symptoms.
PN— pertinent negatives	Investigate likely and related signs and symptoms.

During this exercise, do not try to develop standard questions for each element of the investigation. Rather, let your patient's condition, the nature of the problem, and—later during your career—your experience guide your questioning to garner the pertinent medical information.

Scenario 1 Patient History

Dispatch Information: Responding to a residence for an unresponsive 2-week-old infant.

Scene Size-Up: As your ambulance pulls up to a residential address, a teenage mother is crying while carrying her baby out to the ambulance; no hazards are apparent.

Medical History
A—she doesn't know of any
M—none
P—term pregnancy without complication
L—poor feeding for 2 days
E—elevated temperature today

Scenario 2 Patient History

Dispatch Information: Dispatched to a residence for complications of childbirth.

Scene Size-Up: The father of a newly born infant leads you to a midwife. The midwife is attempting to resuscitate a blue-appearing newborn who is not breathing; no hazards are noted.

Medical History
A—unknown
M—none
P—normal pregnancy
L—no oral intake for several hours
E—first-time labor and delivery

Scenario 3 Patient History

Dispatch Information: Dispatched to the parking lot of a local drug store where a car is standing by with an 18-month-old toddler having a seizure.

Scene Size-Up: A young couple appears extremely upset as they direct your ambulance to their car; the car is running and traffic is busy in the parking lot.

Secure the scene: Turn off the car's engine and have a crew member establish a safety perimeter using cones or scene tape.

Medical History
A—none
M—nonaspirin pain reliever
P—cold and upper respiratory congestion
L—last took medication about 2 hours ago
E—while driving, the father looked in the rearview mirror and saw the child's eyes roll back in her head and the mother observed total body shaking for approximately 30 seconds

Scenario 1 Chief Complaint   "My Baby Is Sick."

O—Baby would not fully awaken from nap about 2 hours ago, has become less responsive
P—only a couple of ounces of formula today, no effect, Tylenol 2 hours ago, no improvement
Q—n/a
R—skin color is mottled, fontanelles are sunken
S—n/a
T—baby has been fussy for 2 days, developed fever today
AS—fewer diapers used in the last 24 hours
PN—no diarrhea or vomiting

(Field Diagnosis: Infection and Dehydration)

Scenario 2 Chief Complaint   "The Baby Is Not Breathing."

O—at birth, neonate was apneic and unresponsive
P—n/a
Q—@1 minute–breathing slow & shallow, heart rate 100 (What is the APGAR score?)
 @5 minute–some spontaneous breathing, no other changes (What is APGAR score?)
R—extremities blue, body pink, limp muscle tone
S—no response to stimuli or pain
T—normal and uneventful 14 hour delivery,
AS—meconium staining noted
PN—term pregnancy w/ no high risk factors

(Field Diagnosis: Fetal Distress-Depressed Neonate)

Scenario 3 Chief Complaint   "Seizures"

O—acute onset, first time, no warning (parents stopped car and loosened car seat straps)
P—n/a
Q—exaggerated body motion
R—whole body (arms legs, torso & head)
S—n/a
T—recent cold and illness, 5 minutes after putting child in car seat,
AS—now, skin very warm and moist, responds only to loud shouts
PN—no seizure today or history of head trauma

(Field Diagnosis: Febrile Seizure)

SCENARIO 4 PATIENT HISTORY

Dispatch Information: Responding to a grocery market where a toddler has fallen from a shopping cart.

Scene Size-Up: A small crowd is surrounding a woman holding a 2-year-old child. The child is crying and has an obvious goose egg on his forehead.

Medical History
A—penicillin
M—Dilantin
P—seizures
L—had lunch 30 minutes ago
E—child stood in shopping cart and fell out onto his head

SCENARIO 5 PATIENT HISTORY

Dispatch Information: Dispatched to a department store for an unconscious 68-year-old woman with a history of heart problems.

Scene Size-Up: A crowd is gathered around an older woman who is lying on the floor, awake but disoriented.

Medical History
A—sulfa drugs and certain antibiotics
M—metaproterenol, isosorbide, and Miacalcin
P—hypertension, cardiac, and osteoporosis
L—nothing to eat today
E—shopping in the department store on a big sale day

SCENARIO 6 PATIENT HISTORY

Dispatch Information: Dispatched to a residence for a fall.

Scene Size-Up: Apartment door is unlocked, and an older gentleman is calling out for help; no hazards noted.

Medical History
A—none
M—Lasix, nitro, potassium, Ventolin, and verapamil
P—cardiac, CHF, URI
L—had breakfast and took all medications right after
E—tripped and fell on scatter rug

SCENARIO 4 CHIEF COMPLAINT   "FALL W/HEAD IMPACT"

O—Sudden (mother had just turned away)
P—Cries louder when bump is touched, mother can comfort child
Q—4 foot fall (cart to hard floor)
R—to anterior forehead
S—minor swelling, size of quarter
T—fall occurred 5 minutes ago
AS—none
PN—patient moves all extremities on mother's request

(Field Diagnosis: Head and possible Neck Trauma)

SCENARIO 5 CHIEF COMPLAINT   "DIZZINESS, COLLAPSE"

O—Suddenly felt weak & dizzy, while shopping, now somewhat confused
P—Lying down, sitting increases dizziness & pulse rate
Q—dizzy and confused
R—n/a
S—oriented to persons, not to time or place
T—no previous episodes or warning for this one, can't remember what she's there for
AS—pale, warm, moist skin; weak, irregular distal pulse
PN—no chest pain dyspnea, or signs of trauma

(Field Diagnosis: Undetermined, rule out Cardiac Syncope)

SCENARIO 6 CHIEF COMPLAINT   "TRIPPED, CAN'T GET UP"

O—pain in left hip after falling
P—pain is worse with movement and palpation
Q—constant severe pain
R—left hip and groin
S—pain is 9 on a scale of 1 to 10.
T—while walking with a cane to the bathroom, tripped on the rug; pain came directly after fall
AS—left leg is shortened and medially rotated
PN—no loss of consciousness, weakness, or dizziness before or after the fall

(Field Diagnosis: Rule Out Fracture/Dislocation of Hip)

SCENARIO 7 PATIENT HISTORY

Dispatch Information: Domestic disturbance, police enroute, not yet on scene.

Scene Size-Up: Two police vehicles outside of single-family residence. A woman with cuts and bruises on her face and arms is being escorted to the ambulance; no other persons or hazards apparent.

Medical History
A—none
M—Zoloft, tramadol
P—depression and chronic back pain
L—last oral intake has been alcohol
E—patient and boyfriend got into a disagreement that turned physical

SCENARIO 8 PATIENT HISTORY

Dispatch Information: Dispatched to the nurse's office at a junior high school in reference to an assault.

Scene Size-Up: Police are on the scene taking a report from a teacher. The teacher was reportedly assaulted by a student; no hazards noted.

Medical History
A—environmental
M—none
P—diet-controlled diabetic
L—sandwich and cola for lunch 40 minutes ago
E—teacher attempted to break up a fistfight between two students

SCENARIO 9 PATIENT HISTORY

Dispatch Information: Dispatched to a motor vehicle collision; one patient with neck pain.

Scene Size-Up: Upon arrival at a motor vehicle collision involving two cars, police direct you to a man complaining of chest pain and a woman who is "signing" to him. Both are standing in a driveway just off the road. Both are obese; no hazards noted.

Medical History
A—peanuts
M—none
P—deaf since birth
L—dinner an hour ago
E—patient's vehicle rear-ended another car at low speed, air bag deployed

SCENARIO 7 CHIEF COMPLAINT   "DOMESTIC DISTURBANCE"

O—police state neighbors report recent fighting and drinking (last hour), patient is evasive and inconsistent during interview
P—n/a
Q—significant developing hematoma to left cheek area (new)
R—numerous abrasions & minor lacerations over head, neck & distal extremities (old)
S—minor trauma
T—old and new wounds
AS—none
PN—rest of assessment normal

(Field Diagnosis: likely Long-term Physical Abuse)

SCENARIO 8 CHIEF COMPLAINT   "ASSAULT, ABDOMINAL PAIN"

O—abdominal pain has persisted after being kicked in the stomach by a student
P—pain has been getting progressively worse since incident
Q—sharp, intermittent, throbbing
R—pain is radiating around into the left flank area
S—pain is 8 on a scale of 1 to 10
T—incident occurred an hour ago
AS—nausea
PN—no vomiting

(Field Diagnosis: Internal Abdominal Hemorrhage)

SCENARIO 9 CHIEF COMPLAINT   "CHEST PAIN"

(Communication is slow due to writing down all Q & As).
O—immediate chest pain occurred after collision
P—pain is worse with inspiration and palpation
Q—pain is sharp and tearing in nature
R—diagonal across chest covered by shoulder harness
S—5 on a scale of 1 to 10
T—distracted by glaring sunlight, her car struck the car stopped in front of her, deploying the air bag in the driver's seat.
AS—difficulty breathing, anxiety, increased difficulties in communication and patient interview
PN—No back or neck pain (reliable reporter), no loss of consciousness

(Field Diagnosis: Musculoskeletal Pain vs. Cardiac)

SCENARIO 10 PATIENT HISTORY

Dispatch Information: Dispatched to a nursing facility for a respiratory distress patient.

Scene Size-Up: A 74-year-old female is unresponsive, lying in her bed. Gurgling respirations are audible from the doorway.

Medical History
A—penicillin
M—a three-page medication administration record is given to you by the staff
P—end-stage lung and brain cancer; CHF, hypertension, dementia; computer-aided dispatch
L—awake for small breakfast 4 hours ago
E—developed labored breathing and became progressively less responsive

SCENARIO 11 PATIENT HISTORY

Dispatch Information: Dispatched to a residence for a 4-year-old who has ingested an unknown product.

Scene Size-Up: Neighbors lead you into the kitchen of a single-family dwelling. The father is washing the face of a 4-year-old girl in the kitchen sink. The child is crying weakly and has burns on her face, nose, and mouth. The mother shows you a milk container that has an unknown gray liquid product in it.

Secure scene: Have the mother take the product outside, but do not discard it. Open windows to air out the house and call for the fire department.

Medical History
A—none
M—none
P—asthma
L—last asthma attack was 3 months ago
E—the child was found screaming and crying in the garage

SCENARIO 12 PATIENT HISTORY

Dispatch Information: Dispatched to a remote farmhouse at the edge of the county line for a 75-year-old sick person.

Scene Size-Up: After a 45-minute response, you arrive at a well-maintained farmhouse to find a 75-year-old woman with an altered mental status under the care of an RN. The nurse reports that the patient has an elevated temperature and an increase in AMS today.

Medical History
A—codeine
M—levodopa, bromocriptine, and amantadine
P—Parkinson's disease
L—oral intake has been minimal for the past 24 hours
E—the central venous access port appears to be infected

Scenario 10 Chief Complaint   "Unconscious"

O—unresponsive starting 30 minutes ago
P—n/a
Q—gurgling in upper airways, crackles in all lung fields
R—n/a
S—unresponsive to any stimuli
T—sudden onset of labored breathing 2 hours ago, progressive worsening
AS—pale skin, decreased SaO2 and rapid, strong pulse
PN—no peripheral edema, oropharynx is clear

(Field Diagnosis: Exacerbation of COPD and CHF)

Scenario 11 Chief Complaint   "Caustic Ingestion"

O—pain & crying immediately upon contact/attempted ingestion
P—face washed with water, reduced crying
Q—facial erythema, blistering and edema
R—face, nose, lips, tongue, and mouth
S—obviously painful but with limited crying
T—child fine immediately before attempted ingestion
AS—parents upset by incident
PN—no wheezing or decreased breath sounds, no attempt at antidote administration, no nausea, posterior throat appears clear of burns

(Field Diagnosis: Accidental Caustic Ingestion with Facial Burns)

Scenario 12 Chief Complaint   "Altered Mental Status"

O—decreasing LOC over last few hours
P—fever medications ineffective
Q—n/a
R—Port-A-Cath site inflamed
S—disoriented to time, place, and person
T—elevated temperature during the day, slow decrease in mental status over last few hours
AS—decreased urine output, mild tachycardia
PN—no respiratory disease, SaO2 98% on room air

(Field Diagnosis: Systemic Infection)